ADVANCES IN LIPID RESEARCH

Volume 13

Advances in Lipid Research

Volume 13

Edited by

Rodolfo Paoletti

Institute of Pharmacology
Milan, Italy

David Kritchevsky

The Wistar Institute
Philadelphia, Pennsylvania

 1975

ACADEMIC PRESS
New York   San Francisco   London
A Subsidiary of Harcourt Brace Jovanovich, Publishers

ACADEMIC PRESS, INC.
111 Fifth Avenue, New York, New York 10003

United Kingdom Edition published by
ACADEMIC PRESS, INC. (LONDON) LTD.
24/28 Oval Road, London NW1

LIBRARY OF CONGRESS CATALOG CARD NUMBER: 63-22330

ISBN 0-12-024913-8

PRINTED IN THE UNITED STATES OF AMERICA

CONTENTS

Lipoprotein Metabolism

Shlomo Eisenberg and Robert I. Levy

Diabetes and Lipid Metabolism in Nonhuman Primates

Charles F. Howard, Jr.

Biliary Lipids and Cholesterol Gallstone Formation

Oscar W. Portman, Toshiaki Osuga, and Naomi Tanaka

The Composition and Biosynthesis of Milk Fat

Stuart Smith and S. Abraham

LIST OF CONTRIBUTORS

Numbers in parentheses indicate the pages on which the authors' contributions begin.

S. ABRAHAM, *Bruce Lyon Memorial Research Laboratory, Children's Hospital Medical Center of Northern California, Oakland, California* (195)

SHLOMO EISENBERG, *Department of Medicine B, Hadassah University Hospital, Jerusalem, Israel* (1)

CHARLES F. HOWARD, JR., *Department of Nutrition and Metabolic Diseases, Oregon Regional Primate Research Center, Beaverton, Oregon, and Department of Biochemistry, University of Oregon Medical School, Portland, Oregon* (91)

ROBERT I. LEVY, *Molecular Disease Branch, National Heart and Lung Institute, National Institutes of Health, Bethesda, Maryland* (1)

TOSHIAKI OSUGA,* *Department of Medicine, University of Tokyo School of Medicine, Tokyo, Japan* (135)

OSCAR W. PORTMAN, *Department of Nutrition and Metabolic Diseases, Oregon Regional Primate Research Center, Beaverton, Oregon, and Department of Biochemistry, University of Oregon Medical School, Portland, Oregon* (135)

STUART SMITH, *Bruce Lyon Memorial Research Laboratory, Children's Hospital Medical Center of Northern California, Oakland, California* (195)

NAOMI TANAKA, *Department of Nutrition and Metabolic Diseases, Oregon Regional Primate Research Center, Beaverton, Oregon* (135)

---

* Present address: Department of Medicine, University of Tsukuba School of Medicine, Sakura-mura, Niihari-gun, Ibaraki-ken 300-31, Japan.

PREFACE

Volume 13 of *Advances in Lipid Research* contains reviews that are somewhat more extensive than those found in earlier volumes. We feel, however, that they cover areas of such great current interest that this departure from custom is justified.

In the past few years advances in the knowledge of lipoproteins have been made on a number of scientific fronts. The first review discusses the present status of the field of lipoprotein metabolism, summarizing and extending existing knowledge in the field. The second article in this volume covers newer aspects of lipid metabolism in diabetes. The frequent suggestions that early atherosclerosis in man may be a prediabetic condition make this review most pertinent.

Another area that has burgeoned in recent years is that concerned with establishment and dissolution of gallstones. Our understanding of the physicochemical basis of gallstone formation has increased and this has led to new nonsurgical approaches to the treatment of gallstones. The third article discusses the gallstone field in depth. The final contribution to this volume deals with the biosynthesis and composition of milk fat and offers new insights into this complex field.

RODOLFO PAOLETTI
DAVID KRITCHEVSKY

CONTENTS OF PREVIOUS VOLUMES

Volume 3

Lipoprotein Metabolism[1]

SHLOMO EISENBERG

Department of Medicine B, Hadassah University Hospital, Jerusalem, Israel

AND

ROBERT I. LEVY

*Molecular Disease Branch, National Heart and Lung Institute,
NIH, Bethesda, Maryland*

[1] In preparation of this study, Dr. Eisenberg was supported in part through the Special Foreign Currency Program of the National Library of Medicine, National Institutes of Health, Public Health Service, U. S. Department of Health, Education, and Welfare, Bethesda, Maryland, under an agreement with the *Israel Journal of Medical Sciences,* Jerusalem, Israel.

I. Introduction

Plasma lipoprotein levels are closely related to a most important process in humans—arteriosclerosis and, in particular, to its clinical manifestation, coronary artery disease. Understanding of the factors affecting lipoprotein levels is therefore of great importance to health and disease, and today constitutes one of the foremost medical challenges.

The biochemistry, biophysics, and physiology of plasma lipoproteins have been reviewed extensively during the last few years. This fact doubtless reflects the enormous flux of information and the rapid progress in this field of research during the last 10 years. Lipoprotein metabolism, however, has been discussed in only a few of these reviews, and in almost none has an attempt been made to integrate lipoprotein structure, function, and metabolism.

Lipoproteins are the transport vehicle in plasma for the otherwise water-insoluble lipids from their organs of synthesis to their sites of utilization. Lipoproteins are found in plasma as discrete entities, containing lipids and specific proteins (apoproteins, apolipoproteins). In order to understand the biological processes involved in the metabolism of lipoproteins and the regulatory mechanisms affecting their plasma levels, they must be regarded as complex particles of unique composition, structure, and function.

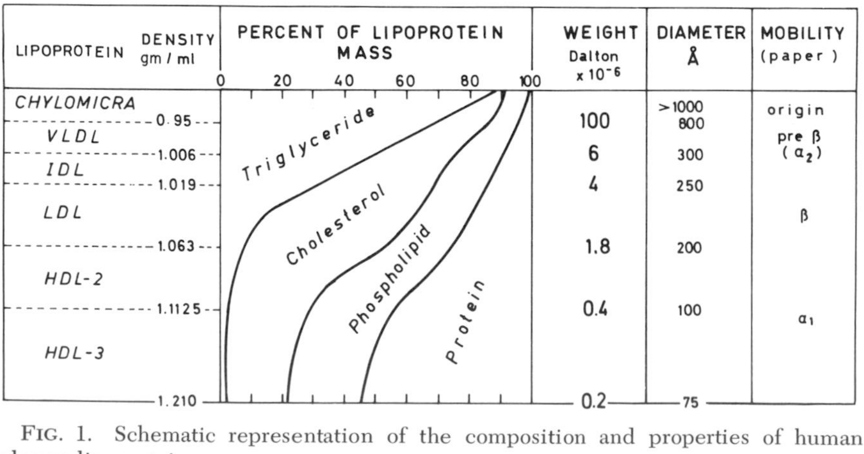

FIG. 1. Schematic representation of the composition and properties of human plasma lipoproteins.

In the present review an attempt will be made to discuss lipoprotein metabolism using an approach which integrates the composition, structure, and function of lipoproteins and regards lipoproteins as discrete and finite particles. To achieve this goal we will first describe pertinent data concerning lipoprotein structure and composition. The synthesis and catabolism of lipoproteins will then be discussed as they relate to the whole lipoprotein particle. Finally, we will try to correlate these routes with mechanisms operating in the regulation of plasma lipoprotein levels and their possible relationship to lipid transport disorders.

II. Lipid and Protein Composition of Lipoproteins

A. The Lipids

All lipoproteins are composed of lipids and proteins. As isolated in the ultracentrifuge, lipoproteins can be viewed as a continuous spectrum of particles with a changing pattern of lipid and protein composition (Fig. 1). The conventional separation of lipoproteins into four families—chylomicrons, very low density lipoproteins (VLDL), low density lipoproteins (LDL), and high density lipoproteins (HDL)—is based primarily on their physical properties and is therefore operational rather than functional. A more functional approach toward the transport of lipids and lipoproteins will be taken here.

The contribution of lipids to total mass of lipoproteins varies from more than 98% in the largest chylomicrons to less than 50% in the smallest high density lipoproteins. Lipoproteins appear to be primarily involved in the transport of triglycerides of either exogenous origin (absorbed from the gastrointestinal tract) or endogenous origin (synthesized and secreted by the liver and the intestinal wall) to their sites of storage or utilization, predominantly in adipose tissue and muscle. All lipoproteins, however, also contain varying amounts of free and esterified cholesterol and phospholipids.

Two lipoprotein families initiate the process of triglyceride transport through the plasma: chylomicrons and VLDL (Table I). The contribution of triglycerides to the lipid mass of these lipoproteins varies from more than 95% to about 30–40%. Within the density range of chylomicrons and VLDL, particles are observed to be poorer in triglycerides and richer in cholesterol, phospholipid, and protein content as they become smaller and more dense (Lossow *et al.*, 1969; Lindgren *et al.*, 1972a,b; Eisenberg *et al.*, 1973a).

The two other major lipoprotein families of human plasma—LDL

Table I

LIPID COMPOSITION OF HUMAN PLASMA LIPOPROTEINS

Lipoprotein	Triglyceride	Cholesterol	Phospholipids	$\dfrac{\text{Ester}}{\text{Free}}$ Cholesterol	$\dfrac{\text{Lecithin}}{\text{Sphingomyelin}}$
	(mg/100 mg lipoprotein–lipid)			(molar ratio)	
Chylomicra[a]	87.7	3.0	8.8	0.88	5.85
VLDL[b]	55.7	16.8	19.3	1.30	4.02
LDL[b]	7.3	59.2	27.8	2.33	2.46
HDL$_2$[b]	6.1	42.5	42.4	2.81	5.08
HDL$_3$[b]	6.7	38.4	40.9	4.38	8.38

[a] Human chyle chylomicrons (Kostner and Holasek, 1972).
[b] Skipski et al., (1967); Skipski (1972).

and HDL—are composed mainly of cholesterol, phospholipid, and protein. Again, one observes that the smaller and heavier particles are richer in protein and poorer in lipid content (Lee and Alaupovic, 1970; Hammond and Fisher, 1971; Lindgren *et al.*, 1972a,b). The role of lipoproteins in general and LDL and HDL in particular in the transport of cholesterol and phospholipids is unclear and speculative. On theoretical grounds lipoproteins may play an important role in cholesterol transport from tissues to the liver—the major organ of cholesterol excretion from the body. This speculation is supported mainly by observations in patients with familial HDL deficiency (Tangier disease; see Section VI) who accumulate cholesterol ester in reticuloendothelial cells throughout the body (Fredrickson *et al.*, 1972a).

Several of the physical characteristics of lipoproteins are related to their lipid content and composition. The flotation properties of lipoproteins are a direct function of the relative contribution of lipids to the total mass and are related to the specific lipids present in each particle. The triglyceride-carrying lipoproteins—chylomicrons and VLDL—are the largest lipoproteins. They range in weight from 5×10^6 to many hundred million daltons, and in diameter from 400 Å to several microns. These large particles scatter light and cause serum and plasma to appear "cloudy" or "milky" when present in increased amounts. Other physical characteristics of lipoproteins, such as surface charge and migration in electric fields, depend primarily on their apoprotein moieties.

Lipoproteins differ considerably in the relative proportion of individual phospholipids, mainly the molar ratio of lecithin to sphingomyelin. They differ also in the molar ratio of free to esterified cholesterol (see Table I). When both ratios are considered, their patterns in the different lipoproteins are not consistent. The molar ratios of total phospholipids to total cholesterol, and of lecithin to sphingomyelin, are higher in VLDL and HDL than in LDL. The molar ratio of esterified to free cholesterol, however, is higher in LDL and HDL than in VLDL. Some of these observations may be partially explained as a function of the length of time that different lipoproteins circulate in plasma (several hours for VLDL and 3–5 days for LDL and HDL), and their exposure to the activity of enzymes present in circulation. It is possible, however, that these differences reflect fundamental variations in ratios of polar lipids (present in the water interphase) to nonpolar lipids or the type and amount of lipid bound to a specific apoprotein.

Studies based on conventional preparative ultracentrifugal procedures, indicate that levels of lipoproteins in fasting normal human

Table II
Serum Lipoprotein Levels in Humans, Dogs, Rats, and Guinea Pigs

Species	VLDL ($d < 1.006$)	IDL ($d = 1.006$–1.019)	LDL ($d = 1.019$–1.063)	HDL$_2$ ($d = 1.063$–1.1125)	HDL$_3$ ($d = 1.1125$–1.21)
			(mg/100 ml of serum)		
Human, males[a]	173	57	380	37	226
Human, females[a]	69	41	330	83	237
Dogs[b]	17	–	30	167	394
Rats[c]	42	2	16	5	123
Guinea pigs[d]	28	Trace	83	12	3

[a] Healthy men and women, 30–49 years (Nichols, 1967).

[b] From Mahley and Weisgraber (1974b) and Mahley et al. (1974a). HDL$_2$ and LDL were isolated at the density fraction of 1.006–1.087 gm/ml and separated by block electrophoresis. HDL$_3$ was isolated at density 1.087–1.21 gm/ml.

[c] From Schonfeld et al. (1974b). LDL, HDL$_2$, and HDL$_3$ were isolated at densities of 1.018–1.05, 1.05–1.07, and 1.07–1.21 gm/ml respectively.

[d] From Sardet et al. (1972). HDL$_2$ was obtained in the density range of 1.063–1.090 gm/ml and had a composition similar to that of LDL. HDL$_3$ was isolated in the density fraction of 1.090–1.21 gm/ml.

plasma vary within a relatively narrow range (Table II). LDL is the major lipoprotein, comprising about 50% of the total lipoprotein mass and carrying about 70% of the plasma cholesterol. VLDL and HDL are the other two lipoproteins normally found in fasting plasma. However, it should be noted that chylomicrons carry by far the bulk of the lipids transported in human plasma during a day (as much as 100 gm of fat and more; Eisenberg, 1973). With age, the levels of LDL and VLDL increase; HDL levels in females are 30–60% higher than those of males of comparable age (Fredrickson and Levy, 1972). These observations are as yet unexplained.

Lipoprotein levels in animals differ markedly, most probably reflecting major differences in lipoprotein metabolism among the different species (Alexander and Day, 1973; Srinivasan *et al.*, 1974). Examples are the dog, rat, and guinea pig (Table II). The pattern of lipoproteins in dogs and rats is characterized by low VLDL levels, very low LDL levels, and relatively high HDL levels. In the guinea pig, an almost complete absence of HDL has been reported. These observations, again poorly understood, lend strong support to the caution with which observations in one animal species can be applied to other species including man.

B. The Apolipoproteins

Apoproteins are present in all plasma lipoproteins. They constitute as little as less than 1% of the chylomicron mass to as much as more than 50% of the mass of the smallest HDL particles. Several different and discernible apoproteins have been isolated and characterized during the last decade from human plasma lipoproteins (Fredrickson *et al.*, 1972b; Shore and Shore, 1972; Scanu and Ritter, 1973; Morrisett *et al.*, 1974). Apolipoproteins isolated from animal species are generally similar to those of the human in their physical properties and biological significance and in their distribution among lipoproteins. The pattern of apoproteins obtained from human and rat lipoproteins is shown in Figs. 2A and 2B. No general agreement exists as yet for the nomenclature of apoproteins. In the present review, the ABC nomenclature (Alaupovic, 1971) will be followed (Table III). According to this system, apoproteins A-I and A-II are the major apoproteins of HDL, apoprotein B is the major protein of LDL and is present also in chylomicrons and VLDL, and apoproteins C-I, C-II, and C-III represent the small molecular weight proteins of human plasma VLDL and HDL.

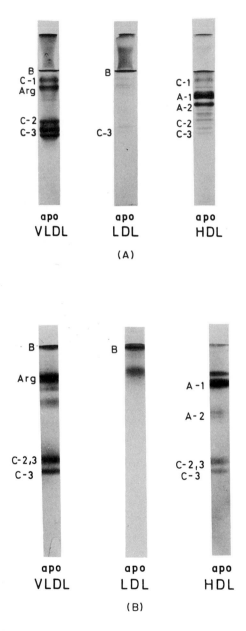

FIG. 2.   Apoproteins of plasma lipoproteins separated by polyacrylamide gel electrophoresis (10% polyacrylamide, 6 M Urea, 0.2 M tris buffer, pH = 8.1). Protein bands stained with 0.054 Coomassie Blue. (A) Human. (B) Rat.

Table III

APOLIPOPROTEINS OF HUMAN PLASMA LIPOPROTEINS

Apoprotein	Lipoprotein	C-terminal	N-terminal	Missing amino acids	Molecular weight	Secondary structure	Carbohydrates
A-I	HDL	Glutamine	Aspartic Acid	Isoleucine, cysteine	2700	α-Helix	+
A-II	HDL	Glutamine	Pyrrolidone carboxylic acid	Histidine, arginine, tryptophan	17000[a]	α-Helix, disordered	±
B	LDL, VLDL	(Blocked?)	Glutamic acid	—	—	β, Disordered?, α-Helix	+
C-I	VLDL, HDL	Serine	Threonine	Histidine, tyrosine, cysteine	7000	α-Helix	0
C-II	VLDL, HDL	Glutamic acid	Threonine	Histidine, cysteine	10000	Disordered	0
C-III	VLDL, HDL	Alanine	Serine	Cysteine, isoleucine	8764	Disordered, α-Helix	+
Arginine-rich	VLDL, HDL	?Alanine	?Lysine	Cysteine	?33000	α-Helix	+

[a] Dimeric form.

1. *Apoproteins A*

a. Human. The two A proteins, A-I and A-II, can be isolated readily from human HDL (Shore and Shore, 1968a,b, 1969, 1972; Rudman *et al.*, 1970; Scanu *et al.*, 1969a, 1972; Kostner and Alaupovic, 1971). Both are soluble in water and urea solutions and contain glutamine at their carboxy-terminal end. They differ, however, in amino-terminal amino acids, amino acid composition, immunological properties, and primary and secondary structure, and are easily separated by various chromatographic techniques. Apoprotein A-I has a molecular weight of 28,300, and is largely helical in structure (Scanu *et al.*, 1969b; Lux *et al.*, 1972a). The protein consists of 245 amino acids, and its primary structure has been recently reported (Baker *et al.*, 1973, 1974a,b; Delahunty *et al.*, 1974). A recent report (Fielding *et al.*, 1972) has indicated that apoprotein A-I may be an activator of the enzyme lecithin–cholesterol acyl transferase (LCAT), an enzyme of major importance for the formation of cholesterol esters in circulation (however, see Kostner, 1974, for another opinion).

Apoprotein A-II, isolated following gel filtration on Sephadex or DEAE-cellulose (diethylaminoethyl cellulose) ion exchange chromatography, is a single protein of molecular weight 17,000. By reduction of a single-S-S-band, two identical peptides of molecular weight 8500 are isolated (Scanu *et al.*, 1971, 1972; Lux *et al.*, 1972b). The peptides consist of 77 amino acid residues (glutamine is the carboxy-terminal amino acid and pyrrolidone carboxylic acid is the amino-terminal residue). The sequence of apoprotein A-II has been reported independently from two laboratories (Brewer *et al.*, 1972; Lux *et al.*, 1972c; Jackson and Gotto, 1972).

The interaction of the A proteins and their cyanogen bromide fragments with lipids has been studied extensively over the last few years. These studies have been summarized recently (Jackson and Gotto, 1974; Morrisett *et al.*, 1974). Both proteins were shown to bind lecithin molecules and to form protein–phospholipid complexes (Lux *et al.*, 1972a,d; Jackson *et al.*, 1972, 1973a,b). Similar observations were reported for apoprotein C-III (Sparrow *et al.*, 1973; Morrisett *et al.*, 1973; Hoff *et al.*, 1973) and for apoprotein C-I (Jackson *et al.*, 1974b). The amount of phospholipids (lecithin and sphingomyelin) that bind to either apoprotein A-I or apoprotein A-II has been recently reported. Assman and Brewer (1974a) have demonstrated that 70–90% of the apoprotein A-II added to a sonicated mixture of either phospholipid can be isolated in the lipid–protein complex density range (1.063–1.25 gm/ml). The ratio of lipid to protein (by weight) varied between 1.1 and 1.9. In contrast, only about 10% of the added apoprotein A-I was recovered with the lipid protein complex. Similar results were obtained when apo HDL was added to the sonicated lipid mixture. The study has thus confirmed previous observations (Gotto and Shore, 1969) that the interaction of apoprotein A-I with lipids may be less avid than that of apoprotein A-II and other apoproteins (apoprotein C-III).

b. *Other Species.* The major proteins isolated from HDL of several animals are not dissimilar to the human apoprotein A. The main A protein of rat plasma HDL is isolated after gel filtration on Sephadex as a single protein peak. It accounts for about 60% of total HDL proteins and has been designated HS-2 or peak IV (Bersot *et al.*, 1970; Koga *et al.*, 1971). There is no immunological cross-reactivity between this apoprotein and other rat plasma apolipoproteins. Swaney and Eder (1974a,b) have reported that rat apoprotein A-I has a molecular weight of 26,000 daltons and possesses amino-terminal aspartic acid and carboxy-terminal alanine. A protein similar to the monomeric form of human apoprotein A-II has also been isolated from rat plasma HDL (Herbert *et al.*, 1974). The protein is devoid of cysteine, histidine, and tryptophan and is rich in glutamine and glutamic acid residues. The carboxy-terminal amino acid is alanine; the amino-terminal residue is blocked. Its content in HDL, relative to that of the major apoprotein A (HS-2), seems to be smaller than that found in humans.

Apoprotein A-I and apoprotein A II have been isolated from plasma HDL of several nonhuman primates (Blaton *et al.*, 1974; Edelstein *et al.*, 1973, 1974; Scanu *et al.*, 1973, 1974a). These apoproteins are very similar to their counterparts in humans in chemical composition, molecular weight, and physical properties. The carboxy-terminal and amino-terminal residues of both the chimpanzee and *Macacus* rhesus proteins are identical to those of the human. In the latter species, apoprotein A-II appears only as a monomer. The amino-terminal amino acid sequence reveals the absence of cysteine at position 6. Apoprotein A-I of several other species (monkey, dog, bull, and chicken) was recently isolated and partially characterized (Assman *et al.*, 1974a,b). The sequence of the 20 amino-terminal amino acids of the A-I protein revealed a high degree of homology to that of the human.

2. Apoprotein B

a. *Human.* Apoprotein B constitutes more than 95% of the LDL proteins and about 40% of VLDL proteins (Gotto *et al.*, 1972). (See Section III,A for detailed discussion of its content in various VLDL particles.) Its concentration in normal plasma varies between 70 and 100 mg/100 ml (Schonfeld *et al.*, 1974b). Apoprotein B is characterized by specific immunological properties, amino acid composition, and secondary structure.

Delipidated apoprotein B is insoluble in water and requires the presence of detergents to maintain the protein in solution. Sodium dodecyl sulfate and sodium decyl sulfate are the most commonly used detergents. The latter detergent is more easily removed by dialysis than the former (Gotto *et al.*, 1968b, 1969). Apoprotein B is also rendered soluble after succinylation or maleation (Gotto *et al.*, 1968c, 1973; Simons and Helenius, 1969; Kane *et al.*, 1970). Carbohydrates constitute about 5% of the mass of apoprotein B (Ayrault-Jarrier *et al.*, 1961; Marshall and Kummerow, 1962; Sloan *et al.*, 1970). These include mannose, galactose, fucose, glucose, glucoseamine, and sialic acids. The location of glycoside chains on apoprotein B, their number, and their sequence are unknown. The amino-terminal amino acid is glutamic acid; the carboxy-terminal amino acid is most probably blocked. The protein has a significant content of beta and disordered structure (Gotto *et al.*, 1968b,c, 1973; Scanu *et al.*, 1969b). The nature of the basic protein subunit is yet unknown. Several investigators have reported data indicating that apoprotein B may contain more than one protein subunit (Simons and Helenius, 1969; Kane *et al.*, 1970; Shore and Shore, 1972; Smith *et al.*, 1972). The molecular weight of the apoprotein B monomer is unknown. Estimates range between 27,000 (Kane *et al.*, 1970) and 250,000 daltons (Smith *et al.*, 1972).

b. Other Species. A protein analogous to the human apoprotein B has been isolated from LDL of several animal species. When studied, various amounts of apoprotein B were found also in the plasma VLDL of those species. Its general features are those of the human apoprotein B, i.e., its solubility properties. In the rat, apoprotein B can be identified in VLDL and LDL. After solubilization in detergent, apoprotein B is isolated at the void volume of a Sephadex column. As in the human, apoprotein B does not enter 10% polyacrylamide gels and is identified at the gel origin. Immunologically, apoprotein B isolated from LDL of primate plasma, as well as the intact LDL particle itself, demonstrate cross-reactivity with human LDL.

3. Apoprotein C

a. Human. At least three different proteins belong to this group of apoproteins: C-I, C-II, and C-III. The three proteins differ in amino acid composition, amino- and carboxy-terminal groups, immunological reactivity, primary and secondary structure, and biological significance. They share in common, however, unique distribution among lipoproteins and certain physiological properties. All three proteins are of similar molecular weight, between 8,000 and 10,000 daltons. The C proteins were originally identified in VLDL by Gustafson, Alaupovic, and Furman (1966). Subsequent studies have demonstrated that apoprotein C is heterogeneous and contains at least three different proteins. These are best separated by ion exchange chromatography using DEAE cellulose (Shore and Shore, 1969; Brown *et al.*, 1969, 1970a,b; Albers and Scanu, 1971; Herbert *et al.*, 1971a). The C apoproteins are isolated also from HDL, especially HDL_2 (d = 1.063–1.1125 gm/ml), as a minor component—5 to 10% of total protein. They are easily and rapidly transferred from VLDL to HDL and vice versa by two different mechanisms: exchange of protein between the lipoproteins and net transfer of apoprotein from one lipoprotein to the other. The two mechanisms are discussed in detail in later sections of the review.

Apoprotein C-I elutes first from DEAE-cellulose. It has a molecular weight of 6631, contains 57 amino acids, has amino-terminal threonine and carboxy-terminal serine. The sequence of this apoprotein was reported in 1972 (Shulman *et al.*, 1972) and confirmed by Jackson *et al.* (1974a,b). The protein contains no carbohydrates and lacks histidine, tyrosine, and cysteine. It comprises about 10% of VLDL protein and 1–2% of HDL protein. Apoprotein C-I contains a large amount of helical structure.

Apoprotein C-II is eluted from DEAE in the second peak. It has amino-terminal threonine and carboxy-terminal glutamic acid. It is frequently referred to as apo-LP glu. The molecular weight of apoprotein C-II is about 10,000 daltons and its structure is primarily disordered. The protein appears to contain no carbohydrates and is lacking histidine and cysteine. Apoprotein C-II comprises 10% of the VLDL proteins and 1–2% of the total HDL protein.

Apoprotein C-III is isolated in at least two, and possibly three, polymorphic forms (Brown *et al.*, 1970a; Albers and Scanu, 1971). The protein contains a carbohydrate side chain attached to threonine, the sixth residue from the C-terminal end of the molecule. The polymorphic forms of apoprotein C-III are related to the molar content of sialic acids: two, one, or none. Apoprotein C-III has amino-terminal serine and carboxy-terminal alanine and contains no cysteine or isoleucine. The protein contains 79 amino acids and its complete amino acid sequence has been reported (Shulman *et al.*, 1974; Brewer *et al.*, 1974). The secondary structure of apoprotein C-III is primarily random coil. Apoprotein C-III comprises 30% of the protein moiety of VLDL and 4–6% of that of HDL.

The various C proteins are of great physiological importance and play an exceedingly important role in fat transport. It is now well established that apoprotein C-II (together with phospholipids) is the specific plasma protein cofactor necessary for the activation of adipose tissue (extrahepatic) lipoprotein lipases (LaRosa et al., 1970). The hydrolysis of nonlipoprotein triglycerides by the enzyme is enhanced 10- to 20-fold when apoprotein C-II and phospholipids are added to the incubation mixture. Apoprotein C-II is abundant in chylomicrons and VLDL particles; its limited content on intermediary triglyceride-rich particles may be responsible for their fate in circulation (see Sections IV,D and VIII). Ganesen et al. (1971) reported that apoprotein C-I may also activate lipoprotein lipases of post-heparin plasma, but this observation remains to be confirmed. Apoprotein C-III has been reported to be a specific inhibitor of the lipoprotein–lipase system (Brown and Baginsky, 1972). Subsequent studies, however, demonstrated decreased activity of the extrahepatic lipase when excess of any of the C proteins is present in the incubation mixture (Krauss et al., 1973a). The mode of action of apoprotein C on the enzymic reaction, especially during degradation of triglyceride-rich lipoproteins, is unknown.

b. *Other Species.* Proteins analogous to human apoprotein C have been identified in VLDL and HDL of several animal species. Where investigated, the C-protein fraction contained the lipoprotein lipase activator. Detailed studies have been carried out in the rat. In this species, apoprotein C comprises about 60% of the total VLDL protein and 20% of that of HDL. Further separation of rat apoprotein C has been achieved by ion exchange chromatography on DEAE-cellulose (Herbert et al., 1974). In analogy to the human, four different C proteins were isolated from rat lipoproteins. Apoprotein C-I lacks tyrosine, cysteine, and histidine, is rich in lysine, and does not contain glycosidic residues. The carboxy-terminal amino acid is alanine and the amino-terminal is aspartic acid. Rat apoprotein C-II is similar to the human in terminal amino acids, but contains histidine. Like its counterpart in humans, the rat apoprotein C-II appears to function as a specific activator of extrahepatic lipoprotein lipase. Apoprotein C-III contains carboxy-terminal proline and amino-terminal aspartic acid and appears in two polymorphic forms. Apoprotein C-III-O does not contain hexosamines or sialic acids and comigrates with apoprotein C-II on polyacrylamide gels electrophoresed in alkaline pH. Apoprotein C-III-3 contains galactosamine and 3 moles of sialic acid per mole of protein.

4. *Other Apoproteins*

Several apoproteins, different from those of apoprotein A, B, and C are consistently found in human plasma lipoproteins. They are usually present in small quantities (less than 10% of total protein). Two of these apoproteins have recently been partially characterized.

An arginine-rich protein was described in the original study of the Shores (1969, 1972) and has received much attention in recent reports (Shore and Shore, 1973, 1974; Shore *et al.*, 1974; Havel and Kane, 1973; Salel *et al.*, 1974). It is isolated from VLDL by DEAE ion exchange chromatography and constitutes 5–10% of total VLDL protein in normal subjects or patients with Type IV hyperlipoproteinemia. The protein is characterized by a high content of arginine—about 10% of the total amino acids. It is a highly structured protein with about 70% helical structure (Shore and Shore, 1973, 1974). The protein appears in several polymorphic forms. The reason for this heterogeneity is unknown. The arginine-rich protein is most probably identical to the protein isolated from human VLDL by Shelburne and Quarfordt (1974). This protein has a molecular weight of 33,000 daltons, an amino-terminal lysine and carboxy-terminal sequence of Leu-Ser-Ala. The arginine-rich protein has been reported to appear in excess amounts in the β-VLDL of patients with Type III hyperlipoproteinemia and possibly also in their normal VLDL and chylomicrons (Havel and Kane, 1973; Salel *et al.*, 1974). It is found also in the LDL density range, and may be present in HDL (Shelburne and Quarfordt, 1974; Havel and Kane, 1973).

An arginine-rich protein has also been found in VLDL obtained from several animal species. The amino acid composition and physical properties of the arginine-rich protein of rabbit VLDL are very similar to those of man (Shore and Shore, 1974; Shore *et al.*, 1974). Of particular interest is the observation that in the rabbit, and other species, the content of this protein is increased several fold when the animal is made hypercholesterolemic by cholesterol feeding. In these animals the arginine-rich protein is associated with abnormal cholesterol-rich lipoproteins (see Section III,D).

Apolipoprotein A-III is a designation suggested by Kostner (1974) for an additional protein isolated from human plasma HDL. The protein, formerly designated "thin-line peptide," is a minor constituent of the HDL proteins. The isolated protein is distinguished from other HDL proteins by its antigenic properties, migration on polyacrylamide gels, and amino acid composition. Serine is suggested to be the carboxy-terminal amino acid. The calculated molecular weight is between 19,000 and 20,350. This apoprotein may play a role in the activation of the enzyme system lecithin–cholesterol acyl transferase, and is also present in the lipoprotein of obstructive jaundice (LP-X).

III. Structure and Function of Lipoproteins

A. CHYLOMICRONS AND VLDL

Chylomicrons and VLDL share many structural features and are therefore discussed together though further knowledge may reveal fundamental differences between the two. These lipoproteins are composed predominantly of triglycerides and contain variable amounts of cholesterol, phospholipids, and apoproteins (Table IV). The molar ratio of free to esterified cholesterol is the highest of all lipoproteins, approximately 1:1; the molar ratio of lecithin to sphingomyelin is about 4:1 (Skipski, 1972; Kostner and Holasek, 1972). Apoprotein B and apoprotein C constitute more than 90% of the total protein moiety of both of these lipoproteins. The presence of small amounts of apoprotein A, has been reported by several investigators, especially in chylomicrons (Rodbell and Fredrickson, 1959; Pearlstein et al., 1971; Kostner and Holasek, 1972; Alaupovic et al., 1972). Others have not been able to detect any A protein in VLDL (Shore and Shore, 1972, 1973; Fredrickson et al., 1972b). Immunoassayable

Table IV
COMPOSITION OF CHYLOMICRONS AND VLDL PARTICLES

Lipoprotein	S_f range	Protein	PL[a]	TG[a]	FC[a]	EC[a,b]
		(mg/100 mg lipoprotein)				
Chylomicrons[c]	2719–10⁵	1.17	2.8	–	–	–
	908–3176	1.81	5.5	–	–	–
	324–1068	2.90	9.4	–	–	–
VLDL[d]	70–370	4.10	19.7	60.1	5.1	11.0
	46–250	6.90	19.9	54.8	6.4	12.0
	17–66	11.10	22.6	43.7	8.4	14.2

[a] PL = Phospholipids; TG = triglycerides; FC = free cholesterol; EC = cholesteryl esters.
[b] Sterol × 1.65.
[c] Adapted from Lossow et al. (1969).
[d] Adapted from Eisenberg et al. (1973a).

apoprotein A-I makes up less than 1% of total VLDL protein (Faineru *et al.*, 1974). Several other apoproteins, and in particular the arginine-rich protein, are consistently found in VLDL. The role of these latter proteins in the formation, stability, and metabolism of chylomicrons and VLDL is not clear. Normal synthesis and/or release of apoprotein B by liver and small intestinal cells is obligatory for the formation of VLDL and chylomicrons. Though apoprotein B may account for less than 1% of the total chylomicron mass, and only a few percent of large VLDL particles, it appears to be essential. VLDL and chylomicrons are not secreted from intestine or liver in the rare inheritable disorder abetalipoproteinemia in which apoprotein B synthesis is defective (see Section IV,A). In this disease, chylomicrons and VLDL are absent from plasma, as is LDL. Noteworthy, high density lipoproteins containing apoprotein A and apoprotein C are found in the plasma of these patients. Chylomicrons isolated from lymph ("primary particles") contain more phospholipids and less protein than circulating chylomicrons ("secondary particles") (Bierman *et al.*, 1965; O'Hara *et al.*, 1966). Most of the protein that is added to chylomicrons in the circulation is apoprotein C. This observation may be partially explained by net transfer of apoprotein C from HDL to chylomicrons, due to the equilibration of apoprotein C between the two lipoproteins. The transfer or adsorption of other proteins, or even smaller lipoprotein fragments to chylomicrons, cannot be ruled out. In the rat, evidence indicating that intestinal VLDL may be secreted with newly synthesized apoprotein B and no apoprotein C will be described in Section IV,A. It appears that apoprotein C may play no role, or only a minor one, in the assembly and secretion of VLDL. It may thus play only a minor role in the primary structure of this lipoprotein.

The classic model usually applied for the structure of chylomicrons and VLDL is that of a lipid core (Schneider *et al.*, 1973). According to this model, the lipoproteins have a neutral "lipid core" structure surrounded by a "surface" of protein and polar lipids. The core contains the nonpolar lipids, triglycerides, and esterified cholesterol; the surface contains apoproteins, phospholipids, and free cholesterol molecules. Several different lines of evidence support this general scheme: (a) Using freezing and thawing procedures, Zilversmit and his associates (Zilversmit, 1965; Yokoyama and Zilversmit, 1965; Salpeter and Zilversmit, 1968) isolated "surface" material fraction from dog chylomicrons. This fraction appeared as a "membrane" when viewed in the electron microscope and is rich in phospholipids and cholesterol. (b) A surface "halo" was demonstrated by electron microscopy to be present in the circumference of VLDL particles (Hamilton,

1968). The inner "core" of the particles was of distinctly different and denser appearance. (c) Free cholesterol, phospholipids (in particular lecithin), and apoprotein C are readily exchangeable between VLDL and other lipoproteins or tissues, indicating that these molecules are present at, or near, the outer surface of the particle. (d) On theoretical grounds, it is reasonable to assume that amphiapatic molecules will be present at oil–water interfaces. (e) The majority of the lecithin molecules present in chylomicrons are hydrolyzable by phospholipases A or C, and in the presence of albumin the lysolecithin formed leaves the chylomicrons without disintegrating the particles (Scow, 1974, unpublished observations). Similar observations were reported for HDL (Ashworth and Green, 1963; Camejo, 1969; Scanu, 1972) and LDL (Aggerbeck and Scanu, 1971).

The "lipid core" model, however, adds very little to the understanding of either the function or the metabolism of chylomicrons and VLDL. A functional view of the structure of these lipoproteins based on an analysis of the differences in physiological behavior of the constituent apoproteins (apoprotein B and apoprotein C) will be presented in later sections of this review.

A more practical approach to the study of the relationship between the nonpolar and the polar moieties of chylomicrons and VLDL is obtained from analysis of density subfractions of these two lipoproteins (Gustafson, 1966; Zilversmit, 1968; Lossow *et al.*, 1969; Fraser, 1970; Hazzard *et al.*, 1970; Lindgren *et al.*, 1972a,b; Sata *et al.*, 1972; Quarfordt *et al.*, 1972a; Eisenberg *et al.*, 1972b, 1973a). Although the methods of preparation of density subfractions vary widely in different studies, several general phenomena are observed (Table IV). Consistently, in all studies: (a) A relationship can be established between size, weight, and flotation rates of different subparticles. (b) The smaller a particle, the fewer triglycerides it contains and the more protein, cholesterol (free and esterified), and phospholipids. (c) Assuming that the particles are spheres and that the protein and the polar lipids are present at the particles' surfaces, and are of constant dimensions, a relatively constant fraction of the surface is covered with these constituents, regardless of particle size.

All these considerations raised the interesting suggestion in the 1960s that smaller particles may be formed from larger particles merely by loss of "core" (neutral lipid) material. However, this suggestion is not compatible with the more advanced analysis of the protein and lipid content of VLDL density subfractions (Eisenberg *et al.*, 1972b, 1973a). Subfractions were prepared from two plasma samples and characterized by analytical ultracentrifugation; their lipid and protein composition was determined. When apoproteins were separated by gel filtration, it was found that the content of apoprotein C in the various fractions was dependent on their density; the fractions of lower S_f rates contained less apoprotein C relative to apoprotein B than those of higher S_f rates (Figs. 3A and 3B). With this

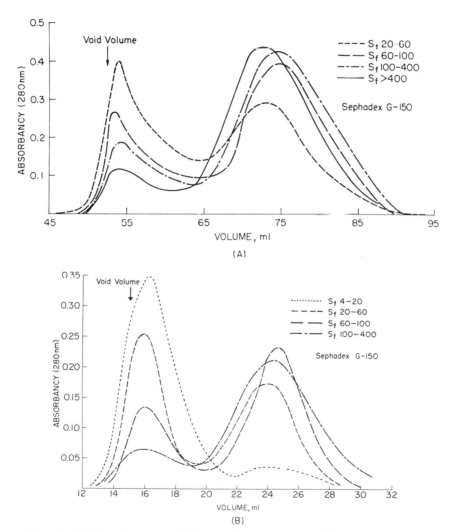

FIGS. 3A AND 3B.   Apoprotein B (first peak) and apoprotein C (second peak) content of VLDL density subfractions. Apoproteins were separated by gel filtration on Sephadex G-150. Data reproduced from Eisenberg *et al.* (1972b) by permission of the publisher.

information one can calculate the molecular weights of median particles of each density subfraction from the median S_f rates (Lindgren
et al., 1972b). Knowing the median molecular weight and the average
composition of the various fractions, it is possible to calculate the
*absolute amount of each lipid and protein constituent in one single
lipoprotein particle*. These results are presented in Fig. 4 together
with comparable data (lipids only) published by other investigators.
The analyzed data demonstrate unequivocally that smaller particles
contain less material of any given lipid constituent than larger particles, and that they are deficient in apoprotein C. In contrast, the content of apoprotein B in all subfractions studied (varying in median
molecular weight between 30.9 and 7.7 million daltons) was of similar
magnitude, did not decrease with decreasing S_f rates, and did not
differ much from that of LDL, measured in one of the two plasma
samples analyzed. It will be shown in later sections of this review that
substantial evidence exists to indicate that small VLDL particles are
formed abruptly from the larger ones. Thus, when regarded as finite
particles, it becomes obvious that VLDL loses some of each lipid constituent when the particles become smaller. The apparent increase in
(relative) content of cholesterol and phospholipids is the result of an
uneven loss of other lipids. Triglycerides disappear from VLDL at the

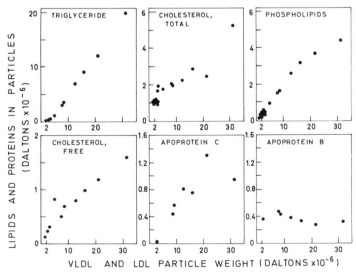

FIG. 4.   Lipid and protein content of VLDL and LDL particles of different weight.
All values are million daltons in one lipoprotein particle. Data used to compose the fig-
ure were published by Hammond and Fisher (1971), Lindgren *et al.* (1972a,b), and
Eisenberg *et al.* (1973a).

fastest rate, whereas the loss of cholesterol and phospholipids occurs more slowly. The data do not permit one to conclude whether free and esterified cholesterol or individual phospholipids (in particular sphingomyelin and lecithin) are removed from VLDL at similar or dissimilar rates.

While these studies do not contradict the fundamental "lipid core" model of VLDL, they raise several fundamental questions and indicate at least a few of the considerations that any VLDL model has to take into account. (1) The model should explain the different behavior of apoprotein B and apoprotein C. (2) If more than one unit of apoprotein B is present in VLDL, the units are necessarily bound together, either structurally or functionally for they always remain together (see Section VIII for a detailed discussion). (3) The model has to allow a loss of cholesterol, phospholipids, and apoprotein C from VLDL, occurring concomitantly with the removal of triglycerides. (4) The content of polar constituents seems to be related to the size and molecular weight of any given VLDL particle. It is thus reasonable to assume that the loss of these constituents is related to the removal of triglyceride from the particle. (5) The model should consider the interesting possibility that apoprotein C, cholesterol, and phospholipids may break off from the VLDL particle in the form of small lipoprotein subunits.

B. LDL

Human plasma LDL, isolated in the ultracentrifuge at the density interval of 1.006–1.063 gm/ml appears under the electron microscope as a homogeneous suspension of spherical particles of similar size and shape. The particles vary in diameter from 170 to 260 Å, with a mean of about 220 Å (Forte and Nichols, 1972; Forte *et al.*, 1968, 1971b). Several investigators have described a substructure to the particle either as being strandlike or as being a set of globular subunits of about 50 Å in diameter (Pollard *et al.*, 1969; Scanu, 1972). About 50% of the LDL mass is cholesterol, predominantly in the esterified form; protein and phospholipids comprise about 20–25% each of the total mass. The presence of small amounts of triglycerides in LDL has been reported by most investigators. The sphingomyelin content of LDL is higher than that in any other lipoprotein with a ratio of lecithin to sphingomyelin of only 2:1.

The major apoprotein present in LDL is apoprotein B. The presence of small quantities of apoprotein C in LDL has been repeatedly reported by Alaupovic and his associates (Lee and Alaupovic, 1970, 1974; Alaupovic *et al.*, 1972). However, even in these studies, appreciable amounts of apoprotein C (more than 5% of the total protein) were found only in the overlap density range of 1.006–1.019 gm/ml. In their most recent report, Lee and Alaupovic (1974) state that apoprotein B and apoprotein C appear to be associated in the density range of 1.006–1.019 gm/ml and to be unassociated in the density range of 1.019–1.053 gm/ml. This observation is in agreement with previous studies demonstrating low, but definite, affinity between apoprotein C and LDL (Eisenberg *et al.*, 1972a). Similarly to the situation in VLDL, but more convincingly, the study indicates that apoprotein C—although present in LDL—is not an integral part of the whole particle. The number of apoprotein B subunits in LDL is unknown; estimates ranging between 2 and 60 have been published (Pollard *et al.*, 1969; Mateu *et al.*, 1972; Scanu, 1972; Smith *et al.*, 1972).

Density subfractions have been prepared from LDL in several studies. It has long been recognized that there is a difference in composition between the fraction of density 1.006–1.019 gm/ml and that of density 1.019–1.063 gm/ml. Metabolically, these two fractions are very different (see Sections IV and VIII). The fraction of density of 1.006–1.019 gm/ml will most probably be distinguished in the future as a descernible lipoprotein form. In three studies, the protein content and lipid composition were measured in several LDL density subfractions, including at least one subfraction of density less than 1.019 gm/ml and at least two subfractions of density greater than 1.019 gm/ml (Lee and Alaupovic, 1970; Hammond and Fisher, 1971; Lindgren *et al.*, 1972a). In all studies, triglycerides were present in appreciable amounts only in fractions of density less than 1.019 gm/ml; their content in the other fractions was far less than 10% of the total LDL mass. There was a general trend toward increased content of protein and cholesterol, especially in the esterified form, in fractions of higher densities. The content of phospholipids was similar in all subfractions. Molecular weights were estimated in two studies (Hammond and Fisher, 1971; Lindgren *et al.*, 1972a), and in both it was possible to calculate the amount of protein and lipid constituents in one particle (Table V). In both studies, the content of lipid constituents in one LDL particle was found to decrease in parallel to its molecular weight, though at different rates. The order of disappearance of lipids from the LDL particles was as follows: triglycerides > free cholesterol > phospholipids > esterified cholesterol. The different rates of disappearance of different lipids thus appear to be responsible for the changing lipid pattern of the LDL subfractions. In contrast, the content of protein in the different subfractions is relatively constant, though it did decrease slightly in one of the three studies. These observations are very similar to those described for the behavior of

Table V
COMPOSITION OF LDL PARTICLES

S_f	Weight (daltons $\times 10^{-6}$)	Protein	PL[a]	TG[a]	FC[a]	EC[a]
			(mg/100 mg lipoprotein)			
Normal[b]	2.7	23	27	11	13	49
20[b]	4.9	18	24	32	18	26
10	3.2	23	24	23	14	39
4	2.5	32	26	16	14	44
10.4–20.0[c]	3.04	16.9	24.8	–	–	–
5.7–12.0	2.17	22.6	23.3	–	–	–
3.5–6.5	1.91	25.5	22.3	–	–	–
10.4–20.0	3.34	17.9	22.2	–	–	–
5.7–12.0	2.25	23.8	22.6	–	–	–
3.5–6.5	1.88	26.6	21.2	–	–	–

[a] PL = Phospholipids; TG = triglycerides; FC = free cholesterol; EC = cholesteryl esters.

[b] Adapted from Hammond and Fisher (1971). The three LDL fractions of S_f rates 20, 10, and 4 were isolated from a patient with Type IV hyperlipoproteinemia.

[c] Adapted from Lindgren *et al.* (1972a).

apoprotein B in VLDL. *Since apoprotein B is the major protein moiety of LDL the general rule that seems to emerge from observations in the two lipoproteins is that a constant amount of apoprotein B is needed to form any chylomicron, VLDL, or LDL lipoprotein particle.* The apoprotein B is bound to lipids, predominantly phospholipids and cholesterol, in an amount which is either similar to or smaller than that present in the smallest LDL particle. A lipoprotein structure is thus suggested which functionally, and possibly also structurally, constitutes a "nucleus" for all apoprotein-B-containing lipoproteins. In larger particles other lipids are also present, and their amount may be many fold greater than that present in the "nucleus." In the absence of the apoprotein B "nucleus"—as in abetalipoproteinemia—lipoproteins containing apoprotein B are not formed. It will be shown later that there is good evidence to regard LDL, at least in part, as a breakdown product of VLDL and possibly also of chylomicrons. The hypothesis of an "apoprotein B nucleus" obviously agrees with this idea. It further suggests that regardless of the size of the lipoprotein particle, there is a need for an "apoprotein B nucleus" for its formation and secretion into the plasma.

Structural models of LDL based on electron microscopy optical properties and nuclear magnetic resonance and small-angle X-ray scattering techniques have been proposed by several investigators (Oncley et al., 1950; Steim et al., 1968; Gotto, 1969; Scanu et al., 1969b; Pollard et al., 1969; Gotto et al., 1973; Mateu et al., 1972). The latest model (Mateu et al., 1972) proposes that LDL is composed of a spherical lipid bilayer of an average diameter of 65 Å covered by a two-dimensional network of protein subunits. The number of these subunits is estimated to be about 60; they have icosahedral symmetry and are each of a molecular weight of about 8000 daltons. Whether such a model agrees with functional and metabolic considerations as detailed above remains to be determined.

C. HDL

The composition and structure of HDL have been investigated extensively during the last 3–4 years. As isolated in the density range of 1.063–1.21 gm/ml, about 50% of the HDL mass is protein, 30% phospholipids, and 20% cholesterol. The lecithin to sphingomyelin ratio is 5:1 and the ratio of esterified to free cholesterol is about 3:1. HDL is customarily divided into two density clases: HDL_2 ($d = 1.063–1.125$ gm/ml) and HDL_3 ($d = 1,125–1.210$ gm/ml). HDL_2 has a mean molecular weight of 360,000 and is composed of 60% lipid and 40% protein. The mean molecular weight of HDL_3 is 175,000, of which 55% is attributed to apoproteins. The lecithin to sphingomyelin and esterified to free choesterol ratios are higher in HDL_3 than in HDL_2.

The protein moiety of HDL is composed of at least two apoprotein groups: A and C. Apoprotein A-I and apoprotein A-II constitute about 90% of the total protein. The available reports (see Scanu, 1972) indicate a ratio of 3:1 of apoprotein A-I to apoprotein A-II in either HDL_2 or HDL_3. Several investigators have reported that within each HDL class, heterogeneous particles can be demonstrated by using physical methods or immunological procedures (Borut and Aladjem, 1971; Eggena et al., 1972; Sundaram et al., 1974). It is still uncertain whether some of the differences among HDL populations are the result of artifacts formed during the isolation of the lipoprotein. These studies, however, raise the important question of the relationship between the two major apoproteins of HDL. Several lines of evidence point to the fact that apoprotein A-I and apoprotein A-II are, at least in part, unassociated, or only poorly associated in HDL particles: (a) Apoprotein A-I, but not apoprotein A-II, is released from HDL following mild treatment of the lipoprotein with physical or chemical agents, even bubbling of oxygen through HDL solutions (Levy and Fredrickson, 1965; Zapol *et al.*, 1969). As much as 50–60% of total plasma immunoassayable apoprotein A-I can be released from HDL during repeated centrifugations of plasma and HDL (Faineru *et al.*, 1974). Release of apoprotein A-I from HDL is responsible for the appearance of the αLP_β form described by Levy and Fredrickson (1965) following storage, centrifugation, freezing and thawing, or urea denaturation of HDL. (b) Specific immunoprecipitation of HDL with antibodies specific for apoprotein A-I and apoprotein A-II have demonstrated the existence of apoprotein A-I particles free of apo A-II (Albers and Aladjem, 1971). (c) Reassembly of HDL results in almost complete disassociation of the A proteins (Scanu *et al.*, 1970; Nichols *et al.*, 1972). After dehydration and rehydration of HDL, 63% of the parent protein is recovered in the fraction of density greater than 1.21 gm/ml. This fraction contains apoprotein A-I combined with small amounts of phospholipids (1% of mass). Apoprotein A-II is recovered mainly in the density of 1.063–1.21 gm/ml with small amounts of apoprotein A-I and apoprotein C-III. (d) In plasma of patients with LCAT deficiency, most of the apoprotein A-I is found in an unassociated form in the fraction of density greater than 1.21 gm/ml (see Section VI). (e) In familial HDL deficiency (Tangier disease, see Section VI), apoprotein A-I is almost absent from plasma, whereas the amount of apoprotein A-II is reduced to 6% of normal, resulting in a ratio of 1:3 between the two apoproteins (Lux *et al.*, 1972e). This ratio is one-tenth of that found in normal HDL. HDL particles containing only apoprotein A-II were recently isolated from the plasma of these patients (Assman *et al.*, 1974d). If the view that apoproteins A-I and A-II are at least partially independent proves to be true, then it may be hypothesized that some of the differences in HDL content in humans (as between males and females) may be related to changing levels and/or metabolism of one of the two apoproteins.

Apoprotein C is present in the HDL density range of humans in relatively small amounts. Apoprotein C comprises 3–5% of HDL_2 protein and 1–2% of HDL_3 protein (Scanu, 1972; Shore and Shore, 1972). It should be noted, however, that when one views protein content in absolute amounts, the apoprotein C present in HDL accounts for more than one-half of the total apoprotein C pool in normal fasting human plasma. It is usually assumed that apoprotein C is not an integral part of the HDL structure. The presence of this protein in HDL is explained as affinity between apoprotein C and constituents on the HDL surface. No direct evidence, however, now exists to conclusively prove this hypothesis. Several other apoproteins have been isolated from HDL. Their characteristics and importance for the integrity and metabolism of HDL are unknown. Electron microscopy of HDL particles (Forte et al., 1968, 1971b; Forte and Nichols, 1972) reveals definite substructure. These observations have been interpreted as compatible with a basic cylindrical subunit with a diameter of 34 Å and long axis of 64 Å. HDL particles varied in the number of subunits from 2 to 7 with most particles resembling a ring containing 4 or 5 subunits. The calculated weight of one subunit is about 60,000 daltons. The figure agrees well with the molecular weights of HDL_2 and HDL_3, assuming that different numbers of subunits are present in each lipoprotein class.

Various structural models of HDL based on chemical, enzymic and physical studies of the intact particle and of particles obtained after reassembly experiments were reviewed recently (Scanu, 1972). The general model emphasizes the presence of most of the proteins and phospholipids in an outside shell of the particle, oriented at a water–lipid interphase. Cholesterol esters are important constituents of any HDL model and are essential for the formation of normal appearing particles (Forte et al., 1971a). Three sophisticated models of the HDL particle were proposed recently. The model, suggested by Assman and Brewer, differs considerably from all former models. It is based on the lipid–protein reconstitution studies already mentioned, and nuclear magnetic resonance spectroscopy of the native and recombined lipoproteins (Assman et al., 1974a,b; Assman and Brewer, 1974a,b). The model predicts that triglycerides and cholesterol esters form an interior "oil droplet" core of the particle. Phospholipids are present in the lipid–water interphase. An amphipathic helical portion near the carboxy–terminal end of apoprotein A-II is interacting hydrophobically with the fatty acid chain of the phospholipids whereas its amino-terminal portion projects into the water environment. The association of apoprotein A-I with the particle is due primarily to a protein–protein interaction with apoprotein A-II. The model suggested by Stoffel et al. (1974) is also based chiefly on nuclear magnetic resonance spectroscopy of reconstituted HDL. By using lipids enriched with ^{13}C at specific positions of the acyl chains, the authors were able to demonstrate a hydrophobic binding of the fatty acyl residues of phospholipids to apoproteins and to exclude strong ionic interactions. The model predicts that the surface of HDL particles is made of the polar head groups of phospholipids and hydrophilic areas of apoproteins, the latter covering more than half of the particle's surface. A different structural association of lipids and proteins in HDL was proposed by Gotto and associates (Segrest et al., 1974; Morrisett et al.,

1974). These investigators have stressed the importance of helical peptide segments of which one side is polar (hydrophilic) and the other apolar (hydrophobic). This structural orientation permits ionic interaction between charged amino acid side chains and polar head groups of phospholipids, and nonionic interactions between the upper portions of the acyl residues (C_2-C_4) and the hydrophobic side of the helix. The model thus assumes amphipathic interaction between phospholipids and apoproteins.

The compatibility of the various models with either the function or the metabolism of HDL remains to be established.

D. OTHER LIPOPROTEINS

1. *The LP(a) Lipoprotein ("Sinking Pre-β-Lipoprotein)*

The LP(a) lipoprotein is found in varying amounts in human plasma at the density interval of 1.055–1.085 gm/ml. This lipoprotein, originally discovered because of its antigenic properties (Berg, 1963), has alpha-2 (prebeta) mobility and is composed of 27% protein, 65% lipid, and 8% carbohydrates (Simons *et al.*, 1970; Rider *et al.*, 1970; Ehnholm *et al.*, 1972; Albers and Hazzard, 1974). The protein moiety of the LP(a) lipoprotein was reported to be composed of 65% apoprotein B, 20% of "LP(a) apoprotein," and albumin (less than 15% of total protein; Ehnholm *et al.*, 1972). The most prevalent lipids of the LP(a) lipoprotein are cholesterol (predominantly esterified) and phospholipids, 41.7% and 19.2% of total mass respectively. Immunochemically, it cross-reacts with LDL, but residual antigenicity is identified with LP(a) after absorption of an anti-LP(a) serum with LDL. LP(a) differs from LDL in both chemical composition (lipid to protein ratio and hexose, hexosamine, and sialic acid content) and physical properties. It is distinguished among the plasma lipoproteins by a disproportionately high molecular rate—5.4×10^6—as compared to its sedimentation properties. In early studies LP(a) was detected in about 30–40% of the individuals tested. In a recent report, however, using a more sensitive assay, LP(a) lipoprotein was identified in 92% of 340 free-living adults (Albers and Hazzard, 1974), supporting the concept that it exists in all individuals. The concentration of LP(a) lipoprotein differs markedly among positive individuals varying from 2–76 mg/100 ml, the mean being 14 mg/100 ml. LP(a) levels are apparently similar in males and females and are independent of age and of plasma cholesterol and triglyceride levels. High levels of LP(a) lipoprotein in certain families may follow autosomal dominant inheritance (Rider *et al.*,

1970; Dahlen *et al.*, 1972; Heiberg and Berg, 1974). The routes of synthesis and catabolism of the LP(a) lipoprotein are yet unknown, as is its physiological significance.

2. The Lipoproteins of Obstructive Jaundice (LP-X)

It has long been recognized that an abnormal lipoprotein, composed predominantly of free cholesterol and lecithin, is present in the LDL density range (d = 1.006–1.063 gm/ml) from patients with obstructive jaundice. This lipoprotein has been isolated and characterized by several investigators during the last 7–8 years (Switzer, 1967; Seidel *et al.*, 1969, 1972; Picard and Veissier, 1970; Hamilton *et al.*, 1971; Quarfordt *et al.*, 1972b). It contains about 65% lecithin, 25–30% unesterified cholesterol, and 5% protein. The lipoprotein migrates on most electrophoretic media slightly slower than normal LDL, and has a flotation rate (S_f) of 9–14. Studies on the protein moiety of the abnormal LDL have revealed that it is composed of albumin (20–40% of total protein) and apoprotein C. The albumin is not detected immunochemically in the intact lipoprotein; it is identified, however, after delipidation or attack by phospholipases (Seidel *et al.*, 1972). Apoprotein C can be identified in the intact particle. These results were interpreted as indicating that albumin is located in the interior of the particle and apoprotein C at its surface.

In the electron microscope, the lipoprotein of obstructive jaundice appears as coin- or disk-shaped particles with a major axis of about 500 Å (Hamilton *et al.*, 1971). Further analysis of the particles suggests that the disks are made of bilayer sheets of 50–60 Å thickness. This suggestion is in agreement with low angle X-ray diffraction analysis of the particles. Of interest is the observation that similar particles are found in the plasma LDL of patients with LCAT deficiency and in the plasma of the cholesterol-fed guinea pig. Similar particles can also be formed by sonication of cholesterol–lecithin micelles with apoproteins (Forte *et al.*, 1971a, 1974; Forte and Nichols, 1972). Thus, the structure of this lipoprotein may be determined by its unusual lipid composition.

The source, metabolism, and fate of this lipoprotein are as yet poorly understood. The disk-shaped lipoproteins are probably formed in plasma since they are not identified in liver cells of mice after ligation of the common bile duct (Stein *et al.*, 1973), whereas they are present in the plasma and the space of Disse.

3. The Lipoproteins of Cholesterol-Fed Animals

Hypercholesterolemia is a well-known consequence of cholesterol feeding in many different animal species. It has been studied in detail in rabbits, guinea pigs, dogs, swine, monkeys, rats, as well as other species. Only recently, however, have the cholesterol-carrying lipoproteins of the different species been isolated and characterized. Two "abnormal" lipoproteins can be isolated from these animals—one of density less than 1.006 gm/ml usually designated B-VLDL and the other of higher density, designated HDL_c. The possibility that very small quantities of these lipoproteins may be present in control animals (fed a normal diet) cannot be completely excluded. The relative contribution of each abnormal lipoprotein varies among the species and depends in part on the magnitude of the cholesterolemia. In guinea pigs (Sardet *et al.*, 1972) 10–12 weeks on diet, hypercholesterolemia is characterized by the appearance of cholesterol-rich lipoproteins in the low and high density range. In either density, the lipoproteins are rich in free cholesterol and phospholipid and are relatively poor in protein. They appear in electron micrographs as long stacks of disks (LDL) or large transparent disks (HDL). The resemblance of these lipoproteins to the abnormal lipoproteins found in plasma of LCAT-deficient patients has been recently discussed (Glomset and Norum, 1973). An unusual feature of these lipoproteins is their content of an apoprotein of a molecular weight of 35,000 not detected in the plasma of control animals. In view of more recent studies in other species (discussed later), it is likely that this apoprotein is the arginine-rich apoprotein. The main difference between the two abnormal lipoprotein forms is the presence of apoprotein B in the low density range and its absence from HDL.

The cholesterol-carrying lipoproteins from rabbits have been investigated recently (Shore and Shore, 1974; Shore *et al.*, 1974; Camejo *et al.*, 1973, 1974). The predominant plasma lipoprotein of the hypercholesterolemic rabbit is found in VLDL. It has beta mobility (B-VLDL), contains 4% protein, 13% phospholipids, and large amounts of cholesteryl esters. In contrast to normal VLDL, only trace amounts of triglyceride are associated with B-VLDL particles. On electron micrographs, the B-VLDL particles appear larger than normal VLDL particles. The apoprotein pattern of these lipoproteins is unique. The arginine-rich protein comprises about 50% and apoprotein B about 40% of the total protein mass. An apoprotein equivalent to the human apoprotein C-I is also enriched in this lipoprotein. The other C-apoproteins, found in control VLDL, are barely detectable in this B-VLDL. Plasma of hypercholesterolemic rabbits is also enriched with LDL, some of which may be due to the presence of HDL_c (Mahley, 1974a).

The abnormal lipoproteins of hypothyroid cholesterol-fed dogs can be isolated either in VLDL or at a density interval of 1.006–1.08

(Mahley and Weisgraber, 1974b; Mahley *et al.*, 1974a). The former lipoproteins have beta mobility (B-VLDL), and the latter alpha mobility (HDL$_C$). HDL$_C$ present in the LDL density range can be separated from LDL by electrophoresis on Geon-Pevikon blocks. When dogs were classified in terms of the magnitude of the cholesterol elevation, differences in relative amounts of B-VLDL and HDL$_C$ were observed. Hyporesponder dogs (plasma cholesterol less than 750 mg/100 ml) were characterized by elevated levels of HDL$_C$ with only 9.5% of the cholesterol in VLDL. In hyper-responder dogs (plasma cholesterol more than 750 mg/100 ml), 65% of the plasma cholesterol was recovered in VLDL mainly as B-VLDL. Both B-VLDL and HDL$_C$ were enriched predominantly with cholesteryl esters. Of interest is the observation that in normal dogs, a lipoprotein fraction with alpha mobility can be isolated at the density interval of 1.006–1.063 (HDL$_1$). It is not dissimilar to HDL$_C$ in electrophoretic mobility, particle size, lipid composition, and apoprotein content. In normal dogs both HDL$_1$ and HDL$_2$ contain apoprotein A-I, apoprotein A-II, as well as the arginine-rich protein and apoprotein C. HDL$_C$ contains chiefly apoprotein A-I and the arginine-rich protein. The major protein constituents of B-VLDL are these same apoproteins as well as apoprotein B.

Hypercholesterolemia in cholesterol-fed rats is also characterized by increased levels of B-VLDL and HDL$_C$ (Lasser *et al.*, 1973; Kuhel *et al.*, 1974; Assman *et al.*, 1974c). These lipoproteins are enriched in cholesteryl esters and share apoprotein A-I, the arginine-rich protein, and apoprotein C. B-VLDL also contains apoprotein B.

B-VLDL and HDL$_C$ are found in swine fed high cholesterol diets (Mahley and Weisgraber, 1974a; Mahley *et al.*, 1974b). In this species, plasma cholesterol may be increased from about 90 mg/100 ml to 350–600 mg/100 ml. The two abnormal lipoproteins contain cholesteryl esters as their major lipid component. The major apoproteins of B-VLDL are apoprotein B and the arginine-rich protein. Those of HDL$_C$ are apoprotein A-I, the arginine-rich protein, and apoprotein C.

These studies unequivocally demonstrate that in many animal species abnormal lipoproteins can be identified in plasma after a drastic change in lipid homeostasis—feeding and absorption of cholesterol in huge amounts (the human equivalent being 50–100 gm per day). In all these species the abnormal lipoproteins share several important characteristics: (a) Two major "new" lipoproteins appear in the plasma, B-VLDL and HDL$_C$. The relative ratio of the two among species may reflect the degree of cholesterolemia (as demonstrated in dogs). (b) With the exception of the guinea pig, these abnormal lipoproteins, regardless of their density, contain cholesteryl ester as their major lipid constituent. Compared to lipoproteins of control animals the cholesterol-rich lipoproteins are relatively poor in protein. (c) The predominant apoproteins of B-VLDL appear to be apoprotein B and the species equivalent of the human arginine-rich protein. Those of HDL_C are apoprotein A-I and the same arginine-rich protein. Apoprotein A-I may also be present in B-VLDL, and proteins of the apoprotein C group are variably detected in either lipoprotein. It is important to note that all these apoproteins can be found in the plasma of normal animals. Whereas the origin, metabolism, and fate of the abnormal lipoproteins are unclear, one might speculate that they may represent elevations of lipoproteins normally present in trace amounts. In turn they may merely represent the fortuitous binding of circulating apoproteins to overlipidated lipoprotein forms.

The relevance of these animal studies to human dyslipoproteinemia is still unclear. B-VLDL not dissimilar to that observed in cholesterol-fed animals is found in plasma of patients with Type III hyperlipoproteinemia (Fredrickson and Levy, 1972; Hazzard *et al.*, 1972; Havel and Kane, 1973; Salel *et al.*, 1974).

IV. Metabolism of Chylomicrons and VLDL

A. SYNTHESIS

The synthesis of chylomicrons takes place in the small intestine during active fat absorption; VLDL is synthesized and secreted by both liver and intestinal mucosal cells at all times. Synthesis of apoproteins has been demonstrated to occur in isolated ribosomes of rat liver (Bungenberg de Jong and Marsh, 1968; Lo and Marsh, 1970) and intestine (Kessler *et al.*, 1970). The lipids are formed in both rough and smooth endoplasmic reticulum (Stein and Stein, 1967, 1974; Hamilton, 1972) where the assembly of lipids and apoproteins occurs. Most of these studies with chylomicrons and VLDL have been conducted in rats; data in humans are limited almost exclusively to the intestine.

A detailed morphological study of lipoprotein formation and intracellular transport in human intestinal absorption cells (Tytgat *et al.*, 1971) has indicated the following sequence: Lipoproteins are first identified in smooth endoplasmic reticulum vesicles at the luminal portion of the cell, a site of active acylation of the absorbed monoglycerides with acyl-CoA derivatives of fatty acids. Oher enzymes active in glyceride formation via the α-glycerophosphate pathway, and the enzymes of phospholipid and cholesterol synthesis are also isolated within the intestinal microsomal fractions (see reviews by Eisenberg, 1973; Stein and Stein, 1974).

Lipoprotein particles are transferred to Golgi organelles and can then be identified there even when lipoproteins are not found in any other cellular substructures. Lipoproteins are then found within smooth vesicles extending from the Golgi area toward the lateral and basal portions of the cell membrane and they leave the cells by reverse pinocytosis.

The sequence of VLDL synthesis in the rat liver is essentially similar to that described in the human small intestinal cells, and has been summarized recently (Marsh, 1971; Margolis and Capuzzi, 1972; Hamilton, 1972; Stein et al., 1972; Stein and Stein, 1974). Osmiophilic particles 300–800 Å in diameter are first observed in the transition zone between the rough and smooth endoplasmic reticulum. Using electron microscopy and radioautography it was possible to identify newly synthesized triglycerides in these particles (Stein and Stein, 1966, 1967). The particles are transported to the Golgi apparatus and reach the sinusoidal cell border inside membrane-bound secretory vacuoles. The VLDL is released into the circulation by fusion of the secretory vacuole with the cell membrane. The role of hepatic cell microtubules in the process of VLDL secretion has been stressed recently (Stein and Stein, 1973b; Stein et al., 1974b). In these studies it was found that in colchicine-treated animals there is an 80% fall in serum VLDL concentration (lipid and protein) concomitant with an accumulation of VLDL particles in the Golgi-derived hepatic secretory vesicles.

The attachment of carbohydrate to the protein moiety of lipoproteins begins in the smooth endoplasmic reticulum but is most marked inside the Golgi apparatus. Lipoproteins are excellent substrates in the Golgi for the nucleotide glycoprotein glycosyl transferases (Lo and Marsh, 1970; Mahley et al., 1971; Bizzi and Marsh, 1973; Delahunty and Mookerjea, 1974). The addition of carbohydrate to lipoproteins may play an important role in the mechanism of their release from cells.

VLDL has been isolated from rat liver and intestinal Golgi cisternae and from organ perfusion effluents from both the liver and the intestine (Mahley et al., 1969, 1970, 1971; Hamilton, 1972; Chapman et al., 1972). The lipoproteins are generally similar to circulating lipoproteins; however, particles from both liver and intestine are richer in phospholipids and poorer in protein than their native counterparts found in plasma. Some of these differences disappear following incubation with plasma or HDL (Hamilton, 1972). The origin of VLDL cholesteryl esters has not been completely elucidated. Transfer of cholesteryl esters from HDL to VLDL in exchange for triglyceride has been demonstrated *in vitro* (Nichols and Smith, 1965; Nichols, 1967; Quarfordt *et al.*, 1971). Lipoprotein particles isolated from either Golgi cisternae or hepatic perfusates, however, contain significant amounts of cholesteryl esters (Mahley *et al.*, 1969; Swell and Law, 1971). Hepatic origin of most of the VLDL cholesteryl esters in rats has also been demonstrated (Roheim *et al.*, 1963; Gidez *et al.*, 1965). In the human, the recent reports of Barter (1974a,b) have suggested that the origin of VLDL cholesteryl esters is hepatic and intraplasmal, with very little to no contribution from high density lipoprotein.

The availability of fatty acids of either endogenous or exogenous origin and the rate of de novo synthesis of fatty acid in the liver have been documented to affect VLDL and chylomicron formation. This is even more obvious for chylomicrons, which are synthesized only during active absorption of fatty acids and monoglycerides from the intestinal lumen. Intestinal VLDL formation is greatly diminished following cholestyramine administration or bile diversion (Ockner *et al.*, 1969; Porter *et al.*, 1971). Both procedures decrease considerably the availability of biliary lecithin fatty acids to the cells of the intestinal mucosa during fasting periods. In the isolated perfused rat liver, the release of VLDL increases or decreases in direct proportion to the concentration of free fatty acids in the perfusate (Ruderman *et al.*, 1968; Alcindor *et al.*, 1970). An analogous condition in humans is seen in uncontrolled diabetes, when free fatty acid levels in plasma are greatly increased (Bierman, 1972). The possible contribution of endogenous fatty acid synthesis to VLDL secretion was investigated in rats by Windmueller and Spaeth (1967). They found that net release of triglycerides and cholesterol into the hepatic perfusate was highly correlated with the rate of hepatic fatty acid synthesis. Carbohydrate feeding and insulin may stimulate liver VLDL synthesis through increased de novo synthesis of free fatty acids (Nikkila, 1969; Fredrickson and Levy, 1972). All these examples, and many more, are compatible with the hypothesis that the synthesis of the triglyceride-rich lipoproteins is dependent on the amount of free fatty acids available to liver and intestinal cells. The possibility that increased flux or synthesis of fatty acids may also affect the nature of the secreted particles has not been adequately explored. In one report it has been demonstrated that carbohydrate feeding may cause secretion of VLDL particles of larger size, richer in triglyceride (Ruderman *et al.*, 1971). The possible role of phospholipid and cholesterol metabolism in the regulation of VLDL or chylomicron synthesis has not been investigated in the human. Cholesterol feeding in several animal species (see Section III,D) results in the appearance in plasma of cholesterol-rich, triglyceride-poor lipoproteins, of density similar to that of VLDL. Virtually nothing is known of the routes of synthesis and secretion of these abnormal lipoprotein particles.

Incorporation of radioactive amino acids into the protein moiety of newly synthesized lipoproteins originating in the liver (Radding *et al.*, 1958; Haft *et al.*, 1962; Windmueller *et al.*, 1973; Bar–on *et al.*, 1973) or intestine (Roheim *et al.*, 1966; Windmueller and Levy, 1967; Windmuller *et al.*, 1970, 1973; Windmueller and Spaeth, 1972) has been demonstrated many times during the last 15 years. The incorporation of radioactive amino acids into specific lipoprotein apoproteins has been reported only recently (Windmueller *et al.*, 1973). VLDL and HDL labeled in their protein moieties have been isolated following liver and intestinal perfusion, and the radioactivity associated with their apoprotein groups as separated by poly-acrylamide gel electrophoresis was determined. In lipoproteins of liver origin, radioactivity was found associated with all apoproteins. However, the amount of label in VLDL apoprotein B was considered to be disproportionately high, and that of VLDL apoprotein C disproportionately low as compared to their known content in plasma VLDL. The results suggest that newly synthesized VLDL of hepatic origin is relatively poor (or absolutely deficient) in apoprotein C content. A similar conclusion was reached by Hamilton (1972) when reviewing unpublished studies on the lipase activation properties of VLDL isolated from the rat Golgi apparatus. In the intestinal perfusion experiment, no radioactivity was found associated with apoprotein C isolated from intestinal lymph VLDL and HDL, indicating that their presence in lymph lipoproteins is due to their transfer from the lipoproteins circulating in the plasma. In agreement with this finding is the observation that apoprotein C is not detected in lipoproteins isolated from the Golgi cisternae of rat intestinal mucosa (Mahley *et al.*, 1971), while it is present in those isolated from the liver (Mahley *et al.*, 1969, 1970). These studies all support the suggestion that *apoprotein C plays a minor role in the synthesis and secretion of VLDL and chylomicrons* and *is of little importance to the structural integrity of these lipoproteins.* They strengthen the hypothesis that the *normal synthesis and release of apoprotein B is fundamental to all these processes.*

That normal synthesis of apoproteins is essential for lipoprotein synthesis and secretion is suggested by still another kind of study. Administration of protein synthesis inhibitors to rats causes a complete inhibition of lipoprotein formation in liver and intestine (Eisenberg, 1973; Stein and Stein, 1974). The possible existence, however, of a preformed apoprotein pool—or a lipoprotein precursor pool—in the liver has been suggested by Bar–on *et al.* (1973). The authors used isolated rat livers perfused with cycloheximide and demonstrated the release of VLDL labeled with leucine and palmitic acid, introduced prior to the cycloheximide.

The specific role of apoprotein B in the formation of plasma lipoproteins is most dramatically illustrated in the rare inheritable disease abetalipoproteinemia. In this disorder apoprotein B is completely absent from plasma while apoprotein A and apoprotein C are present. In abetalipoproteinemia neither chylomicrons, VLDL, nor LDL are released, and the patients exhibit malabsorption of fat and fat-soluble vitamins from birth. Apparently secondary to the inability to synthesize or release apoprotein B, glyceride droplets accumulate in vesicles in the liver and intestine (Levy *et al.*, 1966; Fredrickson *et al.*, 1972a; Partin *et al.*, 1974). Lipoprotein particles are not detected in the various subcellular organelles. Abnormal high density lipoproteins have been identified, however, in the sera of these patients (Gotto *et al.*, 1971; Scanu *et al.*, 1974b; Kostner *et al.*, 1974). A partial defect in apoprotein B synthesis is probably responsible for the low levels of LDL observed in another rare inheritable disorder hypobetalipoproteinemia (Fredrickson *et al.*, 1972a). Whether increased apoprotein synthesis may cause increased lipoprotein synthesis is uncertain. This mechanism has been postulated to explain the hyperlipoproteinemia observed in patients with the nephrotic syndrome and in alcoholics (Marsh, 1971).

B. CATABOLISM OF THE LIPID MOIETY

1. *Lipoprotein Lipases*

The first stage in the degradation of chylomicrons and VLDL is related to triglyceride hydrolysis by the enzyme system lipoprotein lipase. Hypertriglyceridemia is regularly observed in humans and rats with low activity or no activity of lipoprotein lipase and occurs in insulinopenic diabetes (Bagdade *et al.*, 1967), hyperlipemia of pregnancy in starved rats (Scow *et al.*, 1965), familial type I hyperlipoproteinemia (Fredrickson and Levy, 1972), and possibly other conditions. In the present review we will describe briefly only the most recent findings concerned with the activities of the lipoprotein lipases as relevant to lipoprotein metabolism.

Lipoprotein lipase activity is barely detectable in fasting human plasma. Classically, the enzymes are demonstrated in the plasma compartment a few minutes after the injection of heparin. Post-heparin plasma contains several discernible lipolytic activities which may be related, at least in part, to different enzymes. At least two different triglyceride hydrolases are found in post-heparin plasma. The enzymes differ in their pH optimum, inhibition by protamine and concentrated NaCl solutions, and activation by specific apoprotein cofactors. The two enzymes have different tissue origin: One enzyme, identical to the "classic lipoprotein lipase" is of adipose tissue origin, whereas the other originates in the liver (LaRosa et al., 1972; Fielding, 1972; Krauss et al., 1973b; Greten et al., 1974). Both enzymes have been partially purified and characterized. In familial type I hyperlipoproteinemia, there is a complete absence of the extrahepatic triglyceride lipase; the activity of the liver enzyme seems to be present at "normal" levels (Herbert et al., 1971b; Krauss et al., 1974). Further observations demonstrate that these enzymes differ in their activity toward lipoprotein triglycerides, and that the liver enzyme has only limited capacity for hydrolyzing significant amounts of triglyceride from intact glyceride-laden lipoproteins (Krauss et al., 1973b). This is supported by experiments using the isolated perfused liver, which is incapable of catabolizing intact VLDL (Felts and Mayes, 1965; Mayes and Felts, 1967; Felts and Berry, 1971; S. Eisenberg and D. Rachmilewitz, unpublished observations, 1974). The two enzymes may therefore have different functional roles during the process of intravascular triglyceride hydrolysis.

Post-heparin lipoprotein lipase also exhibits distinct activities toward diglycerides and monoglycerides (Greten et al., 1969; Biala and Shafrir, 1969; Nilsson-Ehle and Belfrage, 1972). Another interesting lipolytic activity found in post-heparin plasma is the function of a phospholipase which hydrolyzes fatty acids in the 1-position of phosphatidylcholine and phosphatidylethanolamine (Vogel and Zieve, 1964; Vogel and Bierman, 1967, 1970; Vogel et al., 1971). The enzymic activity results in the formation of lysophosphatide compounds, especially lysolecithin. Phospholipase activity has also been demonstrated in purified milk lipoprotein lipase (Scow, 1974). Zieve and Zieve (1972) have concluded that most of the phospholipase activity of rat plasma originates in the liver. Vogel et al. (1971; Vogel and Bierman, 1970), however, were not able to differentiate the phospholipase and triglyceride lipase activities of post-heparin plasma. The possibility that both the hepatic and extrahepatic enzyme systems are capable of hydrolyzing phospholipids cannot be ruled out. Recent studies, using intact lipoproteins as the enzyme substrate, have indicated that hydrolysis of lecithin to lysolecithin may account for the disappearance of some phospholipids from VLDL after the interaction of VLDL with post-heparin plasma (S. Eisenberg and D. Shore, unpublished observations, 1974) and chylomicrons with the milk enzyme (Scow, 1974). Since lecithin is present on the surface of chylomicrons and VLDL, the post-heparin phospholipase may be active early in the hydrolysis of these large particles.

Of particular interest is the obligatory role of phospholipids and an apolipoprotein cofactor, for the nonlipoprotein triglyceride hydrolysis by extrahepatic lipoprotein lipase. When the partially purified enzyme is incubated with triglyceride emulsions, little activity is observed unless the human apoprotein C-II (carboxy-terminal amino acid glutamic acid) is added to the incubation system (LaRosa *et al.*, 1970; Krauss *et al.*, 1973a). An analogous apoprotein of rat plasma lipoproteins is the specific lipoprotein-lipase activator in this species (Herbert *et al.*, 1973). The mode of action of the activator is as yet unknown. It has been reported that apoprotein C-III (carboxy-terminal amino acid alanine) is a specific inhibitor of the lipoprotein-lipase system, and that this inhibition is reversed by the addition of triglycerides to the incubation mixture (Brown and Baginsky, 1972). Other investigators have found, however, that the enzyme is inhibited by large amounts of each of the C proteins, including apoprotein C-II, and thus the inhibition may represent a nonspecific surface absorption of apoproteins to triglyceride micelles (Krauss *et al.*, 1973a). The activation of lipoprotein lipases of different sources by C proteins other than apoprotein C-II has been reported but not verified (Ganesen *et al.*, 1971). It is obvious that circulating chylomicrons and VLDL provide lipoprotein lipase with both the substrate and the apoprotein and phospholipid cofactor necessary for normal enzyme activity.

Lipoprotein lipase is normally located on the surface of endothelial cells of adipose tissue, skeletal muscle, and heart muscle (Robinson, 1970; Scow, 1970; Blanchette-Mackie and Scow, 1971). The liver enzyme is predominantly associated with the hepatocyte outer membrane (Assman *et al.*, 1973). During the physiological process of chylomicron and VLDL catabolism, the hydrolysis of triglycerides occurs at these sites rather than in the blood stream. Thus factors of possible extreme importance to *in situ* lipoprotein metabolism may be unrecognized when post-heparin plasma is used. Unfortunately, little is known about the interaction of triglyceride-rich lipoproteins and lipoprotein lipase with the endothelial lining of the capillary wall. Some information about this process, however, was recently gathered by Scow and associates, studying the fate of labeled chylomicrons during perfusion of adipose tissue and the lactating mammary gland (Scow *et al.*, 1972, 1973a,b; Blanchette-Mackie and Scow, 1971, 1973). Using both electron microscopy and biochemical approaches and studying chylomicron triglycerides labeled in their glycerol and fatty acid moieties, these investigators were able to demonstrate the following sequence: Chylomicrons are first attached to the capillary endothelial cells presumably at the site of lipoprotein-lipase activity. They are found partially enveloped by the plasma membrane of the cell. Hydrolysis occurs only in chylomicrons attached to the endothelial cells. Within 1–2 minutes, one fatty acid is released from the triglyceride into the circulation. Glycerol is released at a later time, and the molar ratio of glycerol to fatty acids in the perfusate is about 1. These observations were interpreted as indicating that diglycerides formed at the endothelial cell surface are further hydrolyzed inside vacuoles in the cells and at the subendothelial spaces. The glycerol is transferred back to the capillary lumen, whereas the two fatty acids are utilized for the synthesis of tissue triglycerides. The triglyceride-depleted chylomicrons in these studies were subsequently released into the capillary lumen and could then be isolated from the perfusate.

2. *Fate of Chylomicron Lipids*

The rate of disappearance of chylomicron triglyceride from the blood stream is extremely rapid. The half-life time in circulation of triglycerides after injection of labeled chylomicrons into humans is less than an hour (Nestel, 1974) and as short as a few minutes in the rat (Olivecrona, 1962; Olivecrona and Belfrage, 1965; Harris and Harris, 1973). In rats, about 80% of the labeled triglyceride fatty acids are recovered in muscle and adipose tissue, and only 20% in other tissues, principally the liver. A similar distribution of chylomicron triglyceride fatty acids may also occur in humans. An important determinant of chylomicron catabolism is their size: larger particles are catabolized more rapidly than smaller particles (Quarfordt and Goodman, 1966). This interesting observation may be related to the greater affinity of apoprotein C-II and lipoprotein lipase for larger chylomicrons *in situ*. The fate of other lipids especially cholesterol esters and phospholipids has been investigated only in rats. In this species a sharp dichotomy has been found between the fate of chylomicron triglycerides and chylomicron cholesteryl esters (Quarfordt and Goodman, 1967; Stein *et al.*, 1969). The former are channeled to muscle and adipose tissue, whereas the latter are catabolized predominantly by the liver. By coupling electron microscopy with radioautography it has been demonstrated that the chylomicron cholesteryl esters are taken up chiefly by the hepatocytes. Labeled cholesteryl esters were found in Kupfer cells only after the injection of very large amounts of chylomicrons. Similar conclusions were reported after separation of hepatocytes and Kupfer cells by physical procedures (Nilsson and Zilversmit, 1971). Available evidence indicates that the cholesteryl esters are hydrolyzed to free cholesterol and free fatty acids prior to their uptake into the cells. The presence of cholesterol ester hydrolase at the surface of liver cells has been postulated.

All of these results suggest that the process of chylomicron metabolism in rats occurs in at least two different steps: The first affects predominantly triglyceride clearance, occurs in muscle and adipose tissue, and is dependent on the activity of lipoprotein lipase. The second occurs mainly in the liver and involves the catabolism of the cholesteryl ester moiety of chylomicrons. The two steps can be disassociated in rats by a total hepatectomy (Redgrave, 1970). After the injection of chylomicrons into such rats, a particle rich in cholesterol and poor in triglycerides accumulates in the circulation. The particle, designated "remnant" persists in the plasma of the hepatectomized rats. Similar observations in sheep and dogs have also been reported by Bergman *et al.* (1971). These investigators have determined the fate of infused chylomicron triglycerides in unanesthetized animals by sampling plasma aliquots from the aorta, vena cava, and the portal, left hepatic, and jugular veins. Their studies indicate that most of the triglycerides are removed by extrahepatic tissues whereas the liver catabolizes a triglyceride-poor, cholesterol-rich "skeleton." This metabolic pathway is shown schematically in Fig. 5. It should be pointed out, however, that at this time there is no evidence in the literature that demonstrates that human chylomicron remnants are produced or metabolized through similar routes.

3. *Fate of VLDL Lipids*

Numerous studies have been published in the last decade on the kinetics of VLDL triglyceride clearance from the circulation. Most studies have been conducted in humans and in these studies labeled fatty acids or labeled glycerol have been used as precursors of VLDL triglyceride. Several mathematical models have been developed to determine the half-life time of triglycerides in plasma and their synthetic and catabolic rates. The merits and shortcomings of the various models were reviewed recently (Shames *et al.*, 1970). In normal

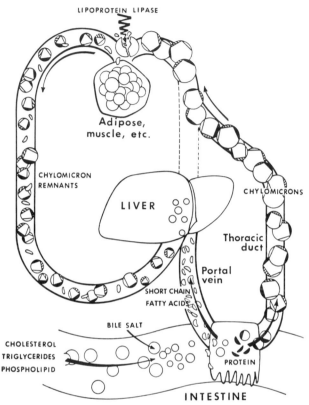

FIG. 5. Schematic representation of chylomicrons metabolism. From Levy *et al.*
(1971).

humans, the half-life time of VLDL triglyceride fatty acid in the
circulation varies between 2 and 4 hours. Increased rates of synthesis
and secretion of VLDL triglyceride are observed when the diet is
enriched in carbohydrates to about 70% of total calories. Most recent
reports indicate that in endogenous hypertriglyceridemia (type IV
hyperlipoproteinemia) the mechanism of removal of triglycerides is
defective (Quarfordt *et al.*, 1970). This conclusion is in agreement
with the observation of Havel *et al.* (1970), who estimated triglyceride
transport from the liver by a direct measurement of the splanchnic
metabolism of free fatty acids and triglyceride.

The clearance of VLDL triglyceride is greatly accelerated following
the activation of the lipoprotein-lipase system by the injection of
heparin. As much as 80% of the VLDL triglycerides are hydrolyzed
within 10–30 minutes of the intravenous injection of heparin and are

cleared from circulation primarily by extrahepatic tissues. To what extent VLDL triglyceride fatty acids are taken up by the liver is not known.

The importance of lipoprotein lipase for the hydrolysis of VLDL triglycerides is best exemplified in patients with type I hyperlipoproteinemia who lack the extrahepatic enzyme. In these patients, the clearance of VLDL triglycerides from the circulation is considerably delayed (Quarfordt *et al.*, 1970).

As in the catabolism of chylomicrons particle size is significant, the larger VLDL particles being more susceptible to lipoprotein lipase than the smaller particles. The distribution of plasma lipoproteins after the injection of heparin, as studied in the analytical ultracentrifuge (Nichols *et al.*, 1968; Eisenberg *et al.*, 1973a), reveals that the major degradation product accumulates in both VLDL and LDL at an S_f interval of 5–60. These lipoproteins persist in circulation for a relatively long period, at least 75 minutes. The density range and metabolic behavior of this post-heparin lipoprotein is strikingly similar to that of the intermediate lipoprotein (see next section.).

The specific activity of VLDL triglyceride fatty acids of particles of different S_f rates before and after the administration of heparin has been measured by Barter and Nestel (1970). Accumulation of smaller VLDL particles subsequent to the injection of heparin was observed, and a precursor–product relationship to the larger pre-heparin particles was recorded. More recently these same authors (1972) have observed a precursor–product relationship between large and small VLDL particles during studies at steady state.

It has long been known that in animals VLDL triglyceride is the precursor of the small amount of LDL triglyceride (Havel *et al.*, 1962). A similar relationship of VLDL and LDL triglycerides has been reported in humans (Quarfordt *et al.*, 1970). All these studies indicate the following sequence of VLDL triglyceride metabolism: *VLDL triglycerides are secreted mainly in the form of large particles* (S_f rate greater than 100). *These particles interact with extrahepatic lipoprotein lipase, lose some of their triglycerides, and form smaller VLDL particles.* LDL triglycerides may represent the end stage of the intravascular triglyceride clearance process.

C. CATABOLISM OF THE PROTEIN MOIETY

Extensive studies on the fate of the protein moiety of VLDL have been carried out in humans and rats. The results obtained from the two species will be discussed separately. No information is available about the metabolism of chylomicron apoprotein *in vivo*.

1. *Studies in Humans*

Gitlin and his associates (1958) were the first to study the fate of lipoprotein apoproteins in humans. Using radioiodinated lipoproteins, these investigators were able to show that following the injection of iodinated VLDL, radioactivity distributes to higher density lipoproteins. Within 12–24 hours of the injection, considerable amounts of the labeled VLDL apoproteins were associated with LDL (S_f 3–9) rather than VLDL (S_f 10–100). These results contrasted with these authors' own experience with labeled LDL and HDL where most of the radioactivity was recovered at all time intervals at the density range of the injected lipoprotein. They thus suggested a precursor–product relationship between VLDL and LDL.

The development of methods for apoprotein separation employing column chromatography and polyacrylamide gel electrophoresis has now enabled extension of these interesting findings to the study of the individual VLDL apoproteins. Extensive studies on the metabolism of iodo-labeled VLDL apoproteins have been conducted at the Clinical Center of the National Institutes of Health (Bilheimer et al., 1971a,b, 1972; Eisenberg et al., 1972a,b, 1973a). In other reports, [75Se]-selenomethionine (Eaton and Kipnis, 1972) and [14C]-leucine (Phair et al., 1972) were used to label the VLDL proteins. Studies on the fate of human VLDL apoproteins injected into monkeys (Schonfeld et al., 1972) and rats (Eisenberg et al., 1973b) have also been published. The results of the different studies, using VLDL labeled by several methods or even unlabeled lipoproteins in monkeys, are essentially corroborative. In the present review, we will describe in detail the results obtained at the NIH in studies of more than 20 normal humans and patients with hyperlipoproteinemia. VLDL, labeled with 125-iodine in its protein moiety was prepared following slight modification of McFarlane's iodine monochloride method. About 50% of the protein-bound radioactivity was associated with apoprotein B, 40% with apoproteins C-II and C-III, and 10% with other apoproteins. Since the kinetic behavior of apoprotein C-II was similar to that of apoprotein C-III, these two were considered together. It is of course recognized that future experiments may discover important metabolic differences between the different C apoproteins.

In preliminary experiments ^{125}I-labeled VLDL was incubated with normal plasma *in vitro*. After incubation, labeled apoprotein C was distributed to other lipoproteins, predominantly HDL. When ^{125}I-VLDL was incubated with HDL, the distribution of ^{125}I-apoprotein C between the two lipoproteins was found to depend on their relative concentration in the incubation mixture. Similar observations were recorded when isolated labeled apoprotein C was incubated with either plasma or lipoprotein mixtures. Since apoprotein C was also readily transferable to VLDL from HDL, it was suggested that the bidirectional transfer of apoprotein C between VLDL and HDL represents an exchange phenomenon. This suggestion has been recently strengthened by further experiments conducted on rats (see next section). *In vivo,* similar observations were recorded immediately after the injection of ^{125}I-VLDL to humans. Labeled apoprotein C was distributed to HDL, and the ratio of radioactivity between VLDL and HDL as determined immediately after the injection was related to their concentrations in plasma (Fig. 6). At later time intervals, labeled apoprotein C, distributed between VLDL and HDL, and its decay from circulation was parallel in the two lipoproteins. All these experiments indicate that apoprotein C represents one single miscible pool which is distributed among VLDL and HDL in proportion to their plasma concentration.

The metabolic fate of apoprotein B was distinctly different from that of apoprotein C. Apoprotein B was always recovered with VLDL following *in vitro* incubations or immediately after the injection of ^{125}I-VLDL to humans. During the first day after the injection, however, apoprotein B disappeared from the density range of VLDL faster

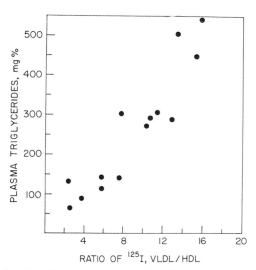

FIG. 6. Ratio of radioactivity associated with VLDL to that in HDL (abscissa) against plasma triglyceride levels. Data obtained 10 minutes after injection of ^{125}I-VLDL to 16 human subjects. Reproduced from Eisenberg *et al.* (1972a) by permission of the publisher.

than apoprotein C did, resulting in a changing pattern of labeled apoproteins in VLDL (Fig. 7). Twenty-four hours after the injection, the contribution of ^{125}I-apoprotein B to the total radioactivity of VLDL was negligible. The labeled apoprotein B was transferred to lipoproteins of intermediate density (1.006–1.019 gm/ml), during the

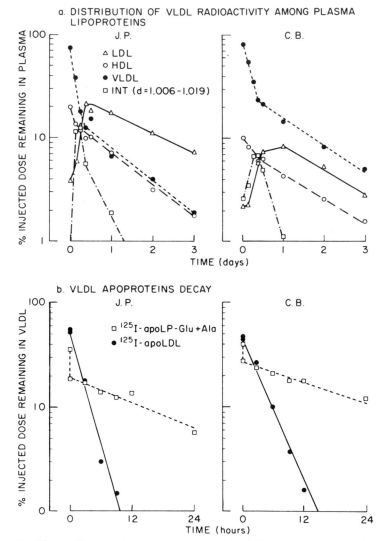

FIG. 7. Plasma lipoprotein radioactivity (top) and VLDL apoprotein radioactivity (bottom) at time intervals after injection of ^{125}I-VLDL to two human subjects. Lipoproteins were separated by ultracentrifugation. VLDL apoprotein radioactivity was determined after delipidation and polyacrylamide gel electrophoresis.

first 6–12 hours. During the next 12 hours radioactivity associated with the intermediate lipoprotein declined rapidly and the ^{125}I-apoprotein B was transferred to LDL (d = 1.019–1.063 gm/ml). Thus within 24–48 hours of injection, labeled apoprotein B was found in LDL and labeled apoprotein C was distributed between VLDL and HDL. The study led to the following conclusions: (a) *The B protein moiety of VLDL is a precursor of the B protein moiety of LDL.* Therefore, some, if not all, of the plasma LDL is formed in circulation and represents a true VLDL "remnant." (b) *The fate of apoprotein C and apoprotein B in VLDL is distinctly different and may even be unrelated.* (c) *The transfer of apoprotein B from VLDL to LDL seems to occur through the formation of a relatively short-lived lipoprotein of intermediate density.*

The relationship between VLDL triglyceride and apoprotein metabolism was further studied in humans injected with ^{125}I-VLDL and then heparin (Fig. 8). Within an hour of the heparin injection, VLDL particles of S_f rates greater than 60 disappeared from the plasma, and particles of S_f rates of 20–60 accumulated (Table VI). The latter particles contained twice as much ^{125}I-apoprotein B compared to [125]Iapoprotein C as the original particles of S_f greater than 60. At this time interval, only a small fraction of the ^{125}I-apoprotein B was associated with intermediate density lipoprotein (d = 1.006–1.019), and almost none with LDL. The further transfer of apoprotein B from small VLDL particles to intermediate lipoprotein and LDL occurred at a relatively slow rate, and was identical to that observed in humans not injected with heparin. The VLDL of S_f rates 20–60 observed in these acute experiments is similar to intermediate density lipoprotein in several respects: (a) It is formed rapidly following triglyceride hydrolysis of larger VLDL particles. (b) It contained more apoprotein B than apoprotein C. (c) Its transformation to higher density lipoproteins was relatively slow and did not appear to depend on the persistence of post-heparin lipolytic activity in plasma. The intermediate lipoprotein thus may represent the end of the first stage of VLDL degradation, a stage primarily determined by the activity of lipoprotein lipase. The mechanism of degradation of the intermediate to LDL is still unknown, as are the factors delaying triglyceride hydrolysis in this lipoprotein form.

These observations are all consonant with previous reports demonstrating accumulation of lipoprotein particles of S_f 12–60 both following the injection of heparin into humans and after *in vitro* incubation of VLDL with lipoprotein lipase (Shore and Shore, 1962; Nichols *et al.*, 1968). They are also in agreement with the previously cited experiments demonstrating a precursor–product relationship between tri-

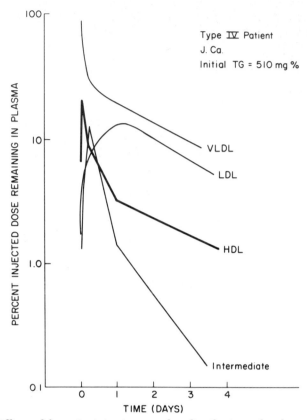

FIG. 8. Effect of heparin injection on the distribution of radioactivity among lipoproteins at time intervals after the injection of ^{125}I-VLDL to a patient with Type IV hyperlipoproteinemia. Reproduced from Eisenberg *et al.* (1973a) with permission of the publisher.

glycerides of large and small VLDL particles and between VLDL and LDL.

The effect of post-heparin lipolytic activity on the distribution of ^{125}I-apoprotein C between VLDL and HDL lipoproteins was investigated in these same studies. Labeled apoprotein C disappeared from VLDL concomitant with the hydrolysis of VLDL triglyceride and was recovered in plasma with HDL. Six hours after the injection of heparin when triglyceride levels reapproached the levels observed prior to heparin administration, ^{125}I-apoprotein C returned to the VLDL density range. It was, moreover, associated with the large, newly synthesized VLDL particles (Table VI).

Table VI

Effect of Heparin Injection on the Distribution of 125I-Apoprotein of VLDL Origin among Plasma Lipoproteins[a]

	Before heparin		After heparin, 45 min		After heparin, 360 min	
	125I-Apoprotein B	Apoprotein C	Apoprotein B	Apoprotein C	Apoprotein B	Apoprotein C
VLDL, S_f > 60	32.8	34.2	2.5	2.6	Trace	19.3
VLDL, S_f 20–60	6.7	3.7	36.8	19.6	10.5	5.5
IDL (d = 1.001–1.019)	Trace	Trace	2.7	0.7	10.4	1.2
LDL (1.019–1.063)	Trace	Trace	1.5	Trace	6.1	Trace
HDL (d = 1.063–1.21)	Trace	3.6	Trace	17.2	Trace	4.7

[a] Adapted from Eisenberg *et al.* (1973a). Data were combined from the two experiments. Apoprotein C represents radioactivity associated with C-II and the two forms of C-III. The results represent percent of injected dose recovered in circulation.

To what extent these conclusions can be applied to chylomicron metabolism is totally unknown. However, a study on the fate of labeled vitamin A absorbed from the intestinal lumen, has indicated that the label is transferred with time from chylomicrons to VLDL and from large VLDL particles to small particles (Hazzard and Bierman, 1970). The possibility that chylomicrons and VLDL are metabolized in humans through similar or even identical routes cannot be overlooked.

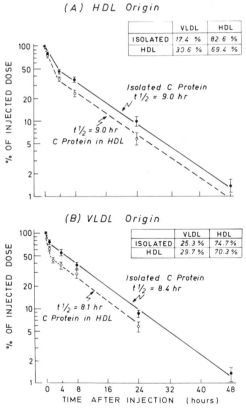

FIG. 9.   Fate of ^{125}I-labeled apoprotein C in the rat. The disappearance of apoprotein C after the injection of intact ^{125}I-labeled HDL (A) or VLDL (B) is shown in solid lines. The disappearance of apoprotein C after the injection of ^{125}I-apoprotein C isolated by gel filtration from either HDL (A) or VLDL (B) is shown in broken lines. Inserts show distribution of ^{125}I-apoprotein C between VLDL and LDL determined 8 hours after the injection. Data calculated from studies of Eisenberg and Rachmilewitz (1973a,b).

2. Studies in Rats

The metabolic fate of rat plasma VLDL apoproteins labeled with 125-iodine has been reported from several laboratories (Eisenberg and Rachmilewitz, 1973a,b; Fidge and Poulis, 1974); it has also been studied using labeled amino acids (Faergeman *et al.*, 1974b). The various studies yield similar results.

Following the injection of ^{125}I-VLDL into rats the distribution of radioactive proteins among lipoproteins was similar to that found in humans. Apoprotein C equilibrated between VLDL and HDL and disappeared from the two lipoproteins at a comparable rate. Of interest was the observation that neither the distribution of apoprotein C among lipoproteins nor its rate of decay from the circulation differed after injections of labeled VLDL, labeled HDL, or labeled C apoprotein isolated from either lipoprotein (Fig. 9). Apoprotein B disappeared from the density range of VLDL ($d = 1.006$ gm/ml) very rapidly, with a half-life time of less than 10 minutes (Fig. 10). Some radio-

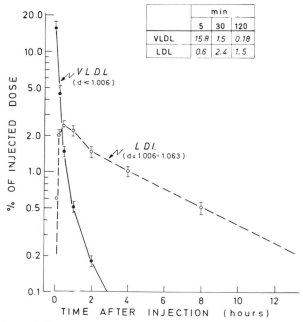

	min		
	5	30	120
VLDL	15.8	1.5	0.18
LDL	0.6	2.4	1.5

FIG. 10. Fate of ^{125}I-apoprotein B in VLDL and LDL after the injection of ^{125}I-VLDL in the rat. Insert shows content of ^{125}I-apoprotein B in the two lipoproteins at three time-points; content is represented as percent of the injected dose. Data calculated from studies of Eisenberg and Rachmilewitz (1973a,b).

activity accumulated in the density range of LDL (d = 1.006–1.063 gm/ml) during the first hour of the study. It was attributed primarily to labeled apoprotein B; however, it did not exceed 2.5% of the injected radioactivity. Since apoprotein B constituted about 16–17% of the injected VLDL radioactivity, about 80–90% of the apoprotein B in VLDL must have been cleared from circulation within the first hour of the injection. Most of the radioactivity that disappeared from the plasma compartment was recovered in the liver. These results have been interpreted to indicate that during the catabolism of VLDL, apoprotein B is cleared from circulation preferentially by liver cells. The pathways of metabolism of rat VLDL are shown schematically in Fig. 11A and those of human VLDL in Fig. 11B. Several lines of evidence indicate that the rapid clearance of apoprotein B occurred after only partial degradation of VLDL: (a) The rate of disappearance of apoprotein B from the plasma compartment was very similar to that reported for triglycerides. (b) During the phase of rapid decay of apoprotein B from circulation, the rate of disappearance of apoprotein C was much slower, indicating that the lipoprotein leaving the blood stream was not intact VLDL. (c) When ^{125}I-VLDL was injected into Triton-WR-1339-treated rats which are incapable of metabolizing VLDL, all radioactivity (including labeled apoprotein B) persisted in the circulation mainly in the VLDL density range.

Similar results were reported recently (Faergeman et $al.$, 1974b) using VLDL labeled in its protein moiety by lysine-^{3}H. Following the injection of tritiated lysine to rats, the apoprotein B specific activity curves indicated a precursor–product relationship between VLDL and LDL. When the labeled VLDL was isolated and reinjected into rats, the half-life time of apoprotein B in the VLDL density range was 6–8 minutes. Some of the labeled apoprotein B was transferred to intermediate density lipoprotein (d = 1.006–1.019) and later to LDL. Less than 10% of the injected apoprotein B however followed this metabolic pathway and the remaining 90% was cleared from the plasma compartment. One hour after the injection, about 60% of the radioactivity was recovered in the liver. Faergeman et $al.$ (1974a) have also studied the fate of the lipid moiety of VLDL in the rat. The half-life time of labeled cholesteryl esters in VLDL was 5–6 minutes. Only 2–5% of the label was recovered in low density lipoproteins, and more than 75% were found in the liver, where the cholesteryl esters were rapidly hydrolyzed. When the labeled VLDL was injected into the supradiaphragmatic rats, 70–80% of the cholesteryl esters persisted in the circulation as compared to only 25% of the triglycerides.

These two studies suggest that VLDL metabolism in rats is different

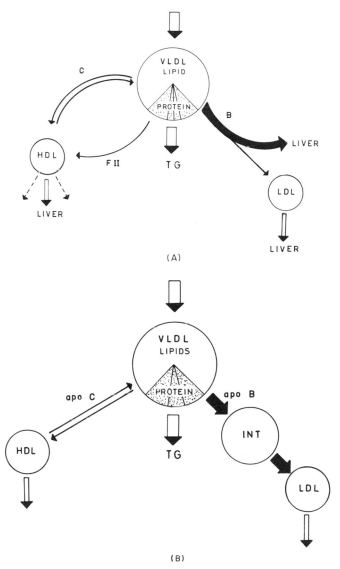

FIGS. 11A AND 11B. Schematic representation of probable pathways for VLDL apoprotein metabolism in rats (A) as compared to that in humans (B). In humans as in the rat, the liver is the probable site of HDL and LDL clearance from the blood stream.

at least in part from that described in the preceding section for he human. In the two species, the metabolism of VLDL apoprotein C and apoprotein B is dichotomous and VLDL particles are converted to LDL. In the rat as compared to man, a major part of VLDL apoprotein B leaves the circulation prior to degradation to LDL (Figs. 11A and 11B). This rapid clearance of apoprotein B from the plasma compartment may explain the low levels of LDL observed in the rat. Whether any of the intermediate density lipoprotein in humans is normally cleared directly from circulation is unknown. If, however, a mechanism of removal of VLDL intermediates operates in humans then the regulation of production and catabolism of this lipoprotein form may be of great importance in regulating plasma LDL levels. The known features of the intermediate lipoprotein are described in the next section.

D. CHARACTERIZATION OF THE INTERMEDIATE LIPOPROTEIN

Only a few studies have been conducted into the physical properties and chemical composition of the intermediate lipoprotein. Shore and Shore (1962) incubated human VLDL (S_f 20–400) with lipoprotein-free plasma obtained after the injection of heparin to humans. Twenty-seven percent (protein content) of the post-lypolysis lipoprotein was recovered at density less than 1.006 gm/ml, and 65% at density 1.006–1.022 gm/ml. The lipoproteins of density 1.006–1.022 gm/ml were isolated from normal plasma and contained about 15% protein, 7% cholesterol, 22–26% cholesteryl esters, 17% phospholipids, and 35–39% triglycerides.

An attempt to characterize the partially degraded rat VLDL was reported recently (Eisenberg and Rachmilewitz, 1973c, 1974). ^{125}I-Labeled VLDL was incubated with lipoprotein-lipase-rich plasma obtained from rats 10 minutes after injection with sodium heparin. Triglyceride-poor VLDL was then isolated by ultracentrifugation at density 1.019 gm/ml. The amount of ^{125}I-lipids and ^{125}I-apoprotein C isolated from VLDL decreased with time (Figs. 12A and 12B). In contrast, the amount of ^{125}I-apoprotein B isolated in VLDL did not change.

FIG. 12.   Effect of lipoprotein lipase-rich (post-heparin) plasma on the ^{125}I-apoprotein composition of VLDL. (A) *Effect of incubation time*—1 mg of ^{125}I-labeled VLDL protein was incubated with 5 ml of rat post-heparin plasma for 0–120 minutes. (B) *Effect of VLDL concentration*—same experiment, carried for only 10 minutes with varying amounts of VLDL. Apoproteins radioactivity was determined after delipidation and polyacrylamide gel electrophoresis. Bars represent percent of triglycerides isolated with VLDL as compared with nonincubated samples. From Eisenberg and Rachmilewitz (1974).

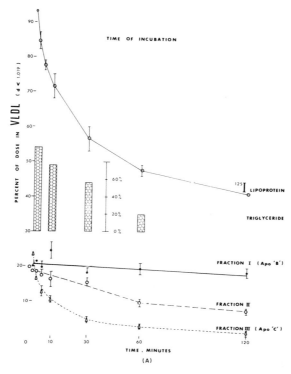

TIME OF INCUBATION

PERCENT OF DOSE IN **VLDL** (d < 1.019)

90—
80—
70—
60—
50—
40—
30—

60%
40%
20%
0%

^{125}I LIPOPROTEIN

TRIGLYCERIDE

FRACTION I (Apo 'B')

FRACTION II

FRACTION III (Apo 'C')

20—

10—

0   10   30   60   120

TIME , MINUTES

(A)

AMOUNT OF **VLDL**

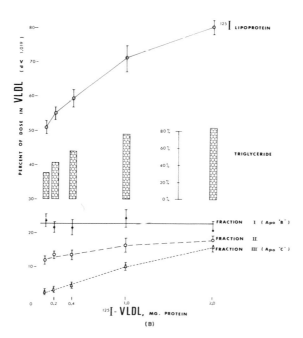

PERCENT OF DOSE IN **VLDL** (d < 1.019)

80—
70—
60—
50—
40—
30—

^{125}I LIPOPROTEIN

80%
60%
40%
20%
0%

TRIGLYCERIDE

FRACTION   I (Apo 'B'')

FRACTION   II
FRACTION   III (Apo 'C'')

20—

10—

0   0.2   0.4   1.0   2.0

^{125}I - **VLDL** , MG. PROTEIN

(B)

When apoprotein fractions were prepared from the *in vitro* produced intermediate lipoprotein using gel filtration on Sephadex G-150, it was possible to determine the relative contribution of each apoprotein to the total protein mass of the lipoprotein as well as the specific activity of each. Not unexpectedly, the only change observed in VLDL incubated with normal plasma was found in the specific activity of apoprotein C (relative to apoprotein B it decreased from 0.82 to 0.44). In samples incubated with post-heparin plasma however, apoprotein C disappeared from VLDL without further decrease of its specific activity, demonstrating a net transfer to HDL.

Further characterization of this triglyceride-poor intermediate lipoprotein included determination of lipid composition, flotation constant (mean S_f rates), and size distribution (determined by electron microscopy). An estimation of the molecular weight of intact VLDL and triglyceride-poor (intermediate lipoprotein) VLDL based on S_f rates yielded a value of 23.1 and 7.0 million daltons respectively. The ratio of these values, 3.3, is similar to that of their volumes, 4.0. From these data it is possible to calculate the amount of each lipid and apoprotein constituent in a VLDL and an intermediate lipoprotein particle (Table VII). Analysis of these calculations demonstrates that during the catabolism of one VLDL particle, all constituents, except apoprotein B, are removed from the particle. Triglyceride and apopro-

Table VII

PHYSICAL PROPERTIES AND CHEMICAL COMPOSITION OF VLDL AND
INTERMEDIATE LIPOPROTEIN PARTICLES

Properties and composition	VLDL	Intermediate lipoprotein
Volume, cubic Å × 10^{-6}	40.1	10.0
S_f rate	114.9	30.5
Particle weight, dalton × 10^{-6}	23.1	7.0
Apoproteins, dalton × 10^{-6}/particle	3.23	1.29
Apoprotein B	0.70	0.73
VS-2[a]	0.73	0.44
Apoprotein C	1.80	0.12
Lipids, dalton × 10^{-1}/particle	19.9	5.7
Triglycerides	14.1	3.1
Phospholipids	3.3	1.4
Cholesterol, free	1.5	0.5
Cholesterol, esterified	1.0	0.7

[a] Apoprotein fraction as defined by gel chromatography on Sephadex G-150 (Bersot *et al.*, 1970). The major apoprotein of this fraction is most probably the arginine-rich protein. From Eisenberg and Rachmilewitz (1974).

tein C disappear at the fastest rate; only 7% of the original apoprotein C and 20% of the triglycerides are recovered with the intermediate lipoprotein particle. About 60% of the free cholesterol and phospholipids and 40% of the esterified cholesterol disappear from VLDL concomitant with the hydrolysis of its triglycerides. In contrast, each intermediate lipoprotein particle retains the full complement of apoprotein B present in the original VLDL particle. *Thus, one and only one intermediate lipoprotein is formed from each VLDL particle.*

In the rat the intermediate lipoprotein had the following characteristics: (a) It was formed from VLDL either *in vivo* or *in vitro* subsequent to the hydrolysis of triglycerides. It contained more triglyceride than LDL and floated in the VLDL density range. The mean S_f rate of the intermediate lipoprotein resembled that of small VLDL particles. (b) The intermediate lipoprotein was almost devoid of apoprotein C; it contained, however, all the apoprotein B present in the original VLDL. (c) The ratio of free to esterified cholesterol in the intermediate lipoprotein was lower than in VLDL. (d) The intermediate lipoprotein seemed to be relatively resistant to lipoprotein lipase. Although about 40% of its total mass is triglycerides, their further hydrolysis—or removal from the particle—occurred at a rate which is considerably slower than that occurring in VLDL.

V. Metabolism of LDL

A. SYNTHESIS

Human plasma LDL is formed largely, if not entirely, in the circulation. As described in detail in the previous section, the major source of LDL is plasma VLDL. If all of the apoprotein B present in VLDL is transferred to LDL, it can account for the production of all LDL particles (Table VIII). In this context, it is interesting to note that many morphological studies in rats have failed to demonstrate LDL particles in liver cells. Two additional hypothetical sources of LDL however, have to be discussed. The first is the possible contribution of chylomicrons to the human plasma LDL pool. Apoprotein B constitutes only 0.1–0.5% of the chylomicrons mass. Assuming a production rate of 70 to 100 gm of chylomicrons per day, it might contribute 10–50% of the circulating LDL. The second possible source of LDL is direct secretion from either the liver or the intestine, especially during periods when triglycerides are available only to a limited extent. This possibility is further discussed in Section VIII of this review.

Table VIII

SOME CALCULATIONS ON APO LDL TURNOVER

VLDL Glyceride flux = 10–20 gm/day

VLDL Protein flux = 2–3 gm/day

Apo-LDL comprises ~ 40% of VLDL apoproteins

Flux of apo LDL = 800–1200 mg/day ⟶

Apo-LDL conc ≅ 75 mg/100 ml

Plasma Apo-LDL pool ≅ 2–2.5 gm

F.C.R. Apo-LDL = 40–50% pool/day

Turnover of Apo-LDL = 800–1200 mg/day

B. Fate of Lipids

Numerous studies have been published on the metabolism and fate of plasma cholesterol in humans (for recent reviews, see Nestel, 1970). The amount of cholesterol bound to lipoproteins in the plasma makes up a very small portion of the body's cholesterol pool. Moreover, cholesterol is readily exchangeable among lipoproteins and between lipoproteins and tissue, and is reutilized for the synthesis of new lipoproteins. These studies therefore measure total body cholesterol turnover rather than that in the plasma.

C. Fate of the Protein Moiety

The turnover of the LDL protein in human plasma has been studied in detail during the last 15 years (Gitlin *et al.*, 1958; Walton *et al.*, 1963, 1965; Hurley and Scott, 1970). Most studies have utilized LDL labeled with radioactive iodine in its protein (apoprotein B) moiety. The disappearance of radioactivity from the plasma compartment in normal humans and in patients with primary or secondary hyperlipoproteinemia has been followed. In all published reports, more than 95% of the apoprotein-bound radioactive iodine was recovered at all time intervals in the LDL density range. The decay of LDL protein from the plasma is biexponential. The distribution of LDL between the intravascular and extravascular compartments, its half-life time in circulation, fractional catabolism rate, and synthetic rate were calculated by use of a simple two-compartmental model. In the recent report on LDL turnover in normal humans and patients with type II hyperlipoproteinemia (Langer *et al.*, 1972; Levy and Langer, 1972), the biological half-life time of LDL protein in normal humans varied between 2.25 and 2.58 days. Sixty-two to 75% of the LDL protein was present in the intravascular compartment. The fractional catabolic rate (fraction of intravascular pool cleared per day) varied between 0.385 and 0.633 and the calculated synthetic rates (milligrams LDL protein per kilogram per day) between 12.0 and 18.2. In patients with type II hyperlipoproteinemia the only metabolic defect noted was a greatly reduced fractional catabolic rate (Table IX).

The effect of diet and drugs on LDL metabolism was also studied by these investigators (Table X). Diets low in cholesterol and rich in polyunsaturated fatty acids decreased the LDL pool size and increased its catabolic rate. Cholestyramine in a dosage of 24 gm/day reduced LDL cholesterol concentrations considerably (32%) in six type II subjects. Concurrent with this, the half-life time of LDL in circulation decreased from a mean 4.8 to 3.6 days and the fractional

Table IX

METABOLIC PARAMETERS OF HUMAN PLASMA LOW DENSITY LIPOPROTEIN[a]

Group (No.)	Treatment	β-Apoprotein level (mg/100 ml)	T 1/2 (days)	Fractional catabolic rate (fraction of IV pool/day)	Synthetic rate (mg/kg/day)	% IV
Normal (10)	Low cholesterol hi P/S diet	63 ± 13	3.08 ± 0.35	0.462 ± 0.077	14.43 ± 1.75	68.4 ± 4.3
Type II (10)	Low cholesterol hi P/S diet	153 ± 30	4.68 ± 0.44	0.237 ± 0.044	15.01 ± 1.71	73.3 ± 5.2

[a] From Langer et al., (1972).

Table X

EFFECT OF DRUG AND DIETARY PERTURBATIONS ON THE METABOLISM OF HUMAN PLASMA LOW DENSITY LIPOPROTEIN

Group (No.)	Treatment	β-Apoprotein level (mg/100 ml)	Half-life time (days)	Fractional catabolic rate (0/0 IV pool/day)	Synthetic rate (mg/kg/day)	0/0 IV
Type II (6)	Low cholesterol diet	170 ± 33	4.90 ± 0.19	21.9 ± 1.4	15.8 ± 2.5	74.9 ± 4.4
	Low cholesterol diet + cholestyramine (24 gm/day)	116 ± 18	3.60 ± 0.31	31.6 ± 3.8	15.9 ± 1.4	75.9 ± 3.2
Type II (2)	Low cholesterol diet (hi P/S = 2)	118	3.9	37.1	14.3	70
	800 mg cholesterol N P/S diet	147	4.9	24.5	14.2	69
Type II (2)	Low cholesterol diet	152	4.5	27.6	16.0	69
	Low cholesterol diet + nicotinic acid (4.5 gm/day)	99	4.6	27.5	10.3	68
Normal (3)	Low cholesterol diet (hi P/S = 2)	60	2.6	51.6	13.4	72
	800 mg cholesterol N P/S diet	77	3.0	40.7	13.7	73
Normal (2)	Low cholesterol diet	60	3.1	45.1	13.1	69
	Low cholesterol diet + nicotinic acid (3 gm/day)	32	3.3	44	6.7	67

catabolic rate increased from 22 to 32%. The synthetic rate of LDL and its distribution between the intravascular and extravascular compartments remained unchanged. The administration of nicotinic acid (3–6 gm/day) in normal humans and patients with type II hyperlipoproteinemia resulted in a similar decrease in LDL pool size. With this drug, however, the biological half-life time of LDL, its fractional catabolic rate, and its distribution did not change, whereas LDL synthetic rate decreased by 30–60%.

These LDL turnover studies further suggest that circulating LDL levels are determined primarily by their removal rate from the plasma rather than their production rate. A linear relationship can be demonstrated during steady state studies between the fractional catabolic rate and levels of LDL in individual subjects. Since LDL is formed chiefly from VLDL, increased LDL formation may be important in determining LDL plasma levels only when VLDL synthesis and conversion to LDL are increased. Possible examples of this are the hyperlipoproteinemia observed in patients with the nephrotic syndrome or alcoholism and the increased LDL levels seen transiently during clearance of endogenous hypertriglyceridemia (Wilson and Lees, 1972). LDL turnover studies have actually indicated increased LDL synthesis in patients with nephrosis (Gitlin *et al.*, 1958) and hyperthyroidism (Walton *et al.*, 1963, 1965). An increased rate of conversion of VLDL to LDL may possibly explain the hyperbetalipoproteinemia observed in some patients treated with clofibrate.

These studies however, provide little insight into the mechanisms operating in the removal of LDL from the circulation or their final degradation by tissue cells. Several recent studies have indicated that the liver may play an important role in lipoprotein catabolism. The rate of disappearance of LDL from the plasma may depend on its rate of removal by the liver and possibly other tissues. In this regard, recent studies reported by Brown and Goldstein (1974a,b) suggest the importance of cell membrane bound receptor sites on the binding and subsequent removal of LDL.

VI. Metabolism of HDL

A. SYNTHESIS

Synthesis and secretion of high density lipoprotein have been demonstrated in both liver and intestine. The relative contribution of each organ to the total amount of circulating HDL is unknown. In rats, the incorporation of labeled amino acids into HDL proteins by intestinal cells was first demonstrated by Roheim *et al.* (1966) and subsequently corroborated by several other investigators. Newly synthesized HDL was isolated from the perfused intestine of the rat (Windmueller *et al.*, 1973). This HDL was found in both the intestinal veins and the lymphatics whereas newly synthesized VLDL was recovered only in the lymphatics (see Section IV,A). When the incorporation of radioactive amino acids into individual HDL apoproteins was measured in the rat intestine, it was found that label was associated with the apoprotein A (predominantly A-I) and not apoprotein C. It is thus likely that the intestinal HDL is secreted in a form devoid of apoprotein C, a situation similar to that reported for intestinal VLDL.

Nascent HDL has been isolated from liver cells, the perfused liver, and Golgi cisternae of the rat (Hamilton, 1972). These HDL particles contain protein, phospholipid, and free cholesterol. They appear on negative staining as a series of lipid bilayers, 45 Å thick and 100–200 Å in diameter. The nascent HDL particles are thus similar to the particles found in the plasma of patients with deficiency of the enzyme lecithin : cholesterol acyl transferase (see below) and to the lipoprotein of obstructive jaundice (LP-X). The esterification of the HDL cholesterol may occur predominantly in the circulation (see next section).

The factors which influence HDL synthesis have not been elucidated as yet. In the human, the level of HDL in plasma varies considerably among individuals and is consistently altered by several physiological and pathological conditions. HDL levels are higher in menstruating women as compared to men of comparable age. They are decreased during diets rich in carbohydrates and are low in patients with hypertriglyceridemia, especially types I and V (Fredrickson and Levy, 1972). Whether some of these changes are due to change in HDL synthesis or catabolism is unknown.

Of particular interest is the lipoprotein pattern of patients with familial deficiency of high density lipoproteins—Tangier disease (Fredrickson *et al.*, 1972a; Lux *et al.*, 1972e). In homozygotes with this disorder, plasma HDL levels are reduced to less than 5% of normal. The clinical picture includes spleenomegaly, orange-colored tonsils, accumulation of cholesteryl ester in reticuloendothelial cells throughout the body and relapsing sensory–motor neuropathy. The small amount of HDL isolated from the patients is very abnormal. It contains only trace amounts of apoprotein A-1 (less than 1% of normal) and reduced levels of apoprotein A-II (about 10% of normal). The ratio of apoprotein A-I to A-II in HDL is decreased by a factor of 30–40. Some of the HDL particles in these patients contain only apoprotein

A-II (Assman *et al.*, 1974d). It is thus possible that formation and secretion of the two major HDL apoproteins are independent of one another, at least in part. However, other possible explanations have not been ruled out. LDL levels are also reduced in Tangier disease, whereas chylomicrons and VLDL tend to accumulate in the circulation.

B. METABOLISM OF LIPIDS AND THE LECITHIN : CHOLESTEROL ACYL TRANSFERASE SYSTEM

HDL lipids undergo constant changes while in the circulation. In addition to exchange of free cholesterol and phospholipids among lipoproteins and between lipoproteins and tissue cells, there is a generation of cholesteryl esters within the HDL particles. The formation of cholesteryl esters is due to transfer of fatty acids from the 2-position of lecithin molecules to unesterified cholesterol resulting in the formation of 1-acyl lysolecithin and esterified cholesterol. The reaction is catalyzed by the circulating enzyme lecithin–cholesterol acyl transferase (LCAT) (Glomset and Norum, 1973). The enzyme is synthesized in the liver and circulates in plasma associated with HDL. It has been reported to be activated specifically by apoprotein A-I (Fielding *et al.*, 1972). The enzyme has been studied in detail, and its mode of action was summarized several years ago (Glomset, 1968). Although the role of the enzyme in lipoprotein metabolism is not yet understood, abnormal lipoproteins are found in the plasma of human patients with a congenital-familial disease due to the absence of the enzyme (Glomset and Norum, 1973; Glomset *et al.*, 1974). The disease has been encountered so far in three Scandinavian families. The clinical picture is characterized by corneal opacities, hemolytic anemia, abnormal lipid composition of erythrocytes, proteinuria, and possible renal failure. Lipid vacuoles are found in cells of the bone marrow and spleen and in the glomeruli. The abnormal lipoproteins present in the plasma of these patients have been described recently in detail (Glomset and Norum, 1973). All their lipoproteins contain abnormally low amounts of cholesteryl esters and high amounts of unesterified cholesterol and lecithin. Triglyceride concentration in relation to other lipids is low in VLDL and high in LDL, as compared to the corresponding lipoprotein of normal humans. Of particular interest is the presence of disk-shaped lipoproteins of varying sizes in the density range of LDL and HDL, not dissimilar to the abnormal lipoprotein of obstructive jaundice. These lipoproteins can be separated by gel filtration, are of very large size, and contain predominantly unesterified cholesterol, lecithin, and some protein. The protein moiety of one of the three LDL subfractions (of intermediate size) was reported to consist of albumin (65%) and apoprotein C (35%), that of the large HDL fraction of apoprotein A. The lipoprotein pattern of the patients has been studied during carbohydrate and fat feeding and following the injection of heparin. In both these studies, the abnormally large LDL particles accumulated under conditions favoring chylomicron formation (fat feeding) or degradation (following heparin injection). It was postulated that the large LDL particles may represent an accumulation of chylomicron surface material. In normals, unesterified cholesterol and lecithin are metabolized by the LCAT system to produce esterified cholesterol which is transferred nonenzymically from HDL to lower density lipoproteins. Such a transfer has been demonstrated (Nichols and Smith, 1965). When plasma from LCAT-deficient patients is incubated with partially purified enzyme, a dramatic change in the pattern of the LCAT patients' lipoproteins occurs (Glomset *et al.*, 1974). The content of cholesteryl esters in plasma more than doubles, the content of abnormally large LDL particles decreases, and that of the normal lipoproteins increases. These changes are associated with changes of the apoprotein content and composition of the lipoproteins: apoprotein B is lost from the density range of both VLDL and HDL and is recovered with LDL; the relative content of apoprotein C and the arginine-rich peptide in VLDL increases; and apoprotein A-I, found after centrifugation mainly with the plasma protein fraction of density greater than 125 gm/ml, is associated with HDL. All these studies were interpreted to indicate that the LCAT system plays an important role in the metabolism of surface material of chylomicrons and possibly VLDL as well. It may provide a means of transferring esterified cholesterol to both VLDL and LDL, and specific apoproteins, such as the arginine-rich peptide, may participate in this transfer reaction. Yet, it should be mentioned that during the normal conversion of VLDL particles to LDL particles, each parent lipoprotein contains enough (or more than enough) cholesteryl ester to account for all the ester found in the resulting lipoprotein (see Figs. 3A and 3B and Section IV,A). This observation is probably true also for chylomicrons. Moreover, the esterified cholesterol content of newly secreted VLDL and chylomicron particles more than adequately accounts for its resulting content in all apoprotein-B-containing lipoproteins. The LCAT system may thus be involved more with the removal of excess unesterified cholesterol and lecithin from the circulation than with the supply of esterified cholesterol to lower density lipoproteins. The mode of clearance of esterified cholesterol from the circulation is unknown, as are the mechanisms of clearance of other HDL lipids.

C. Fate of the Protein Moiety

1. Studies in Humans

Data on the metabolic fate of HDL apoproteins in humans are scarce (Gitlin *et al.*, 1958; Furman *et al.*, 1964) and none are available on the possible different routes of metabolism of the two major A proteins. The half-life time in circulation of the mixture of labeled apoproteins is approximately 5 days. More than 90% of injected HDL protein is recovered within the density range of HDL. About one-half of the HDL is distributed in extravascular compartments. A striking difference in the half-life time in circulation of apoprotein A-I and apoprotein A-II was observed after the injection of ^{125}I-labeled human HDL into rats (Eisenberg *et al.*, 1973b). Preliminary observations at the NIH however (C. Blum, S. Eisenberg, and R. I. Levy, unpublished) suggested that their decay rates were more similar in two normal humans studied. The seemingly contrasting results may be explained by a transfer of apoprotein A-I, but not apoprotein A-II, from human HDL particles to rat HDL, and subsequent independent decay of the rat and human lipoproteins. It thus remains to be demonstrated whether under several different conditions, the two major HDL proteins are metabolized together.

2. Studies in Rats

Data on the metabolic behavior of HDL apoproteins labeled with iodine-125 have been published (Roheim *et al.*, 1971, 1972; Eisenberg *et al.*, 1973b). The results of the two studies are not dissimilar. The rate of disappearance of radioactivity from the plasma and from the density range of HDL was exponential with a half-life time of about 11 hours. About 85–95% of the radioactivity was associated with HDL; 3–5% of the label was associated with VLDL, and about 5% with the plasma protein fraction of density greater than 1.21 gm/ml. About one-half of the radioactivity in the latter fraction represented free iodide transport. In VLDL, about 80% of the radioactivity was due to labeled apoprotein C; these apoproteins accounted for 12% of the injected radioactivity and 7–8% of HDL radioactivity (Eisenberg *et al.*, 1973b). The decay of different apoproteins from the HDL density range differed slightly (Fig. 13). The half-life time of apoprotein A-I was the slowest—12.5 hours (Eisenberg *et al.*, 1973b), resulting in an increased contribution of ^{125}I-apoprotein A-I to total HDL radioactivity from 51% to 62% within 24 hours of the injection. The half-life times of HDL apoproteins calculated by Roheim *et al.* (1972) were similar to those of Eisenberg *et al.* (1973b). The results raise the possibility that

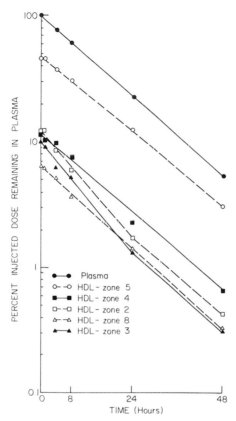

FIG. 13. Decay of radioactive apoproteins after the injection of ^{125}I-HDL to rats. From Eisenberg *et al.* (1973b) by permission of the publisher.

HDL is catabolized, at least in part, in a subunit fashion rather than as a unitary particle. This possibility is certainly true as far as the apoprotein C moiety of HDL is concerned.

VII. Sites and Mechanisms of Catabolism of Lipoproteins

Until very recently, virtually nothing was known about mechanisms involved in catabolism of lipoproteins by tissue cells. During the last few years, however, several different models have been developed to study sites and mechanisms of lipoprotein catabolism. The two major models employed in these studies are the whole animal and cells in tissue culture.

A. Studies in the Whole Animal

As early as 1955 Hotta and Chaikoff reported that hepatectomy caused a sharp decline in the rate of disappearance of labeled cholesterol from rat plasma and concluded that the liver might be the major site of degradation of plasma lipoprotein-bound cholesterol. Studies described in Section IV,B (Quarfordt and Goodman, 1967; Stein *et al.*, 1969) demonstrated that the liver indeed was the major site of catabolism of chylomicron cholesteryl esters. From the studies in hepatectomized rats (Redgrave, 1970), it appears that the liver removed from circulation not only the cholesteryl ester moiety of chylomicrons, but also the other lipid and protein components present in the chylomicron "remnant." The role of hepatocytes as against that of Kupfer cells has been emphasized (Stein *et al.*, 1969; Nilsson and Zilversmit, 1971). The role of the liver in the removal of VLDL "remnants" in rats was described (Eisenberg and Rachmilewitz, 1973a,b; Faergeman *et al.*, 1974a,b). In both laboratories, the liver was shown to concentrate most of the apoprotein B moiety of degraded VLDL. In the latter study, it was demonstrated that the cholesteryl ester moiety of VLDL is also removed by the liver, strengthening the hypothesis that this process represents the clearance of a particle rather than a specific protein or lipid constituent. The morphological details of the clearance of VLDL radioactivity from circulation (Stein *et al.*, 1974b) are described in Section VIII. Since, in fact, VLDL is not taken up from the perfusate during perfusion of the liver, it is possible that during the metabolism of this lipoprotein, a lipoprotein form is produced which is recognized by liver cell receptors and is rapidly cleared from the plasma space. One possible mechanism of removal of lipoproteins from circulation is therefore a "signal" present in the lipoprotein at a specific stage of its metabolism.

The fate of HDL apoproteins was studied in rats (Eisenberg *et al.*, 1973b; Roheim *et al.*, 1971; Rachmilewitz *et al.*, 1972). In the two studies, a concentration of labeled apoproteins was found in the liver. A possible role of the small intestine in the removal of HDL particles from the circulation was also suggested by the latter group. This group has further investigated the fate of the HDL proteins by using electron microscopy combined with radioautography (Rachmilewitz *et al.*, 1972). Six hours after injection, the radioautographic reaction was seen to a greater degree in the hepatocytes than in various cytoplasmic organelles. Concentration of grains was documented over dense bodies, which represented mainly secondary lysosomes (Fig. 14). At this time interval only 19% of the liver radioactivity was recognizable by specific anti-HDL serum. The results indicate that the

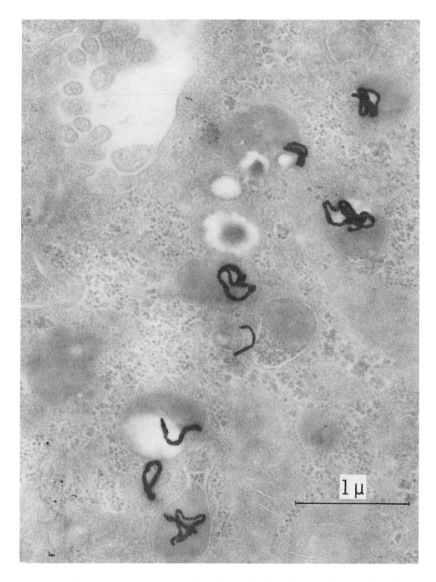

FIG. 14. Electron microscopic radioautograph of rat liver 6 hours after the injection of ^{125}I-HDL. The silver grains are concentrated over dense bodies. (Courtesy of Dr. O. Stein.)

liver participates actively in the catabolism of serum HDL, a conclusion strengthened by the appearance of dialyzable and trichloroacetic acid soluble radioactivity in bile.

In two reports, a concentration of radioactivity in liver was demonstrated after the injection of labeled LDL into humans (Hurley and Scott, 1970) and rats (Hay *et al.*, 1971). Consequently, it has been suggested that the liver is the major site of catabolism of LDL. The recent study of Sniderman *et al.* (1973, 1974) has, however, cast some questions as to the validity of this conclusion. Sniderman *et al.* studied the fate of ^{125}I-LDL in both swine and dogs. As in the previous observations, they found 10–15% of the plasma radioactivity in the liver, whereas other tissues contained only a trace amount of the extravascular labeled lipoprotein. When the experiment was repeated in hepatectomized animals, the authors observed that the rate of catabolism of LDL increased rather than decreased. The following observations were reported in operated swine: (a) Disappearance of an initial fast decay component of plasma radioactivity. This component was always observed in intact animals and presumably represents intravascular and extravascular equilibration of the lipoprotein. (b) A decrease of plasma half-life time from 19.3 ± 0.7 hours to 9.5 ± 0.7 hours. (c) An increase of the LDL fractional catabolic rate from 0.0457 ± 0.0008 to 0.0764 ± 0.0065. (d) An exponential decay of plasma LDL apoprotein concentration. Similar results were also reported in hepatectomized dogs. These investigators have suggested that the liver's role in LDL metabolism is to lengthen LDL lifetime in the plasma rather than to remove and catabolize LDL particles from the circulation. The possible mechanism behind such a phenomenon is unknown. The authors suggest that LDL particles "damaged" by interaction with tissue cells may undergo "repair" in the liver. According to this hypothesis, hepatectomy caused the accumulation of "damaged" particles which were then removed from circulation by extrahepatic tissues at an accelerated rate.

Possibly pertinent to this conclusion is the observation of Starzl *et al.* (1973, 1974) in one girl with type II hyperlipoproteinemia, in whom a porta-caval shunt was performed. In this one subject there was a dramatic decrease in plasma cholesterol and LDL levels.

At the present time, these experiments raise questions rather than give answers. (a) It seems that the *mechanisms of removal of lipoproteins from circulation may be different for the various lipoproteins.* They may even be unrelated. (b) The *primary signal for lipoprotein catabolism appears to be a property of the lipoprotein itself*, at least for chylomicrons and VLDL "remnants." Yet, as discussed in the next sections, the removal of these remnants and other lipoproteins may involve a specific interaction of the lipoprotein particle and cell receptors. (c) Clinical observations in patients with type I and type V hyperlipoproteinemia indicate *that the failure to produce lipoprotein remnants accentuates the operation of secondary mechanisms for the removal of chylomicrons (and VLDL) from the plasma through phagocytosis by reticuloendothelial cells.* (d) Whether signals for accelerated removal of other lipoproteins, e.g., LDL, from the plasma may be of importance in their catabolism remains to be established. (e) *The site of removal of lipoproteins is uncertain, as is the possibility that different lipoproteins are predominantly catabolized by different cells and organs.* (f) *Finally, many more experiments are needed to determine whether different mechanisms of lipoprotein catabolism are operating in the various species.*

B. STUDIES IN TISSUE CULTURES

Many studies during the 1960s have demonstrated that lipids added to growth media have a profound effect on cholesterol metabolism of cells grown in tissue culture. The interaction and subsequent metabolism of lipoproteins with cells, however, has been reported only very recently. Two studies have followed the fate of rat plasma VLDL and HDL labeled with 125-iodine in cultures of rat aortic smooth muscle cells (Bierman *et al.*, 1973, 1974). The uptake of protein and lipid radioactivity increased in proportion to the time of incubation and amount of lipoprotein in the growth medium and a large proportion of either lipoprotein was apparently surface bound and trypsin releasable. By radioautography, label was localized mainly over cell cytoplasm, cell boundary, and, in some cells, over lysosomes. The fate of ingested ^{125}I-HDL was further studied in pulse-chase experiments (Bierman *et al.*, 1974). About 50% of label is released into the medium, of which 75% was TCA precipitable and only a few percent could be identified as being associated with catabolic products (TCA-soluble and chloroform-nonextractable radioactivity). Only 30% of the total releasable radioactivity was precipitable by specific anti-HDL serum. These results indicate that rat aortic smooth muscle cells have a limited capacity to catabolize lipoproteins; however, the cells may possess other mechanisms for the elimination of the ingested lipoproteins. During this process of endo- and exocytosis, however, lipoproteins are modified and lose some of their immunoreactive properties. A specificity in the mechanisms of lipoprotein uptake by the cells is indicated by the observation that on a particle number basis, the uptake of HDL is 4 times greater than that of VLDL. When the uptake of intact VLDL and partially degraded VLDL ("remnant") particles was compared, the latter particles were more readily taken up by the aortic cells (Bierman *et al.*, 1973). These observations are in accord with the hypothesis presented in the previous section that the catabolism of lipoproteins may be determined, at least in part, by the properties of the particles.

A marked species difference in the catabolism of lipoproteins by aortic smooth muscle cells was observed when similar experiments were carried out in cells of human origin (Bierman, 1974). In these cells VLDL is taken up much more avidly than HDL, and the uptake of LDL is even more pronounced.

Additional insight into lipoprotein–tissue cell interactions emerges directly from the studies of the effects of lipid and lipoproteins on sterol metabolism in tissue cultures. The initial investigation (Bailey, 1967, 1973) demonstrated that sterol synthesis in tissue culture cells is suppressed by the presence of cholesterol in the growth medium. Subsequent studies (Rothblat and Kritchevsky, 1968; Burns and Rothblat, 1969; Bates and Rothblat, 1974) have conclusively shown that in cells derived from mouse fibroblasts (L cell line), the rate of sterol synthesis is dependent on the flux of cholesterol into the cell (influx) and from the cell (efflux). The authors have also pointed toward several specific substances affecting sterol metabolism in the cells, lipoproteins being one of the major sterol synthesis suppressing factors. The possible different role of HDL and LDL on the cholesterol flux was postulated in 1969 (Burns and Rothblat, 1969; Rothblat, 1969) and verified recently (Bates and Rothblat, 1974). With either lipoprotein, the cellular sterol levels increase by about 30–50%, more so in the presence of LDL. Sterol synthesis is suppressed, however, only in the presence of LDL, to about 30% of that observed when cells are grown on medium containing delipidated serum. HDL seemed in these experiments to serve as a promoter of sterol efflux from the cells, an observation similar to that reported in Ehrlich ascites cells (Stein and Stein, 1973b). Slightly different results were reported (Williams and Avigan, 1972) using human skin fibroblasts, a system in which both HDL and LDL suppressed the incorporation of acetate into cellular nonsaponifiable lipids.

The mechanism of regulation of cholesterol metabolism in human skin fibroblasts by plasma lipoproteins was recently evaluated when measuring the activity of the enzyme 3-hydroxy-3-methylglutaryl coenzyme A (HMG-CoA) reductase in cells grown in culture (Brown and Goldstein, 1974a,b; Brown *et al.*, 1973a,b, 1974; Goldstein and

Brown, 1974a,b). In normal fibroblasts grown in lipoprotein-free medium, HMG-CoA reductase activity was about 10-fold higher than that of cells grown in the presence of serum obtained from several mammalian species including *Homo sapiens.* When the cells were transferred from serum-containing medium to serum-free medium, enzyme activity increased rapidly, with a peak after 12–16 hours. This increase was inhibited by the addition of cycloheximide or actinomycin D. In a reverse experiment, the addition of serum to cells grown in serum-free medium resulted in a time-dependent decrease of the enzyme activity. The effects of delipidated serum were similar to those of serum-free medium. LDL and VLDL were the two lipoproteins possessing the HMG-CoA reductase inhibitory effect. HDL and serum from patients with abetalipoproteinemia had almost no effect, at the same cholesterol concentrations. The fact that cholesterol in ethanolic solution, and certain cholesterol analogs also, are very efficient in the inhibition of the enzyme suggests that under physiological conditions the mode of presentation of the cholesterol to the cell determines its metabolic effects on cholesterol synthesis. The authors suggest that cholesterol associated with apoprotein B possesses the inhibitory effect whereas that associated with apoprotein A (HDL) does not. In subsequent studies, the cells were shown to specifically bind LDL from the medium, the binding being an obligatory step for the HMG-CoA reductase inhibitory effect. Displacement of LDL from the binding sites was achieved by both whole serum and VLDL but not by HDL, lipoprotein-free serum, or serum from subjects with abetalipoproteinemia. Saturation of LDL binding was achieved at a concentration of 20 μg/ml, and the calculated number of finding sites was 250,000 per cell, assuming that one LDL particle binds to one site. That these phenomena are not restricted to one cell type is indicated by very similar observations reported (Mahley *et al.*, 1974b) on swine aortic smooth muscle cells in culture.

Brown and Goldstein (1974a,b) studied the response of skin fibroblasts obtained from patients with type II hyperlipoproteinemia in the same system. Cells from patients with the homozygous form of the disease demonstrated an absence of cholesterol synthesis inhibition by serum or lipoproteins. The cells, however, did respond to the addition of nonlipoprotein cholesterol to the growth medium in a fashion very similar to that observed with cells from normal humans. The cells also did not bind LDL to any appreciable degree. The biological response to LDL of cells from patients with the heterozygous form of the disease was intermediate between that of cells from normals and from homozygous patients. *These studies have strengthened the pre-*

vious hypothesis of the specific role of LDL in delivering cholesterol to cells through a stage of binding to a specific site. They further support the observation made with ^{125}I-LDL that suggested that familial hyperbetalipoproteinemia (type II hyperlipoproteinemia) resulted from defective LDL clearance.

VIII. Functional, Structural, and Metabolic Interrelationships of Lipoproteins

The metabolic pathways of lipoproteins described in the previous section clearly demonstrate that all major plasma lipoproteins are metabolically related. The purpose of the present section is to integrate these various pathways with the structure and function of lipoproteins. Metabolically, lipoproteins are considered to be composed of substructures, some of which are mandatory for the integrity of the lipoproteins (structural subunits) and others for their function in the transport of fats (functional subunits). Apoprotein B is a part of the major structural subunit of chylomicrons, VLDL, and LDL. Apoprotein A-II appears to be the structural subunit of HDL. Apoprotein C is a functional lipoprotein subunit; it plays an important role in the regulation of the activity of lipoprotein lipases and is not an obligatory constituent of any of the lipoproteins of normal plasma. Apoprotein A-I may also be a functional subunit; it may activate the LCAT enzyme and is not firmly associated with HDL particles. Other structural or functional lipoprotein subunits may be established when more information becomes available concerning the newly described arginine-rich apoprotein.

Lipoprotein subunits are composed of proteins and lipids. Yet, virtually nothing is known about the lipid moiety of the subunits in their native form. As mentioned before (Section III,B), the B subunit may contain an amount of lipid equivalent to, or less than, that present in the smallest LDL particle. The lipids of such a particle are predominantly cholesteryl esters, lecithin, and sphingomyelin. In this subunit, lipids are not only essential for its structure and integrity but also play an important role in its formation and maintenance. The lipids of the other subunits are unknown. Both the A and C proteins bind phosphatidyl-choline (lecithin) *in vitro*. The amount of phosphatidyl choline associated with any apoprotein under physiological conditions is unknown. It is of interest to note, however, that apoprotein A-I found in the fraction of density greater than 1.21 gm/ml contains only trace amounts of phospholipids, and that when apoprotein C is transferred to HDL (i.e., after heparin injection) no appreciable change in HDL phospholipid content can be detected. Thus, these two apoproteins may physiologically be associated with only small amounts of phospholipid.

The assembly and secretion of the triglyceride-rich lipoprotein is dependent on normal synthesis of apoprotein B subunits. The formation of these lipoproteins may be viewed as a process of "lipidation" of a "fundamental unit" built predominantly of apoprotein B, phospholipids, and cholesterol. Whether other apoproteins, such as the arginine-rich protein form an integral part of the "fundamental unit" is yet to be established. Under normal conditions, during the lipidation process, triglycerides are added to this unit, together with relatively small amounts of cholesterol (free?) and phospholipids (lecithin?). The amount of lipids added to the unit depends primarily on the availability of triglycerides. The lipid content and size of the particle secreted may therefore vary; it will, however, contain the same amount of "fundamental unit" material. It has been mentioned earlier that VLDL particles of very large size seem to be secreted during periods of carbohydrate feeding. It is conceivable that triglyceride-poor particles or even LDL may be secreted when the amount of triglyceride is limited. Indeed, in normal monkeys, some LDL and IDL particles may be secreted along with VLDL from the liver or intestine (Illingworth and Portman, 1973).

The abnormal lipoproteins of cholesterol-fed animals are an example of triglyceride-poor cholesterol-rich particles. These particles, in the VLDL density range, exhibit beta electrophoretic mobility, contain apoprotein B, and are enriched with the arginine-rich protein. Although no human counterpart of such lipoproteins has yet been identified, the possibility that similar pathways of lipoprotein formation may exist has to be considered, especially in patients with type III hyperlipoproteinemia.

No information is available in the literature on the mode of assembly, intracellular transport, and secretion of the A and C apoprotein subunits. Both subunits are formed independent of apoprotein-B-containing lipoproteins. They are identified in plasma of patients with abetalipoproteinemia though they may differ some from their normal counterpart. The presence of some apoprotein C subunits in Tangier disease, demonstrates that its formation is independent at least in part of normal apoprotein A particles.

In circulation, all subunits are interrelated and participate in the physiological processes occurring during triglyceride transport. In normal fasting plasma, apoprotein C subunits are distributed between

VLDL and HDL in proportion to their relative concentration in the plasma. They are freely transferred between VLDL and HDL by two mechanisms: (a) exchange and (b) unidirectional transfer. Exchange of apoprotein C among lipoproteins has been clearly demonstrated. It occurs during the steady state, both *in vitro* and *in vivo*. Unidirectional transfer of apoprotein C subunits takes place either from VLDL to HDL or vice versa. It has been documented in several different experiments: (a) Transfer of apoprotein C from HDL to chylomicrons during alimentary chylomicronemia has been demonstrated (Havel *et al.*, 1973). At later periods, when chylomicron triglycerides are cleared from the plasma compartment, the activator protein transfers back to HDL. (b) Similar transfer of apoprotein C from HDL to VLDL probably occurs when newly synthesized VLDL particles enter the circulation. It has been demonstrated that these particles when secreted contain small amounts (liver) or no apoprotein C (intestine). (c) Apoprotein C subunits are transferred to HDL shortly after prompt initiation of VLDL triglyceride hydrolysis by the injection of heparin to humans (Eisenberg *et al.*, 1973b). More than 50% of labeled apoprotein C in VLDL transfers to HDL within 15 minutes of the injection of heparin. Six hours after the injection they are recovered again in the VLDL density range associated with newly synthesized triglyceride-rich particles. Similar observations have been recorded in rats.

The process of delipidation (removal of triglycerides) from either chylomicrons or VLDL involves removal of apoprotein C from the lipoproteins. However, as shown already, it involves also removal of cholesterol and phospholipids, at least from VLDL particles. Moreover, studies on the effect of post-heparin lipolytic activity on VLDL degradation *in vivo* or *in vitro* (Eisenberg and Rachmilewitz, 1974) have clearly demonstrated that a lipoprotein of intermediate density (S_f 12–60) is rapidly formed in plasma. The intermediate lipoprotein is further metabolized—to form LDL only *in vivo*, at a relatively slow rate and independent of the post-heparin lipolytic activity. To account for all of these phenomena the scheme of delipidation may be more complex than a simplified "shrinkage" of particles following triglyceride hydrolysis.

The basic process of delipidation of triglyceride-rich particles occurs at endothelial surfaces of the capillary bed of extrahepatic tissues (Fig. 15). Whether it involves a specific receptor for the lipoproteins, other than the enzyme(s) lipoprotein lipase, is unknown. The attachment of lipoproteins to the enzyme and/or the initiation of lypolysis necessitates the presence of apoprotein C—especially C-II

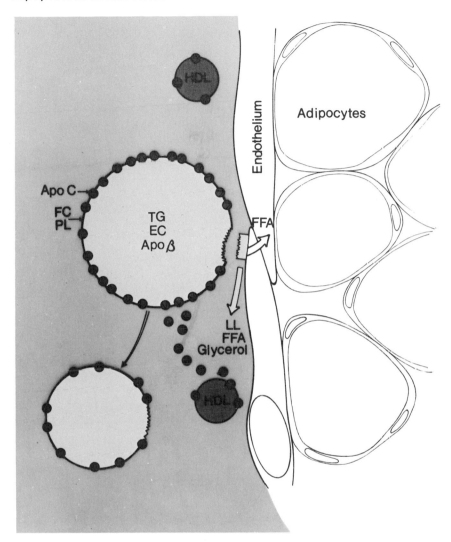

FIG. 15. Schematic representation of lipoprotein-lipase-initiated VLDL catabolism at the capillary vessel wall.

on the surface of the lipoprotein. Organ perfusion studies have clearly demonstrated that the HDL or apoprotein A subunits are not essential for normal lypolysis. Lypolysis occurs in patients with familial HDL deficiency (Tangier disease). The overall process taking place at the site of lypolysis results in hydrolysis of triglycerides and phospholipids (predominantly lecithin) and hydrolysis of cholesterol (predominantly free) and apoprotein C. Whether lecithin is hydrolyzed initially in order to open a "hole" in the surface coat of the lipoprotein and allow direct contact between the enzyme and the triglycerides, or the hydrolysis of the two lipids occurs simultaneously, is unknown. Concomitantly, apoprotein C subunits leave the lipoprotein particle and are transferred to HDL. Some cholesterol (free?) and phospholipids may be transferred to HDL as part of the apoprotein C subunit. Alternatively, the free cholesterol and phospholipids may represent pieces of the surface coat material which has been separated off the lipoprotein and associated with HDL. Partially degraded particles are then released from the enzyme complex back into the circulation. These particles have lost some of each of their lipid constituents and some of their apoprotein C subunits. They contain the full amount of apoprotein B present in the original particle. Since the loss of polar and unpolar constituents is related, the particles contain the same ratio of "surface" (polar) to "core" (nonpolar) material as the original particle. These particles are found in the circulation in VLDL subfractions of lower S_f rates than the original particles and are capable of interacting again with the endothelial lipoprotein lipase. Thus the degradation of any one particle occurs in multiple similar steps and during interaction of the particle with many endothelial lipase sites. From simple surface-to-volume considerations it is apparent that as the particle becomes smaller, each such interaction results in a comparatively greater loss of surface (polar) material than core (nonpolar) material. This consideration is compatible with the observed relationship between apoprotein C and triglycerides in differently degraded VLDL particles. After multiple interactions, the particle loses most of its apoprotein C subunits, phospholipids, and free cholesterol. Its further interaction with the endothelial-bound lipoprotein lipase of extrahepatic tissues becomes limited or may even cease. From a metabolic point of view, this particle represents the true intermediate lipoprotein. It is best defined by its function and metabolic properties rather than by an arbitrary density range. It is a product of VLDL, formed subsequent to the chains of interactions between VLDL and lipoprotein lipase, and in itself is incapable or poorly capable of further interaction with the extrahepatic enzyme. Although it may be regarded as "partially degraded" VLDL, its characteristics are more like "triglyceride-rich" LDL. The main apoprotein of the intermediate lipoprotein is apoprotein B. Relative to intact VLDL, it is rich in cholesteryl esters (and probably sphingomyelin) and poor in free cholesterol and lecithin. It contains however, about 20% of the triglycerides present in the original VLDL. The intermediate lipoprotein thus contains the protein and lipid of the apoprotein B subunit, with an excess of triglyceride and polar lipids. It is found in plasma in the S_f rates of 12–60.

The fate of the intermediate lipoprotein varies in different species. In the normal human, it is further degraded to form LDL. In rats, as well as in some hyperlipidemic states in humans, much of the intermediate lipoprotein may be removed from circulation by the liver.

The mechanisms by which an intermediate lipoprotein particle is either converted to LDL or is catabolized by the liver are obscure. In the rat, the available data suggest that the catabolism of VLDL particles—or their intermediates—occurs in at least two steps. Using electron microscopic radioautography with VLDL labeled predominantly in its protein moiety (Fig. 16), a concentration of radioactivity at the sinusoidal liver cells plasma membranes was observed during the period of rapid disappearance of injected radioactivity from the circulation (Stein *et al.*, 1974b). Radioactive grain density at the cell boundary approached that of the cytoplasm only 120 minutes after the injection. These results further suggested that there was an initial lag period at the liver cells plasma membrane surface prior to interiorization and subsequent catabolism of the lipoproteins. The plasma membrane of liver cells is a site of concentrated activity of several lipid hydrolyzing enzymes, including the hepatic lipoprotein lipase (triglyceride hydrolase), phospholipase A, and cholesterol esterase. Of interest, the activities of the hepatic enzymes are independent of the presence of apoprotein C, and proceed in the apoprotein-C-poor intermediate lipoprotein. It is tempting to hypothesize that the initial lag of the intermediate lipoprotein at the outer cell surface involves binding of the lipoprotein to an enzyme receptor site. The particle then becomes interiorized after some—or most—of its esterified lipids (triglyceride, lecithin, and esterified cholesterol) are hydrolyzed. This proposed mechanism is similar to that shown to take place during the catabolism of chylomicron remnants. It is also compatible with the saturation of VLDL particle uptake by the liver observed shortly after the injection of increasing doses of ^{125}I-VLDL to rats (Stein *et al.*, 1974b). These studies also indicate that the fate of chylomicron remnants and VLDL intermediates in rats is similar and seems a logical explanation for the low levels of plasma LDL in this species.

The mechanism of conversion of an intermediate lipoprotein particle to LDL in humans is unknown. The intermediate particle contains the full complement of apoprotein B and lipid found in any LDL particle. The interconversion involves predominantly removal of

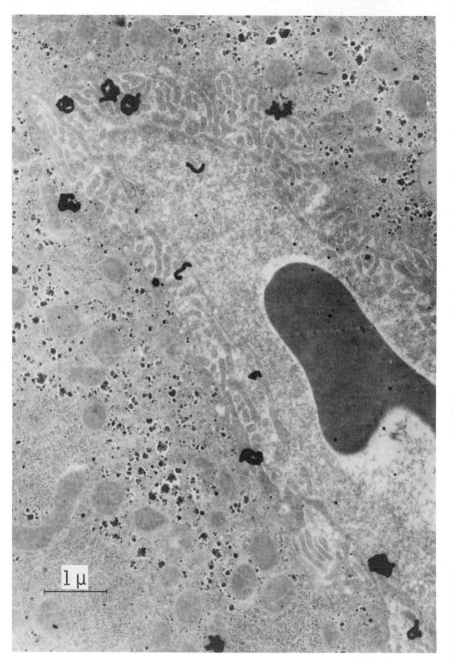

FIG. 16. Electron microscopic radioautograph of rat liver 30 minutes after the injection of ^{125}I-VLDL. The silver grains are concentrated over the hepatocyte sinusoidal cell boundary. (Courtesy of Dr. O. Stein.)

triglycerides from the "apoprotein-C-poor" intermediate along with some cholesterol (free?) and phospholipids. It is tempting to assign the major role of the interconversion of the intermediate to LDL to the hepatic lipoprotein lipase. According to this hypothesis, an intermediate lipoprotein particle would bind to the enzyme site on the liver cell membrane, where it would lose excess triglyceride and polar units in a fashion similar to that described for the extrahepatic lipoprotein lipase. The final particle (in normal man), however, is not catabolized by the cells but is released back to the circulation, where it persists as an LDL particle. The LDL particle then may lose some of its cholesterol and be taken up by tissue cells following specific interactions with different plasma membrane receptors. The possible roles of other enzymes, such as the lecithin:cholesterol acyl transferase in this pathway, are unclear. *The major role of HDL in the pathway appears to be as a flexible "reservoir" of apoprotein C subunits.* Future studies may indicate that HDL participates in other phases of lipopro-

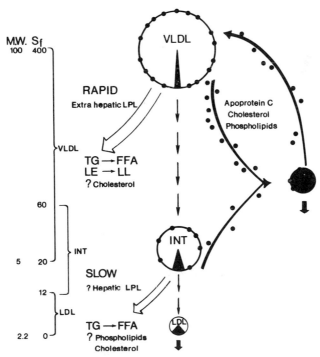

FIG. 17. Schematic representation of the metabolic relationships of human plasma lipoproteins. Dark ball at right represents HDL serving as reservoir for apoprotein C.

tein metabolism, i.e., as a main source for the formation of cholesteryl esters.

Functionally, five lipoprotein families are defined: chylomicrons, VLDL, intermediate lipoprotein (IDL), LDL, and HDL (Fig. 17). These lipoproteins may be defined by virtue of their function and metabolism rather than by their composition, flotation properties, apoprotein content, etc. All of these lipoproteins are linked metabolically and participate in the exceedingly important process of triglyceride transport. Chylomicrons and VLDL are the primary triglyceride-carrying particles transporting triglycerides from liver and intestine to their sites of utilization, predominantly adipose tissue and muscle. They are regarded as bistructural lipoproteins, containing both apoprotein B and apoprotein C subunits. Both are susceptible to the activity of extrahepatic lipoprotein lipase. The action of the enzyme, however, results in the disintegration of the complex lipoproteins and disassociation of the subunits. The apoprotein C subunits are transferred to HDL; the apoprotein B subunit is converted to the intermediate lipoprotein. The intermediate lipoprotein is the product of interaction of the triglyceride-carrying particles with lipoprotein lipase. It is possible that its catabolism involves different enzyme systems, perhaps hepatic lipoprotein lipase, and results in the formation of a "final breakdown lipoprotein product" LDL. Both HDL and LDL are eventually cleared from circulation by tissues, chiefly the liver. Aberrations of one or more of the multiple pathways of this integrated scheme of lipoprotein metabolism in humans result in formation of excessive plasma lipoprotein concentrations—the hyperlipoproteinemias.

References[2]

Aggerbeck, L. P., and Scanu, A. M. (1971). *Circulation, Suppl.* **2**, No. 11, 43–44.
Alaupovic, P. (1971). *Atherosclerosis* **13**, 141.
Alaupovic, P., Lee, D. M., and McConathy, W. J. (1972). *Biochim. Biophys. Acta* **260**, 689.
Albers, J. J., and Aladjem, F. (1971). *Biochemistry* **10**, 3463.
Albers, J. J., and Hazzard, W. R. (1974). *Lipids* **9**, 15.
Albers, J. J., and Scanu, A. M. (1971). *Biochim. Biophys. Acta* **236**, 97.
Alcindor, L. G., Infante, R., Soler-Argilaga, C., Raisonnier, A., Polonovski, J., and Caroli, J. (1970). *Biochim. Biophys. Acta* **210**, 483.
Alexander, C., and Day, C. E. (1973). *Comp. Biochem. Physiol. B* **46**, 295.

[2] In making this list we have attempted to minimize the number of references published prior to 1970. Where possible, the reader is referred to existing reviews on specific phases of lipoproteins composition, structure, and function.

Ashworth, L. A. E., and Green, C. (1963). *Biochem. J.* **89**, 561.

Assman, G., and Brewer, H. B. (1974a). *Proc. Nat. Acad. Sci. U. S.* **71**, 989.

Assman, G., and Brewer, H. B. (1974b). *Proc. Nat. Acad. Sci. U. S.* **71**, 1534.

Assman, G., Krauss, R. M., Fredrickson, D. S., and Levy, R. I. (1973). *J. Biol. Chem.* **248**, 1992.

Assman, G., Sokoloski, E. A., and Brewer, H. B. (1974a). *Proc. Nat. Acad. Sci. U. S.* **71**, 549.

Assman, G., Hight, R. J., Sokoloski, E. A., and Brewer, H. B. (1974b). *Proc. Nat. Acad. Sci. U. S.* **71**, 3701.

Assman, G., Brewer, H. B., Fairwell, T., Mahley, R., and Weisgraber, K. (1974c). *Circulation* **49**, *Suppl.* **3**, 259.

Assman, G., Fredrickson, D. S., Herbert, P., Forte, T., and Heinen, R. (1974d). *Circulation*, **49**, *Suppl.* **3**, 259.

Ayrault-Jarrier, M., Cheftel, R. I., and Polonovski, J. (1961). *Bull. Soc. Chim. Biol.* **43**, 811.

Bagdade, J. D., Bierman, E. L., and Porte, D. (1967). *N. Engl. J. Med.* **276**, 427.

Bailey, J. M. (1967). *Wistar Inst. Symp. Monogr.* **6**, 85.

Bailey, J. M. (1973). *Ciba Found. Symp. Atherogenesis: Initiating Factors* **12**, 63.

Baker, H. N., Jackson, R. L., and Gotto, A. M. (1973). *Biochemistry* **12**, 3866.

Baker, H. N., Gotto, A. M., and Jackson, R. L. (1974a). *J. Biol. Chem.* (in press).

Baker, H. N., Delahunty, T., Gotto, A. M., and Jackson, R. L. (1974b). *Proc. Nat. Acad. Sci. U. S.* **71**, 3631.

Bar–on, H., Kook, A. I., Stein, O., and Stein, Y. (1973). *Biochim. Biophys. Acta* **306**, 106.

Barter, P. J. (1974a). *J. Lipid Res.* **15**, 11.

Barter, P. J. (1974b). *J. Lipid Res.* **15**, 234.

Barter, P. J., and Nestel, P. J. (1970). *J. Lab. Clin. Med.* **76**, 925.

Barter, P. J., and Nestel, P. J. (1972). *J. Clin. Invest.* **51**, 174.

Bates, S. R., and Rothblat, G. H. (1974). *Biochim. Biophys. Acta* **360**, 38.

Bensadoun, A., Ehnholm, C., Steinberg, D., and Brown, W. V. (1974). *J. Biol. Chem.* **249**, 2220.

Berg, K. (1963). *Acta Pathol. Microbiol. Scand.* **59**, 369.

Bergman, E. N., Havel, R. J., Wolfe, B. M., and Bøhmer, T. (1971). *J. Clin. Invest.* **50**, 1831.

Bersot, T. P., Brown, W. V., Levy, R. I., Windmueller, H. G., and Fredrickson, D. S. (1970). *Biochemistry* **9**, 3427.

Biala, Y., and Shafrir, E. (1969). *Clin. Chim. Acta* **23**, 413.

Bierman, E. L. (1972). *Isr. J. Med. Sci.* **8**, 303.

Bierman, E. L., Porte, D., O'Hara, D. D., Schwartz, C. H., and Wood, F. C. (1965). *J. Clin. Invest.* **44**, 261.

Bierman, E. L., Eisenberg, S., Stein, O., and Stein, Y. (1973). *Biochim. Biophys. Acta* **329**, 163.

Bierman, E. L., Stein, O., and Stein, Y. (1974). *Circ. Res.* **35**, 136.

Bilheimer, D. W., Eisenberg, S., and Levy, R. I. (1971a). *J. Clin. Invest.* **40**, 48a.

Bilheimer, D. W., Eisenberg, S., and Levy, R. I. (1971b). *Circulation* **56**, *Suppl.* **2**, 43–44.

Bilheimer, D. W., Eisenberg, S., and Levy, R. I. (1972). *Biochim. Biophys. Acta* **260**, 212.

Bizzi, A., and Marsh, J. B. (1973). *Proc. Soc. Exp. Biol. Med.* **144**, 762.

Blanchette-Mackie, E. J., and Scow, R. O. (1971). *J. Cell Biol.* **51**, 1.

Blanchette-Mackie, E. J., and Scow, R. O. (1973). *J. Cell Biol.* **58**, 689.

Blaton, V., Vercaemst, R., Van De Casteele, N., Caster, H., and Peeters, H. (1974). *Biochemistry* **13**, 1127.
Borut, T. C., and Aladjem, F. (1971). *Immunochemistry* **8**, 851.
Brewer, H. B., Lux, S., Ronan, R., and John, K. M. (1972). *Proc. Nat. Acad. Sci. U. S.* **69**, 1306.
Brewer, H. B., Shulman, R. S., Herbert, P., Ronan, R., and Wehrly, K. (1974). *J. Biol. Chem.* **249**, 4975.
Brown, M. S., and Goldstein, J. L. (1974a). *Proc. Nat. Acad. Sci. U. S.* **71**, 788.
Brown, M. S., and Goldstein, J. L. (1974b). *Science* **185**, 61.
Brown, M. S., Dana, S. E., Dietschy, J. M., and Siperstein, M. D. (1973a). *J. Biol. Chem.* **248**, 4731.
Brown, M. S., Dana, S. E., and Goldstein, J. L. (1973b). *Proc. Nat. Acad. Sci. U. S.* **70**, 2162.
Brown, M. S., Dana, S. E., and Goldstein, J. L. (1974). *J. Biol. Chem.* **249**, 789.
Brown, W. V., and Baginsky, M. L. (1972). *Biochem. Biophys. Res. Commun.* **46**, 375.
Brown, W. V., Levy, R. I., and Fredrickson, D. S. (1969), *J. Biol. Chem.* **244**, 5687.
Brown, W. V., Levy, R. I., and Fredrickson, D. S. (1970a). *Biochim. Biophys. Acta* **200**, 573.
Brown, W. V., Levy, R. I., and Fredrickson, D. S. (1970b). *J. Biol. Chem.* **245**, 6588.
Bungenberg de Jong, J. J. and Marsh, J. B. (1968). *J. Biol. Chem.* **243**, 192.
Burns, C. H., and Rothblat, G. H. (1969). *Biochim. Biophys. Acta* **176**, 616.
Camejo, G. (1969). *Biochim. Biophys. Acta* **175**, 290.
Camejo, G., Bosch, V., Arreaza, C., and Mendez, H. C. (1973). *J. Lipid Res.* **14**, 61.
Camejo, G., Bosch, V., and Lopez, A. (1974). *Atherosclerosis* **19**, 139.
Chapman, M. J., Mills, G. L., and Taylour, C. E. (1972). *Biochem. J.* **128**, 779.
Dahlen, G., Ericson, C., Furberg, C., Lundkvist, L., and Svardsudd, K. (1972). *Acta Med. Scand., Suppl.* **531**, 1.
Delahunty, T., and Mookerjea, S., (1974). *Can. J. Biochem.* **52**, 359.
Delahunty, T., Baker, H. N., Gotto, A. M., and Jackson, R. L. (1974). *J. Biol. Chem.* (in press).
Eaton, P. R., and Kipnis, D. (1972). *Diabetes* **21**, 744.
Edelstein, C., Lim, C. T., and Scanu, A. M. (1972). *J. Biol. Chem.* **247**, 5842.
Edelstein, C., Lim, C. T., and Scanu, A. M. (1973). *J. Biol. Chem.* **248**, 7653.
Edelstein, C., Noyes, C., and Scanu, A. M. (1974). *FEBS (Fed. Eur. Biochem. Soc.) Lett.* **38**, 166.
Egelrud, T., and Olivecrona, T. (1972). *J. Biol. Chem.* **247**, 6212.
Eggena, P., Tivol, W., and Aladjem, F. (1972). *Biochem. Med.* **6**, 184.
Ehnholm. C., Garoff, H., Renkonen, O., and Simons, K. (1972). *Biochemistry* **11**, 3229.
Eisenberg, S. (1973). *In* "Dietary Lipids and Postnatal Development" (C. Galli, G. Jacini, and A. Pecile, eds.), p. 57. Raven Press, New York.
Eisenberg, S., and Rachmilewitz, D. (1973a). *Biochim. Biophys. Acta* **326**, 378.
Eisenberg, S., and Rachmilewitz, D. (1973b). *Biochim. Biophys. Acta* **326**, 391.
Eisenberg, S., and Rachmilewitz, D. (1973c). *Circulation* **47**, Suppl. 2, 111.
Eisenberg, S., and Rachmilewitz, D. (1975). In preparation.
Eisenberg, S., Bilheimer, D. W., and Levy, R. I. (1972a). *Biochim. Biophys. Acta* **280**, 94.
Eisenberg, S., Bilheimer, D. W., Levy, R. I., and Lindgren, F. T. (1972b). *Biochim. Biophys. Acta* **260**, 329.
Eisenberg, S., Bilheimer, D. W., Levy, R. I., and Lindgren F. T. (1973a). *Biochim. Biophys. Acta* **326**, 361.

Eisenberg, S., Windmueller, H. G., and Levy, R. I. (1973b). *J. Lipid Res.* **14**, 446.

Faergeman, O., Mjøs, O. D., and Havel, R. J. (1974a). *Clin. Res.* **22**, 128A.

Faergeman, O., Sata, T., Kane, J. P., and Havel, R. J. (1974b). *Circulation* **49–50**, Suppl. 3, 114.

Faineru, M., Glangeud, M., and Eisenberg, S. (1975). In preparation.

Felts, J. M., and Berry, M. J. (1971). *Biochim. Biophys. Acta* **231**, 1.

Felts, J. M., and Mayes, P. A. (1965). *Nature (London)* **206**, 195.

Fidge, N. H., and Poulis, P. (1974). *Clin. Chim. Acta* **52**, 15.

Fielding. C. J. (1972). *Biochim. Biophys. Acta* **280**, 569.

Fielding, C. J., Shore, V., and Fielding, P. E. (1972). *Biochem. Biophys. Res. Commun.* **46**, 1493.

Forte, T., and Nichols, A. V. (1972). *Advan. Lipid Res.* **10**, 1.

Forte, T., Nichols, A. V., and Glaeser, R. M. (1968). *Chem. Phys. Lipids* **2**, 396.

Forte, T., Nichols, A. V., Gong, E. L., Lux, S. E., and Levy, R. I. (1971a). *Biochim. Biophys. Acta* **248**, 381.

Forte, T., Norum, K. R., Glomset, J. A., and Nichols, A. V. (1971b). *J. Clin. Invest.* **50**, 1141.

Forte, T., Gong, E. L., and Nichols. A. V. (1974). *Biochim. Biophys. Acta* **337**, 169.

Fraser, R. (1970). *J. Lipid Res.* **11**, 60.

Fredrickson, D. S., and Levy, R. I. (1972). In "The Metabolic Basis of Inherited Disease" (J. B. Stanbury, J. B. Wyngaarden, and D. S. Fredrickson, eds.), 3rd ed. p. 531. McGraw-Hill, New York.

Fredrickson, D. S., Gotto, A. M., and Levy, R. I. (1972a). In "The Metabolic Basis of Inherited Disease" (J. B. Stanbury, J. B. Wyngaarden, and D. S. Fredrickson, eds.), 3rd ed., p. 493. McGraw-Hill, New York.

Fredrickson, D. S., Lux, S. E., and Herbert, P. N. (1972b). *Advan. Exp. Med. Biol.* **26**, 25.

Furman, R. H., Sanbar, S. S., Alaupovic, P., Bradford, R. H., and Howard, R. P. (1964). *J. Lab. Clin. Med.* **63**, 193.

Ganesen, D., Bradford, R. H., Alaupovic, P., and McConathy, W. J. (1971). *FEBS (Fed. Eur. Biochem. Soc.) Lett.* **15**, 205.

Gidez, L. I., Roheim, P. S., and Eder, H. E. (1965). *J. Lipid Res.* **6**, 377.

Gitlin, D., Cornwell, D. G., Nakasato, D., Oncley, J. L., Hughes, W. L., and Jancway, C. A. (1958). *J. Clin. Invest.* **37**, 172.

Glomset, J. A. (1968). *J. Lipid Res.* **9**, 155.

Glomset, J. A., and Norum, K. R. (1973). *Advan. Lipid Res.* **11**, 1.

Glomset, J. A., Norum, K. R., Nichols, A. V., Forte, T., King, W. C., Albers, J. J., Mitchel, C. D., Applegate, K. R., and Gjone, E. (1974). *Scand. J. Clin. Lab. Invest.* **33**, Suppl. 137, 165.

Goldstein, J. L., and Brown, M. S. (1973). *Proc. Nat. Acad. Sci. U. S.* **70**, 3804.

Goldstein, J. L., and Brown, M. S. (1974a). *Amer. J. Hum. Genet.* **26**, 199.

Goldstein, J. L., and Brown, M. S. (1974b). *J. Biol. Chem.* **249**, 5153.

Gotto, A. M. (1969). *Proc. Nat. Acad. Sci. U. S.* **64**, 1119.

Gotto, A. M., and Kon, H. (1969). *Biochem. Biophys. Res. Commun.* **37**, 444.

Gotto, A. M., and Kon, H. (1970). *Biochemistry* **9**, 4276.

Gotto, A. M., and Shore, B. (1969). *Nature (London)* **224**, 69.

Gotto, A. M., Levy, R. I., and Fredrickson, D. S. (1968a). *Proc. Nat. Acad. Sci. U. S.* **60**, 1436.

Gotto, A. M., Levy, R. I., Rosenthal, A. S., Birnbaumer, M. E., and Fredrickson, D. S. (1968b). *Biochem. Biophys. Res. Commun.* **31**, 699.

Gotto, A. M., Levy, R. I., and Fredrickson, D. S. (1968c). *Lipids* **3**, 463.
Gotto, A. M., Levy, R. I., Rosenthal, A. S., and Fredrickson, D. S. (1969). *Nature (London)* **219**, 1157.
Gotto, A. M., Levy, R. I., John K., and Fredrickson, D. S. (1971). *N. Engl. J. Med.* **284**, 813.
Gotto, A. M., Brown, W. V., Levy, R. I., Birnbaumer, M. E., and Fredrickson, D. S. (1972). *J. Clin. Invest.* **51**, 1486.
Gotto, A. M., Levy, R. I., Lux, S. E., Birnbaumer, M. E., and Fredrickson, D. S. (1973). *Biochem. J.* **133**, 369.
Greten, H., Levy, R. I., and Fredrickson, D. S. (1969). *J. Lipid Res.* **10**, 326.
Greten, H., Walter, B., and Brown, W. V. (1972). *FEBS (Fed. Eur. Biochem. Soc.) Lett.* **27**, 306.
Greten, H., Sniderman, A. D., Chandler, J. G., Steinberg, D., and Brown, W. V. (1974). *FEBS (Fed. Eur. Biochem. Soc.) Lett.* **42**, 157.
Gustafson, A. (1966). *Acta Med. Scand., Suppl.* **446**, 1.
Gustafson, A. (1966). *Acta MEd. Scand., Suppl.* **446**, 1.
Gustafson, A., Alaupovic, P., and Furman, R. H. (1966). *Biochemistry* **5**, 632.
Haft, D. E., Roheim, P. S., White, A., and Eder, H. E. (1962). *J. Clin. Invest.* **41**, 842.
Hamilton, R. L., (1968). *In* "Proceedings of the Deuel Conference on Lipids, Pub. Health Serv., p. 3. USPHS, Washington, D. C.
Hamilton, R. L. (1972). *Advan. Exp. Med. Biol.* **26**, 7.
Hamilton, R. L., Havel, R. J., Kane, J. P., Blaurock, A. E., and Sata, T. (1971). *Science* **172**, 475.
Hammond, M. G., and Fisher, W. (1971). *J. Biol. Chem.* **246**, 5454.
Harris, K. L., and Harris, P. A. (1973). *Biochim. Biophys. Acta* **326**, 12.
Havel, R. J., and Kane, J. P. (1973). *Proc. Nat. Acad. Sci. U. S.* **70**, 2015.
Havel, R. J., Felts, J. M., and VanDuyne, C. M. (1962). *J. Lipid Res.* **3**, 297.
Havel, R. J., Kane, J. P., Balasse, E. O., Segal, M., and Basso, L. V. (1970). *J. Clin. Invest.* **49**, 2017.
Havel, R. J., Kane, J. P., and Kashyap, M. L. (1973). *J. Clin. Invest.* **52**, 32.
Hay, R. V., Pottenger, L. A., Reingold, A. L., Getz, G. S., and Wissler, R. W. (1971). *Biochem. Biophys. Res. Commun.* **44**, 1471.
Hazzard, W. R., and Bierman, E. L. (1970). *Clin. Res.* **19**, 476.
Hazzard, W. R., Lindgren, F. T., and Bierman, E. L. (1970). *Biochim. Biophys. Acta* **202**, 517.
Hazzard, W. R., Porte, D., and Bierman, D. (1972). *Metab. Clin. Exp.* **21**, 1009.
Heiberg, A., and Berg, K. (1974). *Clin. Genet.* **5**, 144.
Herbert, P. N., Levy, R. I., and Fredrickson, D. S. (1971a). *J. Biol. Chem.* **246**, 7068.
Herbert, P. N., LaRosa, J., Krauss, R. M., Lux, S. E., Levy, R. I., and Fredrickson, D. S. (1971b). *J. Clin. Invest.* **50**, 44a.
Herbert, P. N., Krauss, R. M., Windmueller, H. G., and Shulman, R. S. (1973). *Circulation* **48**, Suppl. 4, 112.
Herbert, P. N., Windmueller, H. G., Bersot, T. P., and Shulman, R. S. (1974). *J. Biol. Chem.* **249**, 5718.
Hoff, H. F., Morrisett, J. D., and Gotto, A. M. (1973). *Biochim. Biophys. Acta* **296**, 653.
Hotta, S., and Chaikoff, I. L. (1955). *Arch. Biochem. Biophys.* **56**, 28.
Hurley, R. J., and Scott, P. J. (1970). *J. Atheroscler. Res.* **11**, 51.
Illingworth, D. R., and Portman, O. W. (1973). *Circulation, Suppl.* **3**, 110.
Jackson, R. L., and Gotto, A. M. (1972). *Biochim. Biophys. Acta* **285**, 36.
Jackson, R. L., and Gotto, A. M. (1974). *N. Engl. J. Med.* **290**, 24 and 87.

Jackson, R. L., Baker, H. N., David, J. S. K., and Gotto, A. M. (1972) *Biochem. Biophys. Res. Commun.* **49,** 1444.
Jackson, R. L., Morrisett, J. D., Pownell, H. J., and Gotto, A. M. (1973a). *J. Biol. Chem.* **248,** 5218.
Jackson, R. L., Gotto, A. M., Lux, S. E., John, K. M., and Fleischer, S. (1973b). *J. Biol. Chem.* **248,** 8449.
Jackson, R. L., Sparrow, J. T., Baker, H. N., Morrisett, J. D., Taunton, O. D., and Gotto, A. M. (1974a). *J. Biol. Chem.* **249,** 5308.
Jackson, R. L., Morrisett, J. D., Sparrow, J. T., Segrest, J. P., Pownell, H. J., Smith, L. C., Hoff, H. F., and Gotto, A. M. (1974b). *J. Biol. Chem.* **249,** 5314.
Kane, J. P., Richards, E. G., and Havel, R. J. (1970). *Proc. Nat. Acad. Sci. U. S.* **66,** 1075.
Kayden, H. J. (1972). *Annu. Rev. Med.* **23,** 285.
Kessler, J. I., Stein, J., Dannacker, D., and Narcessian, P. (1970). *J. Biol. Chem.* **245,** 5281.
Koga, S., Bolis, L., and Scanu, A. M. (1971). *Biochim. Biophys. Acta* **236,** 416.
Kostner, G. (1974). *Biochim. Biophys. Acta* **336,** 383.
Kostner, G., and Alaupovic, P. (1971). *FEBS (Fed. Eur. Biochem. Soc.) Lett.* **15,** 320.
Kostner, G., and Holasek, A. (1972). *Biochemistry* **11,** 1217.
Kostner, G., Holasek, A., Bohlmann, H. D., and Thiede, H. (1974). *Clin. Sci. Mol. Med.* **46,** 457.
Krauss, R. M., Herbert, P., Levy, R. I., and Fredrickson, D. S. (1973a). *Cir. Res.* **33,** 403.
Krauss, R. M., Windmueller, H. G., Levy, R. I., and Fredrickson, D. S. (1973b). *J. Lipid Res.* **14,** 286.
Krauss, R. M., Levy, R. I., and Fredrickson, D. S. (1974). *J. Clin. Invest.* **54,** 1107.
Kuhel, K., Roheim, P. S., and Eder, H. A. (1974). *Fed. Proc., Fed. Amer. Soc. Exp. Biol.* **33,** 828.
Langer, T., Strober, W., and Levy, R. I. (1972). *J. Clin. Invest.* **51,** 1528.
LaRosa, J. C., Levy, R. I., Herbert, P. N., Lux, S. E., and Fredrickson, D. S. (1970). *Biochem. Biophys. Res. Commun.* **41,** 57.
LaRosa, J. C., Levy, R. I., Windmueller, H. G., and Fredrickson, D. S. (1972). *J. Lipid Res.* **13,** 356.
Lasser, N. L., Roheim, P. S., Edelstein, D., and Eder, H. A. (1973). *J. Lipid Res.* **14,** 1.
Lee, D. M., and Alaupovic, P. (1970). *Biochemistry* **9,** 2244.
Lee, D. M., and Alaupovic, P. (1974). *Biochem. J.* **137,** 155.
Levy, R. I., and Fredrickson, D. S. (1965). *J. Clin. Invest.* **44,** 426.
Levy, R. I., and Langer, T. (1972). *Advan. Exp. Med. Biol.* **26,** 155.
Levy, R. I., Lees, R. S., and Fredrickson, D. S. (1966). *J. Clin. Invest.* **45,** 63.
Levy, R. I., Bilheimer, D. W., and Eisenberg, S. (1971). *Biochem. Soc. Symp.* **33,** 3.
Lindgren, F. T., Jensen, L. C., Wills, R. D., and Stevens, G. R. (1972a). *Lipids* **7,** 194.
Lindgren, F. T., Jensen, L. C., and Hatch, F. T. (1972b). *In* "Blood Lipids and Lipoproteins" (G. Nelson, ed.), p. 181, Wiley (Interscience), New York.
Lo, C., and Marsh, J. B. (1970). *J. Biol. Chem.* **245,** 5001.
Lossow, W. J., Lindgren, F. T., Murchio, J. C., Stevens, G. R., and Jensen, L. C. (1969). *J. Lipid Res.* **10,** 68.
Lux, S. E., Hirz, R., Shrager, R. I., and Gotto, A. M. (1972a). *J. Biol. Chem.* **247,** 2598.
Lux, S. E., John, K. M., and Brewer, H. B. (1972b). *J. Biol. Chem.* **247,** 7510.
Lux, S. E., John, K. M., Ronan, R., and Brewer, H. B. (1972c). *J. Biol. Chem.* **247,** 7519.
Lux, S. E., John, K. M., Fleischer, S., Jackson, R. L., and Gotto, A. M. (1972d). *Biochem. Biophys. Res. Commun.* **49,** 23.
Lux, S. E., Levy, R. I., Gotto, A. M., and Fredrickson, D. S. (1972e). *J. Clin. Invest.* **51,** 2505.

Mahley, R. W., and Weisgraber, K. H. (1974a). *Biochemistry* **13**, 1964.

Mahley, R. W., and Weisgraber, K. H. (1974b). *Circ. Res.* (in press).

Mahley, R. W., Hamilton, R. L., and Lequire, V. S. (1969). *J. Lipid Res.* **10**, 433.

Mahley, R. W., Bersot, T. P., Lequire, V. S., Levy, R. I., Windmueller, H. G., and Brown, W. V. (1970). *Science* **168**, 380.

Mahley, R. W., Bennett, B. I., Morré, D. J., Gray, M. E., Thistelwaite, W., and Lequire, V. S. (1971). *Lab. Invest.* **25**, 435.

Mahley, R. W., Weisgraber, K. H., and Innerarity, T. (1974a). *Circ. Res.* (in press).

Mahley, R. W., Assman, G., Brown, G. B., Brewer, H. B., and Wiesgraber, K. H. (1974b). *Circulation* **49–50**, Suppl. 3, 70.

Margolis, S., and Capuzzi, O. (1972). *In* "Blood Lipids and Lipoproteins" (G. Nelson, ed.), p. 825, Wiley (Interscience), New York.

Marsh, J. B. (1971). *Biochem. Soc. Symp.* **33**, 99.

Marshall, W. E., and Kummerow, F. A. (1962). *Arch. Biochem. Biophys.* **98**, 271.

Mateu, L., Tardieu, A., Luzzati, V., Aggerbeck, L., and Scanu, A. M. (1972). *J. Mol. Biol.* **10**, 105.

Mayes, P. A., and Felts, J. M. (1967). *Biochem. J.* **105**, 18c.

Morrisett, J. D., David, J. S. K., Pownell, H. J., and Gotto, A. M. (1973). *Biochemistry* **12**, 1290.

Morrisett, J. D., Jackson, R. L., and Gotto, A. M. (1974). *Annu. Rev. Biochem.* (in press).

Nestel, P. J. (1964). *J. Clin. Invest.* **43**, 943.

Nestel, P. J. (1970). *Advan. Lipid Res.* **8**, 1.

Nichols, A. V. (1967). *Advan. Biol. Med. Phys.* **11**, 110.

Nichols. A. V., and Smith, L. (1965). *J. Lipid Res.* **6**, 206.

Nichols, A. V., Strisower, E. J., Lindgren, F. T., Adamson, G. L., and Coggiola, E. L. (1968). *Clin. Chim. Acta* **20**, 277.

Nichols, A. V., Lux S. E., Forte, T., Gong, E., and Levy, R. I. (1972). *Biochim. Biophys. Acta* **270**, 132.

Nikkila, E. A. (1969). *Advan. Lipid Res.* **7**, 63.

Nilsson, A., and Zilversmit, D. B. (1971). *Biochim. Biophys. Acta* **248**, 137.

Nilsson-Ehle, P., and Belfrage, P. (1972). *Biochim. Biophys. Acta* **270**, 60.

Ockner, R. K., Hughes, F. B., and Isselbacher, K. J. (1969). *J. Clin. Invest.* **48**, 2079.

O'Hara, D. D., Porte, D., and Williams, R. H. (1966). *J. Lipid Res.* **7**, 264.

Olivecrona, T. (1962). *J. Lipid Res.* **3**, 439.

Olivecrona, T., and Belfrage, P. (1965). *Biochim. Biophys. Acta* **98**, 81.

Oncley, J. L., Gurd, F. R. N., and Melin, M. (1950). *J. Amer. Chem. Soc.* **72**, 458.

Partin, J. S., Partin, J. C., Schubert, W. K., and McAdams, A. J. (1974). *Gastroenterology* **67**, 107.

Pearlstein, E., Eggena, P., and Aladjem, F. (1971). *Immunochemistry* **8**, 865.

Phair, R. D., Hammon, M. G., Bowden, J. A., Fried, M., Berman, M., and Fisher, W. (1972). *Fed. Proc., Fed. Amer. Soc. Exp. Biol.* **31**, 421.

Picard, M. J., and Veissier, D. (1970). *Clin. Chim. Acta* **30**, 149.

Pollard, H., Scanu, A. M., and Taylor, E. W. (1969). *Proc. Nat. Acad. Sci. U. S.* **64**, 304.

Porter, H. P., Saunders, D. R., Tytgat, G. N., Brunser, U., and Rubin, C. E. (1971). *Gastroenterology* **60**, 1008.

Quarfordt, S. E., and Goodman, D. S. (1966). *Biochim. Biophys. Acta* **116**, 382.

Quarfordt, S. E., and Goodman, D. S. (1967). *J. Lipid Res.* **8**, 266.

Quarfordt, S. E., Frank, A., Shames, D. M., Berman, M., and Steinberg, D. (1970). *J. Clin. Invest.* **49**, 2281.

Quarfordt, S. E., Boston, F., and Hilderman, H. (1971). *Biochim. Biophys. Acta* **231**, 290.

Quarfordt, S. E., Nathans, A., Dowdee, M., and Hilderman, H. (1972a). *J. Lipid Res.* **13**, 435.

Quarfordt, S. E., Oelschlaeger, H., and Krigbaum, W. R. (1972b). *J. Clin. Invest.* **51**, 1979.

Rachmilewitz, D., Stein, O., Roheim, P. S., and Stein, Y. (1972). *Biochim. Biophys. Acta* **270**, 414.

Radding, C. M., Bragdon, J. H., and Steinberg, D. (1958). *Biochim. Biophys. Acta* **30**, 443.

Redgrave, T. G. (1970). *J. Clin. Invest.* **49**, 465.

Rider, A. K., Levy, R. I., and Fredrickson, D. S. (1970). *Circulation* **42**, Suppl. 3, 10.

Robinson, D. S. (1970). *Compr. Biochem.* **19**, 51.

Rodbell, M. R., and Fredrickson, D. S. (1959). *J. Biol. Chem.* **234**, 562.

Rohcim, P. S., Haft, D. E., Gidez, L. I., White, A., and Eder, H. A. (1963). *J. Clin. Invest.* **42**, 1277.

Roheim, P. S., Gidez, L. I., and Eder, H. A. (1966). *J. Clin. Invest.* **45**, 297.

Roheim, P. S., Rachmilewitz, D., Stein, O., and Stein, Y. (1971). *Biochim. Biophys. Acta* **268**, 315.

Roheim, P. S., Hirsch, H., Edelstein, D., and Rachmilewitz, D. (1972). *Biochim. Biophys. Acta* **278**, 517.

Rothblat, G. H. (1969). *Advan. Lipid Res.* **7**, 135.

Rothblat, G. H., and Kritchevsky, D. (1968). *Exp. Mol. Pathol.* **8**, 314.

Ruderman, H. B., Richards, K. S., Valles De Bourges, V., and Jones, A. L. (1968). *J. Lipid Res.* **9**, 613.

Ruderman, H. B., Jones, A. L., Krauss, R. M., and Shafrir, E. (1971). *J. Clin. Invest.* **51**, 1355.

Rudman, D., Garcia, L. A., and Howard, C. A. (1970). *J. Clin. Invest.* **49**, 365.

Salel, A. F., Shore, B., Shore, V., Mason, D. T., and Zellis, R. (1974). *Clin. Res.* **21**, 637.

Salpeter, M. M., and Zilversmit, D. B. (1968). *J. Lipid Res.* **9**, 187.

Sardet, C., Hansma, H., and Ostwald, R. (1972). *J. Lipid Res.* **13**, 624.

Sata, T., Havel, R. J., and Jones, A. L. (1972). *J. Lipid Res.* **13**, 757.

Scanu, A. M. (1972). *Biochim. Biophys. Acta* **265**, 471.

Scanu, A. M., and Ritter, M. C. (1973). *Advan. Clin. Chem.* **16**, 111.

Scanu, A. M., Toth, J., Edelstein, C., Koga, S., and Stiller, E. (1969a). *Biochemistry* **8**, 3309.

Scanu, A. M., Pollard, H., Hirz, R., and Kothary, K. (1969b). *Proc. Nat. Acad. Sci. U. S.* **61**, 171.

Scanu, A. M., Cump, E., Toth, J., Koga, S., Stiller, E., and Albers, J. J. (1970). *Biochemistry* **9**, 1327.

Scanu, A. M., Edelstein, C., and Lim, C. T. (1971). *FEBS (Fed. Eur. Biochem. Soc.) Lett.* **18**, 305.

Scanu, A. M., Lim, C. T., and Edelstein, C. (1972). *J. Biol. Chem.* **247**, 5850.

Scanu, A. M., Edelstein, C., Vitello, L., Jones, R., and Wissler, R. (1973). *J. Biol. Chem.* **248**, 7648.

Scanu, A. M., Edelstein, C., and Wolf, R. H. (1974a). *Biochim. Biophys. Acta* **351**, 341.

Scanu, A. M., Aggerbeck, L. P., Kruski, A. W., Lim, C. T., and Kayden, H. J. (1974b). *J. Clin. Invest.* **53**, 440.

Schneider, H., Morrod, R. S., Colvin, J. R., and Tattrie, N. H. (1973). *Chem. Phys. Lipids* **10**, 328.

Schonfeld, G., Gulbrandsen, C. L., Wilson, R. B., and Lees, R. S. (1972). *Biochim. Biophys. Acta* **270**, 426.

Schonfeld, G., Lees, R. S., George, P. K., and Pfleger, B. (1974a). *J. Clin. Invest.* **53**, 1458.

Schonfeld, G., Felski, C., and Howald, M. A. (1974b). *J. Lipid Res.* **15**, 457.

Scow, R. O. (1970). *In* "Parenteral Nutrition" (H. C. Menz and D. H. Law, eds.), Chapter 24. Thomas, Springfield, Illinois.

Scow, R. O., Chernick, S. S., and Brinley, M. S. (1965). *Amer. J. Physiol.* **206**, 796.

Scow, R. O., Hamosh, M., Blanchette-Mackie, J., and Evans, E. J. (1972). *Lipids* **7**, 497.

Scow, R. O., Blanchette-Mackie, J., Hamosh, M., and Evans, E. J. (1973a). *Wiss. Veroeff. Deut. Ges. Erhaehr.* **23**, 100.

Scow, R. O., Mendelson, C. R., Zinder, O., Hamosh, M., and Blanchette-Mackie, J. (1973b). *In* "Dietary Lipids and Postnatal Development" (C. Galli, G. Jacini, and A. Pecile, eds.), p. 91 Raven, New York.

Segrest, J. P., Jackson, R. L., Morrisett, J. D., and Gotto, A. M. (1974). *FEBS (Fed. Eur. Biochem. Soc.) Lett.* **38**, 247.

Seidel, D., Alaupovic, P., and Furman, R. H. (1969). *J. Clin. Invest.* **48**, 1211.

Seidel, D., Agostini, B., and Muller, P. (1972). *Biochim. Biophys. Acta* **260**, 196.

Shames, D. M., Frank, A., Steinberg, D., and Berman, M. (1970). *J. Clin. Invest.* **49**, 2298.

Shelburne, F. A., and Quarfordt, S. H. (1974). *J. Biol. Chem.* **249**, 1928.

Shore, B., and Shore, V. (1962). *J. Atheroscler. Res.* **2**, 104.

Shore, B., and Shore, V. (1968a). *Biochemistry* **7**, 2773.

Shore, B., and Shore, V. (1968b). *Biochemistry* **7**, 3396.

Shore, B., and Shore, V. (1969). *Biochemistry* **8**, 4510.

Shore, B., and Shore, V. (1972). *In* "Blood Lipids and Lipoproteins" (G. Nelson, ed.), p. 789. Wiley (Interscience), New York.

Shore, B., and Shore, V. (1973). *Biochemistry.* **12**, 502.

Shore, B., and Shore, V. (1974). *Biochem. Biophys. Res. Commun.* **58**, 1.

Shore, B., Shore, V., and Hart, R. G. (1974). *Biochemistry* **13**, 1579.

Shulman, R. S., Herbert, P., Wehrly, K., Chesebro, B., Levy, R. I., and Fredrickson, D. S. (1972). *Circulation* **46**, Suppl. 2, 246.

Shulman, R. S., Herbert, P., Fredrickson, D. S., Wehrly, K., and Brewer, H. B. (1974). *J. Biol. Chem.* **249**, 4969.

Simons, K., and Helenius. A. (1969). *Scand. J. Clin. Lab. Invest.* **23**, Suppl. 108, 33.

Simons, K., Ehnholm, C., Renkonen, O., and Bloth, B. (1970). *Acta Pathol. Microbiol. Scand. B.* **78**, 459.

Skipski, V. P. (1972). *In* "Blood Lipids and Lipoproteins" (G. Nelson, ed.), p. 471. Wiley (Interscience), New York.

Skipski, V. P., Barclay, M., Barclay, K. R., Fetzer, V. A., Good, J. J., and Archibald, F. M. (1967). *Biochem. J.* **104**, 340.

Sloan, H. R., Kwiterovich, P. O., Levy, R. I., and Fredrickson, D. S. (1970). *Circulation* **42**, Suppl. 3, 8.

Smith, R., Dawson, J. R., and Tanford, C. (1972). *J. Biol. Chem.* **247**, 3376.

Sniderman, A. D., Carew, T. E., Chandler, S., Hayes, S., and Steinberg, D. (1973). *J. Clin. Invest.* **52**, 79.a.

Sniderman, A. D., Carew, T. E., Chandler, S., and Steinberg, D. (1974). *Science* **183**, 526.

Sparrow, J. T., Gotto, A. M., and Morrisett, J. D. (1973). *Proc. Nat. Acad. Sci. U. S.* **70**, 2124.

Srinivasan, S. R., McBride, J. R., Radhakrishamurthy, B., and Berenson, G. S. (1974). *Comp. Biochem. Physiol. B* **47**, 711.

Starzl, T. E., Chase, H. P., Putnam, C. W., and Porter, K. A. (1973). *Lancet* **2**, 940.

Starzl, T. E., Chase, H. P., Putnm, C. W., and Nora, J. J. (1974). *Lancet* **2**, 714.

Steim, J. M., Edner, U. D., and Bargoot, F. G (1968). *Science* **162**, 909.

Stein, O., and Stein, Y. (1966). *Isr. J. Med. Sci.* **2**, 239.

Stein, O., and Stein, Y. (1967). *J. Cell Biol.* **33**, 319.

Stein, O., and Stein, Y. (1973a). *Biochim Biophys. Acta* **326**, 142.

Stein, O., and Stein, Y. (1973b). *Biochim. Biophys. Acta* **326**, 232.

Stein, O., and Stein, Y. (1974). *Proc. Int. Symp. Atherosclerosis, 3rd, 1974* (in press).

Stein, O., Stein, Y., Fidge, A., and Goodman, D. S. (1969). *J. Cell Biol.* **43**, 410.

Stein, O., Baron, H., and Stein, Y. (1972). *Progr. Liver Dis.* **4**, 45.

Stein, O., Alkan, M., and Stein, Y. (1973). *Lab. Invest.* **29**, 166.

Stein, O., Sanger, L., and Stein, Y. (1974a). *J. Cell Biol.* **62**, 90.

Stein, O., Rachmilewitz, D., Sanger, L., Eisenberg, S., and Stein, Y. (1974b). *Biochim. Biophys. Acta* **360**, 205.

Stoffel, W., Zierenberg, O., Tunggal, B., and Schreiber, E. (1974). *Proc. Nat. Acad. Sci. U. S.* **71**, 3696.

Sundaram, G. S., MacKenzie, S. C., and Sodhi, H. S. (1974). *Biochim. Biophys. Acta* **337**, 196.

Swaney, J. B., and Eder, H. A. (1974a). *Fed. Proc., Fed. Amer. Soc. Exp. Biol.* **33**, 2043.

Swaney, J. B., and Eder, H. A. (1974b). *Biochem. Biophys. Res. Commun.* **59**, 513.

Swell, L. and Law, M. D. (1971). *Biochim. Biophys. Acta* **231**, 302.

Switzer, S. (1967). *J. Clin. Invest.* **46**, 855.

Tytgat, G. N., Rubin, C., and Saunders, D. R. (1971). *J. Clin. Invest.* **50**, 2065.

Vogel, W. C., and Bierman, E. L. (1967). *J. Lipid Res.* **8**, 46.

Vogel, W. C., and Bierman, E. L. (1970). *Lipids* **5**, 385.

Vogel, W. C., and Zieve, L. (1964). *J. Lipid Res.* **5**, 177.

Vogel, W. C., Brunzell, J. D., and Bierman, E. L. (1971). *Lipids* **6**, 805.

Walton, V. W., Scott, P. J., Verrier Jones, J., Fletcher, R. F., and Whitehead, T. (1963). *J. Atheroscler. Res.* **3**, 396.

Walton, V. W., Scott, P. J., Dykes, P. W., and Davies, J. W. L. (1965). *Clin. Res. (London)* **29**, 217.

Williams, C. D., and Avigan, J. (1972). *Biochim. Biophys. Acta* **260**, 413.

Wilson, D. E., and Lees, R. S. (1972). *J. Clin. Invest.* **51**, 1051.

Windmueller, H. G., and Levy, R. I. (1967). *J. Biol. Chem.* **242**, 2246.

Windmueller, H. G., and Spaeth, A. E. (1967). *Arch. Biochem. Biophys.* **122**, 362.

Windmueller, H. G., and Spaeth, A. E. (1972). *J. Lipid Res.* **13**, 92.

Windmueller, H. G., Lindgren, F. T., Lossow, W. J., and Levy, R. I. (1970). *Biochim. Biophys. Acta* **202**, 507.

Windmueller, H. G., Herbert, P., and Levy, R. I. (1973). *J. Lipid Res.* **14**, 215.

Yokoyama, A., and Zilversmit, D. B. (1965. *J. Lipid Res.* **6**, 241.

Zapol, W. M., Levy, R. I., Kolobow, T., Spragg, R., and Bowman, R. L. (1969). *Curr. Top. Surg. Res.* **1**, 449.

Zieve, F. S., and Zieve, L. (1972). *Biochem. Biophys. Res. Commun.* **47**, 1480.

Zilversmit, D. B. (1965). *J. Clin. Invest.* **44**, 1610.

Zilversmit, D. B. (1968). *J. Lipid Res.* **9**, 180.

Zilversmit, D. B. (1969). *In* "Structural and Functional Aspects of Lipoproteins in Living Systems" (E. Tria and A. M. Scanu, eds.), p. 329. Academic Press, New York.

Diabetes and Lipid Metabolism
in Nonhuman Primates

CHARLES F. HOWARD, JR.

Department of Nutrition and Metabolic Diseases, Oregon Regional
Primate Research Center, Beaverton, Oregon, and Department of Biochemistry,
University of Oregon Medical School, Portland, Oregon

I. Introduction

Diabetes mellitus occurs spontaneously or it can be induced in nonhuman primates (hereafter, simply primates). In this review, I will: (1) consider the signs and manifestations of diabetes and glucose mismanagement that can occur in primates and, wherever possible, draw analogies to human beings; (2) use available data to discuss changes in lipids and lipid metabolism; and (3) assemble for the first time the available literature on spontaneous and induced diabetic syndromes in primates.

Most animal models that are used to duplicate human disease fail to manifest all the metabolic changes and syndromes seen in human patients; nevertheless they are indispensable to studies of selected aspects of these diseases. Primates, which are more closely related taxonomically to man than are other laboratory animals, can be especially valuable to such studies; even with them, however, direct analogies may not be warranted. For instance, there are known metabolic and evolutionary disparities between human beings, apes, monkeys, and prosimians. In addition to the various genus–species differences, there is an almost infinite variety of environmental conditions under which these primates live. Finally, the changes that are inadvertently produced during most studies may exacerbate potential metabolic defects. Among such changes are diet, stress induced by confinement, and a breakdown in the normal social structure that exists among the primates in the wild. As a further complication, primates are as heterogeneous as human beings so that individual monkeys often react quite differently. Thus, in studies involving primates, there is a need to define the genus–species, to identify the environmental changes that may contribute to the disease state, and to recognize differences in individual primates. Only then can cautious comparisons be drawn between disease manifestations presented in the primate model and those in the human being. A major aim with primate models of diabetes is to find those in which the primary metabolic aberrations lead to secondary manifestations such as atherosclerosis and microangiopathies of the retina, kidney, and muscle capillaries.

II. Defining Diabetes Mellitus

There are problems in determining how analogous the diabetic signs observed in primates are to those in human beings. Since the primates are often few in number, human criteria may serve as initial guides and these can then be modified after intensive studies on more monkeys.

The most common criteria for establishing a diagnosis of diabetes are those relating to carbohydrate mismanagement: hyperglycemia, glucosuria, and responses to intravenous or oral glucose tolerance loads. Of equal interest are the insulin levels, blood lipids (cholesterol, triglyceride, phospholipid, nonesterified fatty acids), ketones in blood and urine, and acidosis. Often the full spectrum of diabetic signs is not present in any one primate model so that those signs related to carbohydrate management form the major criteria.

Table I brings together data from all relevant studies on diabetes in primates reported by the various investigators covered in the text. Abnormal values are listed only if they differed from the control measurements and were considered to be indicative of diabetes in that species. Thus for a number of studies just the normal values are listed. This does provide more information for establishing what is normal so that "abnormal" can be more readily ascertained for each genus-species. In some instances, normal values are included even if no abnormal results were reported. This provides a broader base for establishing what is normal for a genus-species so that "abnormal" can be more readily ascertained. In some instances, the primate genus-species have been reclassified to be in accord with current or more widely accepted taxonomy (Napier and Napier, 1967), e.g., Sokolo-verova (1960) *Comopithecus hamadryas* to *Papio hamadryas;* Coran *et al.* (1972) *Papio doguera* to *Papio anubis;* Britton and Kline (1939) *Aotus zonalis* to *Aotus trivirgatus.* It should be emphasized that taxonomic classification can seldom be precise; further, members or groups of the same genus-species may differ radically among themselves, depending on habitat, inheritance within the group, and general living environment. Thus classification serves as the best available guide for considering various primates for models.

A. FASTING SERUM, PLASMA, OR BLOOD GLUCOSE (FSG, FPG, FBG)

The range of glucose in the plasma or serum of primates is generally close to that of human beings, i.e., 50 to 110 mg/dl (mg% or mg/100 ml). Variations are evident from some workers, even with the same genus-species. *Macaca mulatta* (rhesus monkey) is the species most commonly used. Fasting blood glucose (FBG) generally registers on the low side of human values; only a few reports show higher values. Concentrations of more than about 125 to 135 mg/dl are roughly the point at which hyperglycemia can be diagnosed; many of the reported abnormal values are much higher. In Table I and elsewhere, no consideration is given to the method of glucose measurement or to whether plasma or serum was assayed. Fasting, usually overnight, was reported in most cases and was assumed in the rest.

Table I

NORMAL AND ABNORMAL CARBOHYDRATE AND LIPID MEASUREMENTS IN NONHUMAN PRIMATES[a,b]

Reference	Normal		Abnormal			Other	Normal[c]	Abnormal
	Glucose (mg/dl)	K (%)	Procedures	Glucose (mg/dl)	K (%)			
			Papio ursinus					
Allan and Leonsins, 1958; Gillman et al., 1958a	70–94	—	Pancreatectomy	66–666	—	Total lipid Cholesterol Phospholipid	362–679 117–204 7–14.5	320–2426 78–780 10–35
			Papio anubis					
Cerchio et al., 1971	(109)	—	Hemorrhagic shock	177 ± 28	—	—	—	—
Coran et al., 1972	130 ± 6	—	Hemorrhagic shock	252 ± 20	—	IRI	19.0 ± 6.1	7.6 ± 0.8
			Papio hamadryas					
Sokoloverova, 1960	64–130	—	Spontaneous	224–323	—	Cholesterol	67–172	700
			Papio-?					
Tseng, 1972	53 ± 6	—	Pancreatectomy	395 ± 15	—	—	—	—
			Macaca mulatta					
Arora et al., 1971	117.2 ± 3.3	—	Cold injury	172.7 ± 6.8	—	Triglyceride FFA Cholesterol Cortisol	48.1 ± 0.9 300 ± 6.7 192.6 + 8.9 36.1 ± 8.5	87.6 ± 4.9 650 ± 45.3 62.5 ± 4.7
Banerjee et al., 1966	133 ± 7	1.2	Antibiotics	—	—	Cholesterol Phospholipid FFA	94 ± 6 206 ± 12 346 ± 48	 567 ± 41
Banerjee et al., 1967	109 ± 9	(1.4)	Antibiotics	—	—	Triglyceride Cholesterol Phospholipid Betalipoprotein	(81)–(99) 130 ± 8 192 ± 6 (63)–(66)	(118)–(129) 217 ± 8 (72)–(74)

Reference								
Beck, 1969	(54.7)	(4.55)	Progesterone	(45.8)	(6.35)	IRI Growth hormone	(27.8) (7.6)	— —
Beck, 1970a	—	(7.24)	Progesterone	—	(5.19)	—	—	—
Bloodworth et al., 1973	—		Alloxan	300–800	—	—	—	—
Chapman and Fulton, 1938	—		Pancreatectomy	14–410	—	—	—	—
Chakravarti and Pal, 1970	—		Alloxan	—	—	Total lipid Cholesterol Phospholipid	388 ± 25 99 ± 5 188 ± 14	590 ± 35 162 ± 11 249 ± 12
DiGiacomo et al., 1971			Spontaneous	200–325	—	—	—	—
Fiser et al., 1974	72 ± 8	(2.2)	Infection	151 ± 11	(1.1)	—	—	—
George et al., 1974	65 ± 2	2.49 ± 0.06	Endotoxemia	—	—	IRI Glucagon Cortisol	47.2 ± 3.9 399 ± 39 19.7 ± 1.7	— 512 ± 41 23.4 ± 1.9
Gibbs et al., 1966, 1969			Alloxan	170–508	—	Cholesterol: low fat high fat	(190) (265)	(342) (475)
Hamilton and Brobeck, 1963, 1965	57–75	1.5	Hypothalamic lesions	177–214	0.48	—	—	—
Hamilton et al., 1972	87.9 ± 5.2	3.8 ± 0.1	Hypothalamic obesity	—	2.46 ± 0.24	Triglyceride IRI FFA	45.2 ± 5.3 92.0 ± 13.4 450 ± 40	175.6 ± 6.1 619.8 ± 55.5 570 ± 50
			Spontaneous	254–300	0.70–0.87	Triglyceride FFA Cholesterol	— — 133.1	274–927 1050–1200 267–367 (317.0)

(Continued)

Table I (*Continued*)

Reference	Normal		Abnormal					
	Glucose (mg/dl)	K (%)	Procedures	Glucose (mg/dl)	K (%)	Other	Normal[c]	Abnormal
Hiebert et al., 1973a,b	73.3 ± 12.1	1.97	Hemorrhagic shock	164 ± 35	(1.26)	—	—	—
			Hemorrhagic shock + adrenalectomy	40 ± 8	(2.38)	IRI Cortisol	69 ± 19 49.2 ± 10.5	17.0 ± 0.9 —
Kirk et al., 1972	93 ± 9.8	(2.0)	Spontaneous	162–688	0.7–1.3	—	—	—
Lewis et al., 1969	—	2.06–3.10 (2.5)	Neurological trauma	—	1.04–2.20 1.65 ± 0.15	—	—	—
Lipman et al., 1972	—	3.83–6.30 4.81 ± 0.26	Immobilization	—	1.86–3.30 2.69 ± 0.23	—	—	—
Maller and Hamilton, 1968	—	(> 2.0)	Spontaneous	—	(0.61)	—	—	—
Martin et al., 1971	—	—	Pregnant	—	—	Triglyceride Cholesterol Phospholipid NEFA	117.6 ± 5.3 145.4 ± 4.8 213.4 ± 5.1 393 ± 26	729 ± 6.0 119.4 ± 9.4 740 ± 124
Mintz et al., 1972	35 ± 2.2	5.9 ± 0.3	Pregnant Pregnant + streptozotocin	91 ± 21 —	2.11 ± 0.26 4.28 ± 0.29	IRI	70 ± 10.5	47.5 ± 5.5
Mirsky et al., 1942	60–100	—	Pancreatectomy	200–400	—	—	—	—
Pitkin and Reynolds, 1970	54–91 (61)	3.8 ± 0.8	Streptozotocin	160–350	(<0.99)	IRI	(34.3)	—

Reference								
Poirier et al., 1955	(133)	—	Immobilization	188–236	—			
Polikarpova and Shulyattikova, 1962	77–138 97 ± 3	—	Irradiation	129–259	—			
Rakieten, 1965, 1969	60–116	—	Streptozotocin	132–600	—			
Ramfjord, 1952	47–63	—	Alloxan	125–237	—			
Ranson et al., 1938			Hypothalamic lesions	192–240	—			
Schein et al., 1973	80–122	—	Streptozotocin	208–720	—			
Smith et al., 1936a,b	101–115	—	Hypophysectomy	45–76	—			
Smith et al., 1972	(71)	(2.5)	Adrenalectomy	—	—			
Valerio et al., 1969, 1971	60–100	—	Pregnant and postpartum	212–330	0.83			
Wakeman and Morrell, 1931	—	2.12	Infection	—	0.86			
Wilson et al., 1971	—	(1.73)	—	—	—	IRI	(10)	—
			Macaca nigra					
Howard, 1972b	45–115	1.83–3.21 (2.35)	Spontaneous	139–500	0.53–1.12 (0.67)	Triglyceride Cholesterol Prebetalipoprotein	37–163 100–172 3–20	82–205 10–34
Howard, 1974a	91.0 ± 7.3	2.15 ± 0.09	Spontaneous	166 ± 29	0.58 ± 0.09	Triglyceride IRI Prebetalipoprotein NEFA	97.3 ± 7.1 24.4 ± 1.9 17.6 ± 1.2 798 ± 78	188 ± 41 13.0 ± 1.3 34.2 ± 6.1 1190 ± 128
			Macaca nemestrina					
Howard, 1972a; Howard and Peterson, 1973	60–94	2.0–3.1	Streptozotocin	107–350	0.05–1.35	—	—	—

(Continued)

Table I (*Continued*)

Reference	Normal		Abnormal					
	Glucose (mg/dl)	K (%)	Procedures	Glucose (mg/dl)	K (%)	Other	Normal[c]	Abnormal
			Macaca fascicularis					
Altshuler *et al.*, 1971	77.5 ± 3.4	—	—	—	—	Cholesterol	116 ± 3	—
Jones, 1974	40 – 80		Spontaneous	160–320	—			
Vogin and Oser, 1971	99.2 ± 4.1		—	—	—	Cholesterol	123.3 ± 2.0	—
			Macaca cyclopis					
Howard and Palotay, 1975	100	>2.0	Spontaneous	550	0.85	Triglyceride Prebetalipoprotein IRI	<100 <20 25	155 36.4 6.8
Like and Chick, 1974	54 ± 2		Glucocorticoids	75 ± 7	—	IRI	120 ± 45	1217 ± 388
Taylor *et al.*, 1973	81.2 ± 3.0					Cholesterol	116.9 ± 4.5	
			Mandrillus leucophaeus					
Howard and Palotay, 1975	—		Spontaneous	300	0.29	IRI	—	13.9
			Cebus capuchinus					
Britton and Kline, 1939	87–132 (105)		Emotional stress	(129)	—			
			Leontocebus geoffroyi					
Britton and Kline, 1939	112–156 (128)		Emotional stress	(171)	—			
			Ateles geoffroyi					
Britton and Kline, 1939	79–105 (93)		Emotional stress	(120)	—			

Reference			Condition	Species (value)		Parameter	Normal	Abnormal
Britton and Kline, 1939	100–184 (130)		Emotional stress	*Aotus trivirgatus* (180)	—			
Davidson et al., 1967; Davidson and Blackwell, 1968	50–75	2.23 ± 0.03	Spontaneous	*Saimiri sciureus* 510–750	1.38–0.03	Cholesterol	192 ± 10	—
						NEFA	820 ± 60	—
						IRI	18.2 ± 1.4	—
Lehner et al., 1971, 1972	—	(1.22)	Alloxan	203 ± 35	(0.44)	Triglyceride	20 ± 2	27 ± 4
						Cholesterol	150 – 293	189 – 676
							228 ± 18	575 ± 79
						Betalipoprotein	54 ± 1	68 ± 4
Wilson et al., 1971	—	1.49	—	—	—	IRI	(10)	—
Schwaier, 1973	90–110		Spontaneous	*Tupaia belangeri* 140–16?	—			
Rabb et al., 1966	53, 217(?)		Spontaneous	*Urogale everetti* 285–490	—			

[a] Presentation of data: Dash between numerals indicates range of values; ± is a mean with a standard error of the mean; parentheses enclosing numbers indicate a mean without S.E.M.; a single measurement has no parentheses.

[b] Units: triglyceride, cholesterol, total lipid, and phospholipid = mg/dl; FFA = µEq/liter; lipoprotein = % of total measured; IRI = µU/ml; glucagon = pg/ml; cortisol = µg/dl.

[c] Normal values are listed to provide baseline information from each study. Abnormal values are included only when they differed enough from normal values to indicate carbohydrate mismanagement or diabetes.

B. Glucosuria

Glucose in the urine almost always indicates glucose mismanagement and is therefore regarded as prime evidence of a potential diabetic condition. This is reported either as +1 or +4 measured with test-tape or test-sticks or as glucose concentrations per volume of urine. Glucosuria is reported only in the text.

C. Glucose Tolerance Test

Because of the difficulty of administering substances orally to primates, the glucose tolerance test is most commonly run intravenously (IV-GTT). The sampling time for blood withdrawal for calculating "K" (Lundbaek, 1962)[1] varied with investigators. In some instances, the K values listed in Table I were recalculated to include the earliest sampling times and to utilize values taken during clearance before glucose reached normal levels. This allows more meaningful comparisons. The oral glucose tolerance test (O-GTT) has been used less often. Both the IV-GTT and O-GTT are usually compared against human standards, but to achieve the most accurate diagnosis of the diabetic state in the primate, members of each species should serve as their own controls. Most of the normal K values derived from IV-GTT were 2.0 or higher for the *Macaca mulatta*. Several exceptions are seen in Table I: Banerjee *et al.* (1967) had a value of 1.4 but the monkeys' FBG were high though not hyperglycemic; Hamilton and Brobeck (1963, 1965) reported values of 1.3 to 1.5 but later (Hamilton *et al.*, 1972) presented normal K values of >2.0; and Wilson *et al.* (1971), using a lower concentration of glucose, reported an average K value of slightly less than 2. All the rest were 2.0 and ranged up to values as high as 5 to 7. Problems encountered were glucose concentrations insufficient to stress the monkeys and sample times not taken early enough or often enough after glucose administration. Squirrel monkeys had an average value of 2.23 (Davidson *et al.*, 1967), but from the same laboratory later values were 1.22 (Lehner *et al.*, 1971, 1972); Wilson *et al.* (1971) also found a lower K. Other species (Howard, 1972a,b, 1974a; Howard and Palotay, 1975) had normal K values of >2.0. Abnormal values indicating substantial impairment were often less than 2.0 and there were some less than 1.0. Although many of the results are analogous to human conditions, they again

[1] $K = \dfrac{0.693 \times 100}{t_{1/2}}$ % glucose decrease per minute where $t_{1/2}$ is the time for the glucose concentration to decrease by half.

point out the need to eventually define normal and abnormal within each genus-species. Thus, for example, in the report of progesterone-induced impairment in an IV-GTT (Beck, 1970a), the decrease in K from 7.2 to 5.2 is statistically significant but meaningful only in the rhesus monkey. Similarly, Hamilton and Brobeck (1965) found a normal K of 1.5 but the abnormal drops to 0.48.

D. INSULIN

Primate insulin is commonly measured by immunoreactive techniques. One hazard worth noting in the use of assays for immunoreactive insulin (IRI) is that immunogenic cross-reactivity exists among insulins from Old World primates, man, and other mammals but only minimal cross-reactivity with New World monkeys (Mann and Crofford, 1970; Moloney and Goldsmith, 1957). Reports of insulin in nanograms (e.g., Wilson *et al.*, 1971) have been converted to μU/ml by the use of 1 mg insulin = 25 U.

Another concern with insulin is the therapeutic regimen necessary to maintain a diabetic primate. The source of insulin is apparently no problem since there is sufficient immunocross-reactivity as mentioned above; but dosage is a problem. Sufficient insulin to abolish glucosuria often leads to hypoglycemia and insulin shock. Thus most investigators administer enough insulin to keep the primate alive and slightly hyperglycemic but not enough to risk death.

E. LIPIDS

The increase in blood lipids during diabetes mellitus is of major concern in the development of vascular complications in human beings. Thus among primate models, the most useful to compare with human beings will be those with alterations in lipid metabolism and lipid concentrations. The fact that not all primates have these changes may reflect the severity and duration of metabolic impairment, genus–species differences, dietary regime, or experimental procedures. Some of the observable differences listed in Table I are briefly covered here.

1. *Cholesterol*

This is the lipid component most often studied in relation to the development of atherosclerosis. Changes in cholesterol concentrations are usually induced by dietary means although some are due to carbohydrate abnormalities. In spontaneously diabetic primates, Sokoloverova (1960) reported increased cholesterol in *Papio hamadryas* as did Hamilton *et al.* (1972) in their *Macaca mulatta,* but Howard (1972a) found no differences in *Macaca nigra.* In primates with in-duced diabetes, cholesterol was increased in pancreatectomized *Papio ursinus* (Allan and Leonsins, 1958; Gillman *et al.,* 1958a) and alloxan-treated *Saimiri sciureus* (Lehner *et al.,* 1971) and *Macaca mulatta* (Gibbs *et al.,* 1969; Chakravarti and Pal, 1970); those of Lehner *et al.* (1971) and Gibbs *et al.* (1969) also received cholesterol in the diet but the diabetic monkeys had significant increases in serum cholesterol over the controls. Decreased cholesterol was found during pregnancy in primates in one instance (Martin *et al.,* 1971). Other values in Table I are from reports of normal concentrations or from experiments wherein no changes were noted.

2. *Triglycerides*

The lipemic changes associated with diabetic primate models are often due to increased triglycerides (TG). These constitute important criteria for assessing the severity of diabetes. Most primate species have lower concentrations of triglyceride than man, so the term "hypertriglyceridemia" can only be properly related to the norm of each particular primate. Normal values in Table I are generally less than 100 mg/dl. Although some of the abnormal values are still com-paratively low (see, e.g., Arora *et al.,* 1971; Lehner *et al.,* 1971), most of them indicate that metabolic aberrations cause abnormal values at about 125 mg/dl and above (Hamilton *et al.,* 1972; Howard, 1974a).

3. *Lipoproteins*

Changes in lipoproteins have seldom been reported. β-Lipopro-teins have been examined in relation to cholesterol changes. In their work on drug effects, Banerjee *et al.* (1966, 1967) found no dif-ferences; and only normal values, determined by paper elec-trophoresis, are in Table I. Using antihuman β-lipoprotein precipita-tion serum and paper electrophoresis, Lehner *et al.* (1971, 1972) found that alloxan diabetic squirrel monkeys had higher β-lipoproteins than control monkeys fed a similar diet containing cholesterol. Howard (1972b, 1974a; Howard and Palotay, 1975) used agarose gel elec-trophoresis and found increased pre-β-lipoprotein in spontaneously diabetic primates. Srinivasan *et al.* (1974) compared serum lipopro-teins among chimpanzees and Old and New World monkeys. There were marked inter- and intraspecies differences. Chimpanzees had lipoprotein profiles most nearly like human beings and New World monkeys were least like man, especially in pre-β-lipoprotein.

4. *Nonesterified or Free Fatty Acids (NEFA, FFA)*

Several investigators have reported increases concomitant with diabetes or carbohydrate mismanagement: a doubling of NEFA during pregnancy (Martin *et al.*, 1971), increased FFA immediately after cold injury (Arora *et al.*, 1971), increased FFA in hypothalamic obese and spontaneously diabetic rhesus monkeys (Hamilton *et al.*, 1972), and increased NEFA in spontaneously diabetic *Macaca nigra* (Howard, 1974a). But Banerjee *et al.* (1966, 1967) found no changes in their drug-treated rhesus monkeys. Thus this lipid component generally follows the patterns seen in human beings.

5. *Phospholipids*

The earlier literature lists this as lipid phosphorus. Phospholipid changes are usually of lesser magnitude than those of other lipids; hence it often requires greater duration or severity of carbohydrate metabolic abnormalities to reveal phospholipid alterations. As with triglycerides, phospholipid concentrations are most accurately assessed when they are compared against normal concentrations in the same primate species. Only a few phospholipid changes are noted in Table I: Allan and Leonsins (1958); Gillman *et al.* (1958a) in depancreatectomized baboons; Chakravarti and Pal (1970) in alloxan diabetic rhesus monkeys; and Martin *et al.* (1971) in pregnant rhesus monkeys.

F. SECONDARY COMPLICATIONS

Such secondary complications as atherosclerosis and microangiopathies have been assessed in relation to human diabetes. Most models do not achieve the same broad manifestations or severity found in man. Induced diabetes often fails to cause these abnormalities to develop, even with longer observation times. Spontaneous diabetes presents potentially better opportunities for metabolic aberrations to develop into secondary complications over a period of years during which these metabolic and hormone interrelations change because of genetic defects. Thus it more closely approximates human diabetes.

III. Primates with Spontaneous Diabetes

Spontaneous diabetes has been discovered in primate species in which there is evidence of glucose mismanagement or of some other

diabetic signs without any other manipulation than diet and confinement. These primates reflect genetic weaknesses or a predisposition
toward diabetes which is precipitated by environmental stress.
Whether feral primates have a spontaneous diabetic syndrome is a
moot point since it has been reported only in animals after variable
periods of captivity. However, a predisposition to diabetes can be assumed since some primates show diabetic signs shortly after confinement.

Isolated cases with little history sometimes provide clues in the
search for primate models that might be more fully exploited. In the
documented cases that follow the next section on brief case histories,
diabetes had developed sufficiently to indicate not only carbohydrate
mismanagement and altered lipid metabolism but even some secondary complications.

A. MINIMUM CLINICAL DESCRIPTIONS

Some reports of "diabetes" in primates present only the diagnosis
without much supporting information. The earliest report of spontaneous diabetes observed in a monkey (ape?) was quoted by Fröhner
(1892, citing Leblanc, 1851). Prosectors at the London Zoo have
reported several cases; Hamerton and Rewell (1947) reported the
death of a green monkey (*Cercopithecus aethiops sabeus*) apparently
from diabetic coma, and Hill (1951) diagnosed diabetes in a King
colobus monkey (*Colobus polykomus*), an East African bushbaby
(*Galago crassicaudatus kikuyensis*), and later a Mona monkey (*Cercopithecus mona*) and a Stuhlmann's monkey (*Cercopithecus mitis
stuhlmanni*; Hill, 1957). Trant (1967) reported that her pet Sykes
monkey (*Cercopithecus albogularis*) had had diabetes mellitus for the
last 4 years of life, had required insulin injections, and eventually had
succumbed after developing peripheral neuritis and diabetic gan-
grene of the limb. Reuther (1967) described a diabetic male chimpanzee (*Pan troglodytes*) at the San Francisco Zoo. Spontaneous
diabetes has also been reported in rhesus monkeys (*Macaca mulatta*).
Martin *et al.* (1969) identified rhino-orbital phycomycosis with possible diabetes; secondary fungal infections of this type in the class
Phycomycetes are often associated with diabetes mellitus. Gray *et al.*
(1972) reported "pseudodiabetes" in a rhesus monkey with serum
glucose concentrations up to 400 mg/dl and a +4 glucosuria. An
orangutan (*Pongo pygmaeus*) at the Seattle Zoo also had diabetes (J.
Foster and L. Dillingham, personal communication). This mature
male had the recognizable signs of polydipsia, polyuria, and poly-

phagia with loss of weight. There was glucosuria, hyperglycemia with >350 mg/dl, and decreased IRI.

B. Supported Diagnoses

Sufficient clinical and necropsy information is available in some cases to substantiate a diagnosis of diabetes mellitus similar to that in human beings. The first well-documented case is that by Sokolo-verova (1960) of a postpartum hamadryas baboon (formerly *Comopithecus hamadryas*, now *Papio hamadryas*) which had devel-oped polydipsia, polyrexia, and polyuria in 1956 after bearing her first infant; she excreted 80 to 145 gm of urinary sugar per day. Blood glucose and cholesterol were increased (Table I) and she had an ab-normal glucose tolerance test (oral?). Insulin ameliorated the gluco-suria but the dosage had to be lowered because of resultant hypogly-cemia.

Lang (1966) reported that half of 200 squirrel monkeys (*Saimiri sciureus*) had sustained high glucose in response to an oral glucose tolerance test. A bimodal distribution of results of the O-GTT led him to propose two populations with inherent capabilities for handling glucose. No reference was made to a diabetic state *per se.* Subsequently Davidson *et al.* (1967) in the same laboratory examined 50 adult female squirrel monkeys and found a similar distribution. Generally abnormal glucose tolerance was linked to impaired pan-creatic response, which was diagnosed with tolbutamide tests. No other signs of diabetes were reported in these particular monkeys, but comments were made about a few other squirrel monkeys in their colony that had overt diabetes—rapid physical deterioration before death, hyperglycemia, polyuria, glucosuria, and marked degranula-tion of the β-cells. The two populations had similar serum cholesterol and NEFA. Atherosclerosis has also been reported in squirrel monkeys (Middleton *et al.*, 1964), but in Davidson and co-workers' report (1967) carbohydrate impairment and serum lipid increases were not correlated. According to Davidson and Blackwell (1968), clearance of glucose in some impaired squirrel monkeys was im-proved with the administration of trivalent chromium. On the basis of glucose management, Wilson *et al.* (1970) did not find two popula-tions among their squirrel monkeys, but they did conclude that squirrel monkeys have a greater intolerance to orally administered glucose than rhesus monkeys, probably with its origins in genus–species differences. Ausman *et al.* (1972) proposed that a com-mercial diet fed to squirrel monkeys caused greater intolerance to oral glucose and concluded that a defined diet with glucose may have developed the monkeys' capabilities to manage glucose better than a commercial diet, which contains more sugar as sucrose. Wilson *et al.* (1970) also noted that glucose absorption may be a problem in squirrel monkeys since almost all IV-GTT were near normal even when the O-GTT showed more abnormal responders. In my experience, squirrel monkeys offer less than an ideal primate model for studying diabetes or glucose management. In addition to their excitability, which seems to cause variations in fasting analyses and responses to diabetogenic drugs, a series of IV-GTT run on the same monkeys over a period of several years often produced results that were sometimes normal, sometimes abnormal. Brown *et al.* (1970) noted the high concentrations of plasma corticoids in restrained squirrel monkeys and later (Brown *et al.*, 1971) the rapid release of growth hormone upon restraint. These responses to stress may explain the variable results often obtained with this species.

Diabetes has often been reported in rhesus monkeys (*Macaca mulatta*). Valerio *et al.* (1969) reported hyperglycemia and a K of 0.83 in a postpartum female that had delivered an 849-gm infant; by 3 months postpartum, the fasting glucose had returned to near normal. The same female subsequently delivered a stillborn infant (738 gm; Valerio *et al.*, 1971) and then maintained an elevated blood glucose of 150 to 286 mg/dl. She developed polydipsia, +4 glucosuria, and eventually bilateral cataracts. DiGiacomo *et al.* (1971) reported diabetes mellitus in an adult male that had cachexia, polydipsia, and hyperglycemia. Insulin therapy lowered blood glucose but shock ensued even though hyperglycemia was sustained. The monkey lived another 15 months with hyperglycemia and +3 to +4 glucosuria before dying of unknown causes. Fine yellow streaks and focal intimal thickening were noted in the aorta and there were gingival ulcers. In a comment, they also alluded to two females which had borne large infants and had had abnormal glucose tolerance results.

Kirk *et al.* (1972) reported two female rhesus with impaired IV-GTT, hyperglycemia, and +4 glucosuria; cataracts developed in one. Although these two females were from a group of 350 monkeys that had received whole body irradiation some years previously, this 0.6% incidence is not substantially different from what has appeared in nonirradiated populations; this makes it unlikely that the irradiation contributed to the subsequent development of diabetes. Maller and Hamilton (1968) had two rhesus monkeys that had been in the laboratory for nearly 7 years develop hyperglycemia, glucosuria, and K values of 0.61% decrease per minute. In well-documented subsequent work (Hamilton *et al.*, 1972), two "middle-aged" (12 to 14 years old) obese rhesus monkeys developed spontaneous diabetes with hyperglycemia, decreased K values, decreased fasting IRI, and a 40-fold diminution in IRI response to an IV-GTT. Spontaneously obese rhesus monkeys without overt diabetes had normoglycemia and normal K values, but IRI was six times higher than in normal rhesus monkeys of similar age. Plasma lipids were elevated in both the spontaneous obese and the diabetic obese rhesus monkeys (Table I). On lipoprotein electrophoresis, spontaneously obese monkeys had a moderately higher and diabetic obese monkeys a markedly higher increase in both pre-β-lipoprotein and β-lipoprotein than normal monkeys. Blood triglycerides of spontaneously diabetic monkeys receiving insulin increased from 221 to 282 mg/dl when insulin was withdrawn and cholesterol rose from 164 to 286 mg/dl (Hamilton and Lewis, 1975).

A diabetic condition has been found among a few multiparous rhesus monkeys which delivered overweight infants at the Oregon Primate Center (C. F. Howard, unpublished observations). IV-GTTs were abnormal and TG were elevated; in one autopsied monkey, the islets of Langerhans were completely infiltrated with amyloid.

In a group of 300 cynomolgus or crab-eating macaques (*Macaca fascicularis*) maintained on high sucrose diets, Jones (1974) found that three 8- to 9-year-old females lost weight, became depressed, anorexic, and hyperglycemic. One died soon after diagnosis and of the two surviving monkeys, one receives daily insulin and the other has hyperglycemia of 170 mg/dl and an abnormal O-GTT. Severe periodontal disease and gingivitis have developed in two of the three monkeys. Jones also notes that the high sucrose diet plus the stresses of captivity may predispose these monkeys to diabetes. Observations on the pancreatic histology were not reported by Jones (1974), but in a *Macaca fascicularis*, Sheldon and Gleiser (1971) found amyloidosis which obliterated the normal architecture in the islets of Langerhans. Amyloid was not present in other tissues; no clinical information was given in their report.

The most extensive studies on any primate species with spontaneous diabetes have been those on the black Celebes apes (*Macaca nigra;* Howard, 1972b). The major group is a closed breeding colony at the Oregon Primate Center that began with 1 male and 13 mature females. With subsequent births, deaths, and purchases, about 60 *Macaca nigra* have been available for study. Some data are also available from monkeys examined at zoos and at the Yerkes Regional Primate Research Center. The major diagnostic tool, the IV-GTT, gave K values of about 1.8 and greater for normal monkeys and of less than 1.0 for diabetic monkeys. About 50% of the monkeys examined

from all sources have K values of less than 1.8. With increasing severity, fasting glucose, triglycerides, pre-β-lipoproteins, and nonesterified fatty acids increased, and K and IRI decreased. A major factor in
the development of diabetes is amyloid infiltration into the islets of
Langerhans which obliterates cells and reduces insulin secretory
capacity; some infiltration is found even in monkeys which appear to
be clinically normal. Amyloid infiltration is only part of the picture; in
a few cases there is hyperinsulinemia and in others the circulating IRI
is below normal even though the β-cells appear viable.

Increased triglycerides and pre-β-lipoprotein correlate with hyperglycemia and diminished IRI and K. This is particularly significant
since the commercial diet consumed by these monkeys has only 2 to
3% triglyceride in the diet and less than 0.01% cholesterol. Thus,
triglyceride and pre-β-lipoprotein arise from endogenous lipogenic
origins. There is no correlation between the metabolic status and
cholesterol concentrations.

Atherosclerosis (Howard, 1973a, 1975b) was more common among
clinically diabetic monkeys than among normal monkeys. Normal
aortas had minimal sudanophilia, roughening, and thickening, and
a few small discrete lesions. Diabetic monkeys had aortas with extensive sudanophilia and thickening, and lipid and musculoelastic lesions in some cases involved more than 80% of the surface. The
thickness of the basement membrane around the capillaries of the
muscle correlated with IRI, FBG, K, and TG (Howard, 1974b 1975a).
As the severity of the diabetic signs increased, the thickness of capillary basement membrane increased significantly (20%) both in compu-
tations of average (Siperstein et al., 1972) and of minimum (Williamson et al., 1969) thickness in mature monkeys with a well-defined
metabolic status.

The conclusion reached for *Macaca nigra* is that the high incidence
of this species-specific diabetes mellitus arises because of prolonged
inbreeding within a small sector of the Celebes island. As with other
primate species, this genetic predisposition among feral animals is
probably exacerbated by diet and confinement.

Prosimians also develop spontaneous diabetes. Rabb et al. (1966)
found 2 of 6 tree shrews (*Urogale everetti*) with bilateral cataracts,
polyphagia, polydipsia, glucosuria, and acetonuria. Most of the diagnostic monitoring was by examination of the urine. Normal blood
glucose values were not reported but were compared with those of a
common tree shrew (*Tupaia glis;* 53 mg/dl); one of the nondiabetic
Urogale everetti with a slight glucosuria had an FBG of 285 mg/dl, and
the two overt diabetics were grossly hyperglycemic (Table I). Vacuolated cells within the islet of Langerhans of the male diabetic are

shown in their photomicrograph with no recognizable β-cells; they appear similar to the vacuolated, amyloid-infiltrated islets of others (Sheldon and Gleiser, 1971; Howard, 1972b; Howard and Palotay, 1975). Amyloidosis in primates may be a major contributory factor to the development of diabetes mellitus.

Dr. Anita Schwaier (1973, and personal communication) describes another prosimian species of tree shrews (*Tupaia belangeri*) which may also develop a spontaneous diabetic syndrome. Several members in this colony have glucosuria and polydipsia with blood glucose values of 100 to 160 mg/dl versus the normal values of 90 to 110 mg/dl. IV-GTT *K* values are impaired in older animals, males, and in those in which there are distinct stress reactions. One 8-year-old female *Tupaia belangeri* has consistent glucosuria and ketonuria with an FBG of 160 mg/dl. Among prosimian bushbabies (*Galago crassicaudatus*) here at the Oregon Primate Center (C. F. Howard, Jr., unpublished observations), cataracts and FBG values in excess of 150 mg/dl have been found.

C. General Comments on Spontaneously Diabetic Primates

Diabetes mellitus, or at least carbohydrate impairment, can be found in all species of primates—human, ape, monkey, and prosimian. The prevalence may be even greater than reported because many investigators have not looked for diabetic signs in the primates with which they work. These signs in primates appear to be qualitatively and, in some cases, quantitatively analogous to those in human beings. The underlying metabolic mechanisms may mimic those in certain types of human diabetes, particularly those in which insulin deprivation plays a major role. Certainly the lipid alterations in many cases approximate those seen in human diabetes. In most reported instances, there was increased triglyceride, nonesterified fatty acid, β-lipoprotein, and pre-β-lipoprotein. Although cholesterol was generally increased in diabetes, there was a more definite link between the diet consumed and the concentration of circulating cholesterol than between diet and the other lipid increases.

IV. Induced Diabetes

A. Techniques

Inducing diabetes by interfering with the ability to secrete insulin was first accomplished by pancreatectomy and later by the use of diabetogenic drugs. Severity varied with the species, individual primate, and induction technique. Diabetes in these primate models is analogous to human juvenile-onset diabetes and to certain severe cases of adult-onset diabetes in which insulin secretory capacity is reduced or abolished.

1. Pancreatectomy

Pancreatectomy was studied first in dogs and rabbits (Houssay, 1937). Collip *et al.* (1937) reported the first pancreatectomies in primates, rhesus monkey (*Macaca mulatta*). Glucosuria, hyperglycemia, and transient ketonuria developed. Although they stated that no insulin therapy was necessary for most of the monkeys, they did not confirm total pancreatectomy. Of 12 rhesus monkeys in which complete pancreatectomies were confirmed by Chapman and Fulton (1938), 6 survived on a high carbohydrate diet without insulin for 1 to 10 months. Glycosuria and ketonuria were present in fed monkeys but hypoglycemia developed upon fasting; acidosis did not develop in their monkeys. Total liver lipid in the 6 monkeys that had died within a week was 19 to 23%; those surviving longer were within the normal range of 2.5 to 7%. Unlike these models, the pancreatectomized rhesus monkeys of Mirsky *et al.* (1941, 1942) required insulin therapy. When insulin was temporarily discontinued, ketosis developed, and when food was withdrawn, acidosis leading to coma and death ensued. They concluded that their monkeys showed a diabetes mellitus similar to that induced in dogs. Tseng (1972; Tseng *et al.*, 1972) depancreatized baboons (*Papio-?*) to study the development of glomerulerosclerosis. Hyperglycemia and +3 to +4 glucosuria were present and the mesangial matrix in the kidney increased significantly.

Monitoring body weight is a convenient way to assess the health of a diabetic monkey since sudden weight loss often reveals incipient complications. In a series of 10 pancreatectomized baboons maintained on insulin, Gillman and Gilbert (1959a) reported that 7 weighed the same as before pancreas removal and only 2 gained enough to reach the expected weight of baboons of corresponding age.

2. Alloxan

This compound was first used as a diabetogenic agent in rabbits (Jacobs, 1937; Dunn *et al.*, 1943) and soon after in monkeys. Development of diabetes follows the same course in all animals: transient hypoglycemia after insulin release from the necrosing β-cells followed by sustained hyperglycemia, glucosuria, and eventually acidotic coma and death. Banerjee (1944) and Goldner and Gomori

(1944) induced sustained diabetes in rhesus monkeys (*Macaca mulatta*) with 300 mg alloxan per kilogram body weight and 150 mg per kilogram respectively. However, when Siliprandi (1947) administered only about 100 mg alloxan per kilogram to a rhesus monkey, the diabetes was transient for about 3 weeks. This indicates not only individual responses but also variations in the efficacy of different alloxan preparations which may not cause sufficient necrosis of enough β-cells to achieve permanent diabetes. Ramfjord (1952) observed this difficulty with alloxan and administered high or cumulative doses; he also pointed out the toxicity of alloxan to the liver and kidney. Thus, any metabolic alterations had to account not only for insulin insufficiency but for changes resulting from hepatic and renal toxicity.

Gibbs *et al.* (1966, 1969) studied the development of glomerulerosclerosis in alloxan-diabetic rhesus monkeys. Greater basement membrane developed in the mesangium of the glomerular tuft, lenticular cataracts appeared, and microaneurysms were noted in 5 of 14 retina. Their best regimen for height and weight gain, as well as for prevention of cataract development, was a diet with high fat plus administration of high insulin dosage. Low daily insulin led to hyperlipemia and ketosis with death in 3 to 5 days. Atheroma developed with the high-fat diet in both normal and diabetic monkeys.

Bloodworth *et al.* (1973) reported diffuse glomerulerosclerosis with proliferative mesangial changes and a few retinal microaneurysms in alloxan rhesus diabetic monkeys maintained for 7 years. Rose *et al.* (1967) induced alloxan diabetes in rhesus monkeys to study periodontal diseases.

3. *Streptozotocin*

This has become the diabetogenic agent of choice since it has greater specificity against β-cells with fewer discernible toxic effects on liver and kidneys. The initial work (Rakieten, 1965, 1969) established that streptozotocin-induced diabetes in monkeys and other animals follows a course similar to that of alloxan-induced diabetes, i.e., the insulin released by necrosing β-cells causes hypoglycemia, and, depending on the quantity and efficacy of the streptozotocin to cause necrosis, the insulin lack leads to hyperglycemia, glucosuria, and eventually ketoacidosis and death. O-GTT were abnormal after diabetogenic doses had been given. Pathological findings included mottled, fatty liver and changes in retinal endothelial cells along with intercapillary strands; gross retinal microaneurysms were not noticeable. Nicotinamide protected against the diabetogenic action of streptozotocin (Schein *et al.*, 1973) but not against its toxicity to the liver. Pitkin and Reynolds (1970) used 45 to 60 mg streptozotocin per kilogram body weight to produce diabetes in rhesus monkeys: impaired IV-GTT, hyperglycemia, and decreased IRI. Mintz *et al.* (1972) induced diabetes in female rhesus monkeys with streptozotocin and studied the effects of the diabetic state on the normal and pregnant female (see section on pregnancy). Howard (1972a) infused 20 mg streptozotocin per kilogram body weight directly to the pancreas and induced diabetes in *Macaca nemestrina*. Subsequently (Howard and Peterson, 1973) these streptozotocin-diabetic monkeys developed bilateral cataracts. The severity of the cataracts related directly to the duration and intensity of diabetes; this in turn related to the degree of β-cell degranulation or necrosis in the islets. In the few streptozotocin-treated rhesus monkeys examined by them, Salazar *et al.* (1973) found no significant differences in the width of the basement membranes of muscle capillaries. Rhesus monkeys with streptozotocin-induced diabetes were also used to study gestational age and fetal growth (Peterson *et al.*, 1972) and to test various modes of insulin administration (Cohn *et al.*, 1972).

More recent investigators have been interested in using primates as models for transplantation studies. Jersky (1972) in the chacma baboon (*Papio ursinus*) and Kemp *et al.* (1972) performed total pancreatectomies and transplanted the whole pancreas with minimal success. Groenewald and Louw (1973) induced diabetes in vervet monkeys (*Cercopithecus aethiops pygeretherus*) by pancreatectomy, alloxan, and streptozotocin but could not isolate sufficient islets by the collagenase digestion technique for transplantation. Scharp *et al.* (1974) reported an improved technique for isolating islets of Langerhans and transplanted these with some success into streptozotocin-diabetic monkeys.

These induction techniques were generally designed to produce diabetes that would approximate as closely as possible human diabetes. Not only were many of the metabolic changes noted and studied, but efforts were often made to develop such secondary complications as atherosclerosis or microangiopathies. Lipid changes were noted in some instances but were not stressed. The changes in lipids and lipid metabolism, however, were an integral part of some studies; the following section reviews work in which lipid alterations were studied more extensively. Many of the changes have as a basis the interrelations of glucose and fatty acid metabolism (Randle *et al.*, 1963).

B. Lipid Alterations in Induced Diabetes

Lipid alterations in primates with induced diabetes correlated with alterations in carbohydrate metabolism. Chacma baboons (*Papio ur-*

sinus) depancreatized by the technique of Allan and Leonsins (1958) developed glucosuria within 24 hours; insulin therapy was required. During insulin deprivation (Gillman *et al.*, 1958c), serum glucose rose rapidly and was followed by increased lipids (Table I). Total lipids increased first, then lipid phosphorus and cholesterol. Nephlometry, which was used to analyze for total lipids, would measure increased turbidity from increased particles; these would be mostly very low density lipoprotein (pre-β-lipoprotein) and perhaps chylomicrons. The net result indicated primarily triglyceride changes. When insulin therapy was restored, glucose decreased quickly followed by the total lipids within a day; lipid phosphorus and ketone bodies returned to near-normal levels only after 3 days, and after an initial decrease in the first day, cholesterol returned to basal concentration only after 5 days. Glucosuria and hyperglycemia were still evident after an overnight fast; thus the glucose-utilizing mechanisms are more sensitive to the actions of insulin while it takes longer to reestablish the necessary metabolic system to deal effectively with lipids. Among the lipids, triglycerides respond less rapidly than glucose but more rapidly than phospholipids and cholesterol. Daily injections of insulin maintain the lipids at near-normal concentrations even when transitory hyperglycemia and glucosuria are present. The severity of ketosis and lipemia in baboons did not correlate, the individual animals varying widely in their response to insulin deprivation and restoration.

These workers (Savage *et al.*, 1959) found that normal baboons had 2.1 to 5.5% of their total liver weight as fat whereas pancreatectomized baboons maintained on insulin ranged from 2.9 to 10.4%; without insulin for 4 days, these latter baboons increased their fat content from 20.9 to 34.3%. Gilbert and Gillman (1960) found no significant differences in the coronary arteries of *Papio ursinus* in various normal and endocrine-deficient states. However, the baboons may have been too young and the examination period after pancreatectomy too short to allow any significant alterations in the arteries to become evident. Gillman and Gilbert (1970) have reviewed their work on pancreatectomized baboons and various aspects of metabolic and hormonal interrelationships.

Gibbs *et al.* (1969) noted that discontinuing insulin therapy to alloxan diabetic rhesus monkeys caused hyperlipemia which led to ketosis and death within 3 to 5 days; cholesterol concentrations rose from near-normal concentrations of 190 to 342 mg/dl on a low-fat diet and from 265 to 475 mg/dl on a high-fat diet (egg plus butter). In juvenile rhesus monkeys maintained on a diet with 4% fat content, Chakravarti and Pal (1970) studied the effects of lipemia and hemodynamic disturbances on thrombus formation. Alloxan monkeys had increased total lipids, cholesterol, and phospholipids (Table I), but the diabetic endogenous lipemia failed to induce thrombogenesis in this species. C. F. Howard, Jr. (unpublished observations) found that in *Macaca nemestrina* with streptozotocin-induced diabetes, triglycerides increased to 150 to 190 mg/dl over baseline levels of 40 to 60 mg/dl commensurate with increases in pre-β-lipoprotein from 10 to 15% up to 30%. Despite differences in the severity of diabetes, triglyceride and pre-β-lipoprotein concentrations correlated with hyperglycemia. As in other primates, including human beings, lipid increases were less evident in immature monkeys (< 4 years).

C. LIPOGENESIS

The lipogenic capacities of diabetic primates have been examined. Savage *et al.* (1960a) administered [2-^{14}C]-pyruvate intravenously to normal and pancreatectomized *Papio ursinus* and examined the lipogenic capabilities of blood and tissues. The incorporation of ^{14}C into triglycerides of serum and tissues was greater in depancreatized baboons, with or without insulin therapy, than in normal controls. The ^{14}C in triglyceride fatty acids was 5 times greater in serum and 2 times greater in liver of diabetic baboons when compared with normals. In depancreatized baboons not receiving insulin therapy, the kidneys contained 30 times more triglyceride fatty acid radioactivity than the kidneys of baboons receiving insulin, omental fat contained twice as much, and muscle content was lowest; these last three tissues were virtually devoid of radioactivity in normal baboons. Within triglycerides, 90 to 98% of the ^{14}C was in the glycerol moiety. These results are similar to those of Howard (1973b) who administered [2-^{14}C]-glucose to normal squirrel monkeys and found 60 to 80% of the ^{14}C in the glycerol moiety of fat and liver. This emphasizes the need to establish specific sites of radiosubstrate incorporation when assessing lipogenic capacities. Savage *et al.* (1960b) proposed that because of a shunting of [2-^{14}C]-pyruvate into glycerol, which then serves as a substrate for fatty acid esterification, there is greater ^{14}C incorporation in the triglycerides of diabetic baboons without insulin than in normal or diabetic monkeys with insulin. These radioactive studies showing increased triglyceride synthesis corroborate the quantitative data that diabetic baboons accumulate more fat than normal animals.

Concomitant studies on phospholipid synthesis in the same depancreatized baboons (Savage *et al.*, 1960d) showed increased phospholipid radioactivity, but only in those baboons without insulin therapy. This also confirms earlier observations (Gillman *et al.*, 1958a) that insulin withdrawal increases triglycerides rapidly but phospholipids more slowly and only after longer periods of insulin deprivation. In the serum, liver, and kidney of depancreatized baboons without insulin therapy, phospholipid fatty acids increased 2 to 5 times more than normal but were about the same or lower in normal and pancreatectomized baboons with insulin. These changes were less than for triglycerides or cholesterol.

In the same series of experiments, Savage *et al.* (1960c) examined cholesterol (purified through dibromide) synthesis and found that cholesterol radioactivity was 18 times higher in the serum and 15 times higher in the liver of depancreatized baboons without insulin than in the serum and liver of normal animals; depancreatized baboons with insulin had about 2-fold greater radioactivity than the normals. These workers concluded that the liver is the most likely source of the incorporation of higher amounts of radioactivity in the triglycerides, phospholipids, and cholesterol in diabetics than in normal baboons. Although active lipogenesis led to increased lipemia and some translocation, the increased storage in the liver may indicate defective mobilization in diabetes.

Lehner *et al.* (1971) noted hyperglycemia, reduced K values, and increased FSG in alloxan-diabetic squirrel monkeys. When cholesterol was added to the diets of both normal and diabetic monkeys, atherosclerosis developed more severely in the aortas and coronary arteries of the alloxan-diabetic monkeys than in those of the controls. Subsequently (Lehner *et al.*, 1972), the *in vitro* incorporation of radioactive acetate and mevalonate into cholesterol in the liver, ileum, and aorta of alloxan-diabetic monkeys was significantly reduced. Liver slices from normal monkeys on a diet supplemented with cholesterol incorporated 7 and 3 times more mevalonate and acetate respectively than slices from cholesterol-fed alloxan diabetics; incorporation in normal monkeys without cholesterol was 78- and 200-fold greater, respectively, than in the diabetics. Aortas from controls with and without dietary cholesterol incorporated 6 to 11 times more mevalonate and acetate respectively than aortas from the diabetics. These results concur with those from similar *in vitro* studies in other normal and diabetic animals including man which indicate that synthetic capabilities are impaired with diabetes; they contrast with the *in vivo* results in baboons (Savage *et al.*, 1960c). The reason for the discrepancy is not known, but the spectrum of metabolic controls, including feedback mechanisms induced by dietary cholesterol and the interrelationships with bile acid synthesis and excretion, which affect cholesterol synthesis *in vivo*, would be curtailed *in vitro* where only a limited number of enzymic steps are measured. Species differences seem a less likely explanation.

V. Stresses Which Can Cause Alterations in Carbohydrate Metabolism

A number of stress conditions produce transient or permanent changes in carbohydrate and lipid metabolism. Such changes often reflect concern with the "diabetic-like" conditions that occur in human patients. The following covers work that dealt with the kind of stress that produces changes in glucose management in primates in order to gain some insight into the underlying metabolic aberrations which cause these phenomena in human being. Stress is taken to be any stimulus, physical or emotional, which affects the metabolic homeostasis of the primate.

A. IRRADIATION

Whole body irradiation of primates sometimes causes aberrations in carbohydrate metabolism. Within 30 minutes after "acute radiation" in rhesus monkeys, Anderson (1963) found marked hyperglycemia which had subsided by 2 hours later and had returned to normal by 4 hours. Preadministration of chemical protective agents modified the hyperglycemic response. As mentioned earlier, the two diabetic monkeys reported by Kirk *et al.* (1972) had been irradiated. However, the delay of several years in the appearance of diabetic signs and the low incidence in their population make it highly improbable that the irradiation was a major cause of the diabetes. Immature rhesus monkeys exposed to 700 r of X-ray for about 30 minutes (Polikarpova and Shulyatikova, 1962) remained normoglycemic or slightly hypoglycemic until about day 5 when they became hyperglycemic; they died at 1 week. Glycogen content had generally decreased by the time of death. The conclusion, which can be applied to other irradiation cases, was that a sufficient amount of irradiation can cause a general debilitating condition and that catabolic processes in general are accelerated during the period before death. Carbohydrate alterations reflect numerous metabolic changes throughout the body.

B. IMMOBILIZATION

Normal human beings confined to bed or immobilized in other ways sometimes develop glucose intolerance. Lipman *et al.* (1972), who

compared human beings confined to bed for 3 days and monkeys immobilized vertically for 2 to 16 weeks, found both had decreased K
values from IV-GTT. Poirier *et al.* (1955) immobilized rhesus
monkeys for 4 hours with and without additional stresses. Glucose
increased significantly by the end of the first hour but returned to a
lower concentration by 4 hours; cholesterol showed no changes. A
painful stimulus superimposed on the restraint hastened the hyperglycemia but did not alter the magnitude. They concluded that catecholamines suppress insulin release and cause transient hyperglycemia.

C. EMOTION

Emotional and behavioral stresses have been examined for their effect on carbohydrate management. Britton and Kline (1939) threat-
ened caged animals, including New World monkeys, and found blood
glucose levels increased 23 to 35% over the fasting concentrations
(Table I). Hypothalamic stimulation, sufficient to produce behavioral
excitement in unanesthetized, chair-adapted rhesus monkeys (Natelson *et al.*, 1973), caused an increase in plasma glucose within 15
minutes which was sustained during the 60 minutes of stimulation.
Insulin rose initially but then declined to near-normal concentrations.
Involvement of epinephrine was documented by ablation of the adrenals which reduced or abolished the insulin response and the concomitant hyperglycemia. In an intriguing study, Hamilton and Kuo
(1974) caged together 3 rhesus monkeys with hyperinsulinemia
(greater than 200 μU/ml) and then examined various blood components. By 8 weeks, the most dominant monkey still had a high concentration of immunoreactive insulin while the other two had decreased
to normal ranges. No changes were noted in blood lipids and glucose
values during this period. Kanfor (1962) allowed hungry and fed
monkeys to observe other monkeys feeding. The "hungry observers"
had marked reduction in blood sugar until the visual stimuli were
removed, when the blood sugar returned to normal. "Fed observers"
experienced no changes.

D. INFECTION

Infection often causes carbohydrate mismanagement in human
beings. In rhesus monkeys infected with yellow fever, Wakeman and
Morrell (1931) found diminished absorption of orally administered
glucose and decreased K values; impairment of hepatic function was
a major contributory factor. After inducing *Escherichia coli* septicemia

in baboons (*Papio anubis*), Cryer *et al.* (1971) found hypoinsulinemia and hyperglycemia within 15 minutes. Increased catecholamine excretion in the urine indicated that infection probably triggered the release of catecholamines, which suppressed insulin secretion and resulted in hyperglycemia. This was further documented by means of an α-adrenergic receptor blockage (phentolamine) (Cryer *et al.*, 1972b) which also prevented the septicemic hyperglycemia. Rhesus monkeys injected with either *Salmonella typhimurium* or *Diplococcus pneumoniae* (Fiser *et al.*, 1972) reacted differently to the two infections; variable, but different, changes in triglycerides, phospholipids, cholesterol, free fatty acids, and lipoproteins were caused by each infecting agent and aggravated by the duration and severity of the disease. Use of the *Salmonella typhimurium* endotoxin (Fiser *et al.*, 1974) caused increased triglycerides and decreased K. George *et al.* (1974) induced a mild infection with *Diplococcus pneumoniae* and thereafter found a slight increase in insulin response to IV-GTT, hyperglucagonemia, but no change in K.

E. Hemorrhagic Shock

Human beings who suffer from hemorrhagic shock often have glucose intolerance and hyperglycemia. Primates have been studied to explain the metabolic mechanisms underlying shock. In several reports from one group (Moss *et al.*, 1970, 1972; Cerchio *et al.*, 1971, 1973; Siegel *et al.*, 1972), hemorrhagic shock in baboons (*Papio anubis*) caused an IRI decrease of 20 to 30 μU/ml within 15 to 20 minutes but a return to baseline levels by 2 hours. Glucose increased to almost 200 mg/dl by 1 hour and remained high even after insulin had returned to normal. Examination of the portal vein revealed intermittent variations in IRI during the experiment despite an apparent equilibrium in the periphery. These authors proposed that the fact that sensitivity to tolbutamide was reduced during hemorrhage was due to an α-adrenergic blockade or the suppression of insulin release by catecholamines. Sustained hyperglycemia in the absence of decreased insulin would arise from humoral and metabolic factors outside the pancreas. Coran *et al.* (1972) found similar carbohydrate and IRI results in baboons (*Papio anubis*) with hemorrhagic hypotension and also noted that FFA increased only after $2\frac{1}{2}$ hours. Hiebert *et al.* (1972, 1973a,b) noted hyperglycemia and decreased K in hemorrhagically shocked *Papio anubis*. By adrenal ablation and consequent removal of catecholamines, the hyperglycemic response was lessened. They concluded, as have others, that epinephrine is a major hormone which responds to hemorrhagic stress. It acts to suppress insulin release as well as effecting changes in glucose and insulin metabolism in the periphery. Adrenal cortex hormones, cortisol especially, also increase during hemorrhagic shock (Hiebert and Egdahl, 1972) but the mode of their actions is less clear; metabolic activities to provide glucose can be envisioned as one role.

F. Nondiabetogenic Compounds

Certain pharmacological agents and antimetabolites may have direct or indirect side effects on glucose management in human beings. A diazoxide analog (AO-25) (Wolff *et al.*, 1968; Grant *et al.*, 1970) used to overcome hypoglycemia in human patients had possible antidiuretic or adverse side effects on blood pressure. Both groups found transient hyperglycemia as a result of insulin suppression when the drug was administered either intravenously or orally in monkeys; there were no long-range effects. Tetracycline compounds (Banerjee *et al.*, 1966, 1967) impaired the tolerance to intravenously administered glucose in rhesus monkeys, but fasting blood sugar was the same as in controls without the drug. Intravenous tetracycline administration caused significant increases in cholesterol, phospholipids, and free fatty acids whereas intramuscular administration caused significant increases only in phospholipids, triglycerides, and lipoproteins. In the latter instance, the drug affected carbohydrate and lipid metabolism throughout the animal system but did not directly affect insulin release from the pancreas. Values given in Table I (Banerjee *et al.*, 1966, 1967) are selected from several experiments to represent different normal values and significant changes to abnormal.

According to Smith *et al.* (1972, 1973), 2-deoxy-D-glucose competes with glucose in the periphery to inhibit both metabolic transport and intracellular utilization of glucose. Hyperglycemia develops and there is an epinephrine-mediated suppression of insulin release. An interesting side effect is development of hyperphagia as a result of apparent glucose privation. Unlike the peripheral effects of 2-deoxy-D-glucose, mannoheptulose (Viktora *et al.*, 1969; Johnson *et al.*, 1969) administered orally to monkeys acts directly on the β-cells (Simon *et al.*, 1972) to prevent glucose-mediated insulin release. A 60% reduction of plasma insulin causes a 60 to 100% increase in glucose; gluconeogenesis may also be promoted. As in other animals, tolbutamide (Miller *et al.*, 1966; Wilson and Martin, 1970) enhances insulin release from the pancreatic β-cells in rhesus monkeys. The return of IRI to normal levels within 3 hours, during which glucose remained low, indicated some metabolic activity of tolbutamide at sites other than the β-cell.

G. CENTRAL NERVOUS SYSTEM EFFECTS

Central nervous system lesions often have direct and indirect effects on carbohydrate management in human beings. Ranson et al. (1938) found that of 50 rhesus monkeys with hypothalamic lesions one developed a pathological adiposity that led to diabetes mellitus. An initial polyphagia and weight gain were followed by polydipsia, polyuria, glucosuria, hyperglycemia, and impaired response to administered insulin, and at autopsy, hydrophic degeneration of the islets of Langerhans was observed. In a series of studies, Hamilton and co-workers examined rhesus monkeys which had developed hyperphagia and obesity after electrolytic lesions in the ventromedial hypothalamus. Hamilton and Brobeck (1963, 1965) had 3 of 7 rhesus monkeys with obesity and glucosuria; 1 of the 7 developed an abnormal IV-GTT, with decreased K, and bilateral cataracts. In later reports (Hamilton et al., 1972; Hamilton, 1972), individual and groups of normal rhesus monkeys and those with lesions were described and compared with middle-aged monkeys (12 to 14 years) that had spontaneously developed obesity. Fasted blood glucose was similar in all 3 monkeys, but K was significantly decreased and fasting IRI was increased almost 7-fold in both the spontaneous and hypothalamic obese monkeys. Triglyceride, cholesterol, β-lipoprotein, and pre-β-lipoprotein levels were increased in both types of obese monkeys over those of normal controls. Insulin refractiveness and impaired release of growth hormone in response to insulin administration mimic the results often observed in obese human beings with possible diabetes mellitus. Cornblath et al. (1971), stressing that more attention should be paid to the species used, found that lesions in the amygdaloid nuclei of the stumptail macaque (Macaca speciosa) led to increased free fatty acids and greater K during a tolerance test; Macaca mulatta treated similarly did not show significant differences from the controls. Kennard et al. (1947) performed bilateral frontal lobectomies in rhesus monkeys but found no alterations in blood sugar as had been produced in cats.

Hypothalamic hypophysiotropic peptides have also been studied in primates. Somatostatin was initially found to inhibit the secretion of growth hormone, but recent work (Koerker et al., 1974a,b) illustrates that somatostatin also inhibits secretion of glucagon and insulin. Hypoglycemia occurs even with the decrease in insulin. This apparent discrepancy has not yet been resolved but these workers concluded that the involvement of glucagon in glucose homeostasis was a major determinant.

H. DIET

Such dietary manipulations as qualitative or quantitative changes in fat or sugar content and starvation often produce transient changes in carbohydrate management (Coltart and Crossley, 1970; Crossley and Macdonald, 1970; Lang and Barthel, 1972). The differences often appear to be due to adaptive enzymic changes, and the metabolism can be returned to normal with the resumption of a balanced diet. Protein-deficient diets alter at a fundamental level the ability of monkeys to manage carbohydrate. In acute experiments of 3 weeks' duration carried out by Ausman and Hayes (1970) and Ausman *et al.* (1972), infant squirrel monkeys fed diets with only 2.3% of the calories as protein developed hyperglycemia, glucosuria, and impaired ability to clear orally administered glucose. Increasing the protein content to just 4.6% eliminated glucose mismanagement but there was still no weight gain. These authors offer as a prime reason for these aberrations the inadequate synthesis or release of insulin. They also emphasize the marked variations among individual squirrel monkeys in response to various laboratory procedures and note differences between this species and others. They also question whether the slight increases in protein content from 2.3 to 4.6% and improvement in glucose tolerance could be attributed to increased chromium (Davidson and Blackwell, 1968).

I. ENDOCRINE RELATIONSHIPS

The severity and expression of human diabetes mellitus has long been linked with the effects of other endocrine secretions, and animal studies have attempted to mimic these effects (Houssay, 1937).

1. *Hypophysis*

Interest in the pituitary gland resulted from early observations that hypophysectomy ameliorates diabetes. The results in nonhuman primates were similar to those in other experimental animals and in human beings (Houssay, 1936; Luft and Cerasi, 1967; Merimee and Rabin, 1973). The effects of growth hormone are both indirect (via other endocrine glands) and direct (on the pancreatic islets of Langerhans). Smith *et al.* (1936a,b) showed that hypophysectomy in rhesus monkeys, as in other animals, produced hypoglycemia and increased sensitivity to administered insulin. Diabetes in pancreatectomized rhesus monkeys (Chapman and Fulton, 1938) was ameliorated by hypophysectomy with less glucosuria and decreased blood glucose. In pancreatectomized baboons (Gillman et al., 1958a,b), ketonemia and lipemia were selectively alleviated by hypophysectomy, the insulin requirement for maintenance was decreased to one-third to one-fifth, and glucosuria and hyperglycemia were ameliorated, though still noticeable. Total lipids, which increased after pancreatectomy, decreased after hypophysectomy to near-normal concentrations even without insulin. Hypophysectomy also prevented the fatty livers that usually developed after pancreatectomy (Gillman and Gilbert, 1958). One feedback mechanism that may be involved in controlling the lipolytic effects of growth hormone has been studied in primates. Cryer et al. (1972a) found that intravenous fat with heparin increased the free fatty acid level in serum sufficiently to significantly reduce the concentration of growth hormone secretion.

Certain properties inherent within the growth hormone molecule itself seem to confer species specificity. Growth hormone obtained from simian sources and administered to fasting hypophysectomized rhesus monkeys gave the predicted hypoglycemia and convulsive action, but bovine growth hormone was without effect (Knobil et al., 1961). Neither growth hormone preparation had any effect on normal fasted monkeys. Tashjian et al. (1965) found that cross-reactivity of primate growth hormones with human growth hormone antibody varied with species. The apes (gibbon, chimpanzee, and orangutan) gave 65 to 91% cross-reactivity, Old World monkeys (rhesus, pigtail, etc.) had 48 to 62% fixation, whereas squirrel monkeys had only 10%. Abrams et al. (1966) found similar results; rhesus monkey growth hormone had less reactivity than human growth hormone against human antibody but was better than squirrel monkey growth hormone. These results further emphasize species differences and, parenthetically, show the closer evolutionary relationship of human beings to apes than to New World monkeys.

2. Adrenal Glands

The effects of the adrenal cortex and medullary hormones on carbohydrate management have also been studied in primates. Adrenalectomy of rhesus monkeys (Greep et al., 1952; Knobil et al., 1954; Hofmann et al., 1954) caused death unless glucocorticoids were administered. Hypoglycemia and increased K were observed but an adequate dosage of cortisone or 17-hydroxycorticosterone therapy afforded complete replacement. Gilbert *et al.* (1960a) examined how pancreatectomy followed by adrenalectomy affects *Papio ursinus.* Adrenalectomy restored blood glucose, total lipids, and cholesterol to near-normal levels, but the lipid phosphorus remained high. Ketone bodies increased 10 to 50 times in pancreatectomized baboons and were lowered by adrenalectomy to only 2 or 3 times higher than normal levels even without insulin. In a subsequent work (Gilbert *et al.*, 1960b), cortisone or hydrocortisone were effective as replacement hormones but deoxycorticosterone was not. Administration of cortisone and hydrocortisone to pancreatectomized-adrenalectomized baboons on insulin therapy caused hyperlipemic fatty livers which were similar to those in pancreatectomized baboons with intact adrenals and no insulin therapy (Gillman and Gilbert, 1959b). Deoxycorticosterone, however, lowered all lipids to the levels in pancreatectomized baboons on insulin therapy. These results confirm the multiple roles of adrenal corticoids in controlling insulin release and maintaining blood glucose homeostasis by various metabolic actions in other organs.

Like and Chick (1974) administered glucocorticoids to *Macaca cyclopis;* serum IRI rose significantly as pancreatic IRI decreased but blood glucose also increased. Cessation of glucocorticoids allowed glucose and serum IRI to return to near-normal concentrations but pancreatic IRI was significantly increased. Like and Chick correlated this increase with increased β-cell replication. Rivière and Combescot (1954) earlier had reported effects of various hormones on β-cells in monkeys but attributed the hyperplasia and hypertrophy mainly to pancreatic cells peripheral to those in the islets.

Epinephrine acts in rhesus monkeys as it does in other animals and man (Kris *et al.*, 1966; Miller and Soeldner, 1969). Infusion prevents or suppresses insulin release with consequent increases in glucose; termination of infusion allows insulin release to control glucose. Thus, of the adrenal hormones, the action of epinephrine is best characterized as acting directly on β-cell insulin release whereas glucocorticoids may act either directly on the pancreas or indirectly on the gluconeogenic capabilities of other tissues.

3. *Pregnancy Effects*

The stress imposed by pregnancy often causes transient carbohydrate mismanagement and may also disclose a prediabetic state. The diabetic primates reported by Sokoloverova (1960) and Valerio *et al.* (1971) were found after pregnancies. Martin *et al.* (1971) monitored plasma lipids during pregnancy in the rhesus monkey but found that most of them unexpectedly decreased. Wide fluctuations were noted and the only increases were in nonesterified fatty acid and triglyceride; both cholesterol and phospholipid dropped and did not return to normal levels until postpartum. This does not bear out the usual observations (e.g., Gupta et al., 1967; Knopp et al., 1973) of significant and sustained increases in most of the lipids during human pregnancy. Pitkin et al. (1970) found hyperinsulinemia and enhanced insulin response to glucose in pregnant female monkeys but no significant differences in plasma glucose and glucose tolerance. Mintz et al. (1972) analyzed glucose, IRI, and K in normal pregnant rhesus monkeys and in those given streptozotocin. In the normal pregnant monkeys, the K was significantly decreased just before parturition, but FBG and IRI were not altered significantly. In streptozotocin-induced diabetes, the monkeys had variable degrees of diabetes. FBG increased whereas K and, as might be expected, IRI decreased; this was especially evident just before the termination of pregnancy.

The steroid hormones that increase during pregnancy or that are contained in contraceptives are antagonistic to the action of insulin, cause excessive destruction of insulin, or produce insulin resistance in the periphery. Nelson and Overholser (1934, 1936) administered estrone (estrogen) to partially and totally pancreatectomized rhesus monkeys; in most cases, hyperglycemia and glucosuria were ameliorated but there was eventual death. The effects of contraceptive steroid medications on monkeys have been investigated by Beck (1969; Beck and Wells, 1969). Progesterone administration to normal female rhesus monkeys increased the insulin response during glucose tolerance test, but the clearance of glucose was not significantly altered nor were fasting glucose and insulin significantly different; there was a small but significant increase in peripheral resistance to insulin. Later, Beck (1970a) found that progesterone caused a slight, significant decrease in K from 7.2 to 5.2, but this still indicates rapid clearance of glucose by the monkey. Human chorionic somatomammotropin (HCS) (Beck, 1970b) did not significantly alter K but, when given simultaneously with progesterone, did cause a significant decrease of the mean K from 7.2 to 4.5; again, this is still rapid clearance. HCS minimized or enhanced the diabetogenic effects of progesterone (peripheral resistance and islet insensitivity). The addition of estriol (Beck and Hoff, 1971) improved clearance through increased peripheral utilization; estradiol though had less efficacy in correcting carbohydrate mismanagement. These results with hormone administration to normal monkeys approximate some of the results in pregnant monkeys (Pitkin et al., 1970), i.e., changes in insulin response and peripheral resistance but unaltered fasting glucose or glucose clearance. These results also indicate that there is indeed a complex interaction between the many hormones present during the normal menstrual cycle, during pregnancy, and in contraceptive steroids which affect glucose utilization and carbohydrate tolerance in different ways.

J. MISCELLANEOUS STRESSES

Arora *et al.* (1971) subjected one limb of rhesus mokeys to −30° C for 1 hour; glucose, free fatty acid, triglyceride, cholesterol, and cortisol increased immediately afterwards but by the third day did not differ from those of controls. Head injuries to rhesus monkeys (Lewis *et al.*, 1969) decreased *K* values immediately after injury but they returned to normal within a week. The degree of brain damage could not be correlated with intolerance. Both groups of investigators proposed that increased stress involves adrenal gland secretions which act to produce metabolic changes. Bloom and co-workers (1973) subjected chair-restrained rhesus monkeys to several stimuli, including noise, rectal distention, electric current, etc. There was a 2.5 to 5 times greater release of glucagon, no significant change in IRI, and only small increases in glucose.

VI. Summary

Work covered in this review includes the causative factors for diabetes mellitus, or carbohydrate mismanagement, and the consequent changes in lipids and lipid metabolism. Most cases arose from insulin deprivation: (1) spontaneous diabetes in many of the primates was a result of amyloid infiltration into the islets of Langerhans; (2) induction of diabetes, whether surgically or with diabetogenic drugs, effectively removed β-cells for insulin secretion; (3) stress conditions usually elicited catecholamine production which suppressed insulin secretion. To the limited extent that insulin lack approximates only human juvenile or severe adult onset diabetes, these primate models are directly analogous to part of the spectrum of human diabetes. However, in the larger sense, the metabolic consequences from whatever cause elicited responses that are applicable to the conditions in human diabetes. Changes in homeostasis resulted in hyperglycemia and glucosuria which were accompanied by increased lipid concentrations; restoration of insulin, whether from external therapy or resumption of normal secretion, returned metabolites toward normal. However, over a long period of time, slight insults from carbohydrate and lipids effectively caused such secondary manifestations as atherosclerosis and microangiopathies; failure to develop these to the extent and severity found in human beings seemed to result mainly from failure to experimentally approximate the human condition, especially insufficient time lapse and age. Thus, these primate models when used within their limitations are analogous to many of the conditions that occur in human beings with diabetes or carbohydrate-lipid mismanagement.

ACKNOWLEDGMENTS

This is publication No. 746 from the Oregon Regional Primate Research Center, supported by General Research Support Grant RR 05969 and Animal Resources Branch Grant RR 00163, both from the Division of Research Resources, National Institutes of Health. Work from this laboratory was supported by funds from the Kroc Foundation, Eli Lilly Co., and Public Health Service grants AM 12601 and HL 16661.

I appreciate the efforts of the following members of the Oregon Regional Primate Research Center staff: JoAnn Wolff, Lynne Bonnett, and Laurie Medill for their laboratory assistance and reference work; Dr. James Palotay of the Department of Pathology and Dr. Arthur Hall of the Department of Animal Science; and Margaret Shetler and Margaret Barss for their editorial assistance.

References

Abrams, R. L., Parker, M. L., Blanco, S., Reichlin, S., and Daughaday, W. H. (1966). Hypothalamic regulation of growth hormone secretion. *Endocrinology* **78**, 605–613.

Allan, J. C., and Leonsins, A. J. (1958). Total pancreatectomy in the baboon (*Papio ursinus*). *S. Afr. J. Med. Sci.* **23**, 241–244.

Altshuler, H. L., Stowell, R. E., and Lowe, R. T. (1971). Normal serum biochemical values of *Macaca arctoides, Macaca fascicularis,* and *Macaca radiata*. *Lab. Anim. Sci.* **21**, 916–926.

Anderson, D. R. (1963). Species difference in postirradiation hyperglycemia. *Radiat. Res.* **19**, 191.

Arora, R. B., Tariq, M., and Siddiqui, H. H. (1971). Effect of experimental cold injury on the levels of blood lipids, cortisol and glucose in monkeys. *Pharmacol. Res. Commun.* **3**, 107–111.

Ausman, L. M., and Hayes, K. C. (1970). Alteration of carbohydrate metabolism in infant squirrel monkeys. *Fed. Proc., Fed. Amer. Soc. Exp. Biol.* **29**, 364.

Ausman, L. M., Hayes, K. C., and Hegsted, D. M. (1972). Protein deficiency and carbohydrate tolerance of the infant squirrel monkey (*Saimiri sciureus*). *J. Nutr.* **102**, 1519–1528.

Banerjee, S. (1944). Alloxan diabetes in monkeys. *Lancet* **2**, 658–659.

Banerjee, S., Kumar, K. S., and Bandyopadhyay, A. (1966). Carbohydrate and lipid metabolism in animals treated with pyrrolidinomethyl tetracycline. *Proc. Soc. Exp. Biol. Med.* **122**, 652–657.

Banerjee, S., Kumar, K. S., and Bandyopadhyay, A. (1967). Effect of oxytetracycline and tetracycline on glucose tolerance and serum lipids. *Proc. Soc. Exp. Biol. Med.* **125**, 618–620.

Beck, P. (1969). Progestin enhancement of the plasma insulin response to glucose in rhesus monkeys. *Diabetes* **18**, 146–152.

Beck, P. (1970a). Reversal of progesterone-enhanced insulin production by human chorionic somatomammotropin. *Endocrinology* **87**, 311–315.

Beck, P. (1970b). The role of human chorionic somatomammotropin (HCS) and gonadal steroids in gestational diabetes. *Acta Diabetol. Lat.* **7**, 529–541.

Beck, P., and Hoff, D. L. (1971). Estriol modification of the effects of progesterone and human chorionic somatomammotropin on glucose tolerance and plasma insulin in rhesus monkeys. *Diabetes* **20**, 271–275.

Beck, P., and Wells, S. A. (1969). Comparison of the mechanisms underlying carbohydrate intolerance in subclinical diabetic women during pregnancy and during postpartum oral contraceptive steroid treatment. *J. Clin. Endocrinol. Metab.* **29**, 807–818.

Bloodworth, J. M. B., Engerman, R. L., and Anderson, P. J. (1973). Microangiopathy in the experimentally diabetic animal. *Advan. Metab. Disord.* **2**, Suppl. 2, 245–250.

Bloom, S. R., Daniel, P. M., Johnston, D. I., Ogawa, O., and Pratt, O. F. (1973). Release of glucagon, induced by stress. *Quart. J. Exp. Physiol. Cog. Med. Sci.* **58**, 99–108.

Britton, S. W., and Kline, R. F. (1939). Emotional hyperglycemia and hyperthermia in tropical mammals and reptiles. *Amer. J. Physiol.* **125**, 730–734.

Brown, G. M., Grota, L. J., Penney, D. P., and Reichlin, S. (1970). Pituitary-adrenal function in the squirrel monkey. *Endocrinology* **86**, 519–529.

Brown, G. M., Schalch, D. S., and Reichlin, S. (1971). Hypothalamic mediation of growth hormone and adrenal stress response in the squirrel monkey. *Endocrinology* **89**, 694–703.

Cerchio, G. M., Moss, G. S., Popovich, P. A., Butler, E., and Siegel, D. C. (1971). Serum insulin and growth hormone response to hemorrhagic shock. *Endocrinology* **88**, 138–143.

Cerchio, G. M., Persico, P. A., and Jeffay, H. (1973). Inhibition of insulin release during hypovolemic shock. *Metab., Clin. Exp.* **22**, 1449–1458.

Chakravarti, R. N., and Pal, G. (1970). Effect of lipaemia and acute haemodynamic disturbances on thrombus formation in rhesus monkeys. *Indian J. Med. Res.* **58**, 223–229.

Chapman, S. W., and Fulton, J. F. (1938). Pancreatectomy in the monkey. *Amer. J. Physiol.* **123**, 35.

Cohn, M. L., Chez, R. A., Hingson, R. A., Szulman, A. E., and Trimmer, M. (1972). Use of jet insulin injection in diabetes mellitus therapy. *Diabetes* **21**, 39–44.

Collip, J. B., Selye, H., and Neufeld, A. (1937). Experimental pancreatic diabetes in the monkey. *Amer. J. Physiol.* **119**, 289–290.

Coltart, T. M., and Crossley, J. N. (1970). Influence of dietary sucrose on glucose and fructose tolerance and triglyceride synthesis in the baboon. *Clin. Sci.* **38**, 427–437.

Coran, A. G., Cryer, P. E., Horwitz, D. L., and Herman, C. M. (1972). The metabolism of fat and carbohydrate during hemorrhagic shock in the unanesthetized subhuman primate: Changes in serum levels of free fatty acids, total lipids, insulin, and glucose. *Surgery* **71**, 465–469.

Cornblath, M., Levitsky, L. L., and Kling, A. (1971). Response to intravenous glucose in juvenile macaque monkeys. Effect of central nervous system lesions and species difference. *Diabetes* **20**, 156–161.

Crossley, J. N., and Macdonald, I. (1970). The influence in male baboons of a high sucrose diet on the portal and arterial levels of glucose and fructose following a sucrose meal. *Nutr. Metab.* **12,** 171–178.

Cryer, P. E., Herman, C. M., and Sode, J. (1971). Carbohydrate metabolism in the baboon subjected to gram-negative (*E. coli*) septicemia. I. Hyperglycemia with depressed plasma insulin concentrations. *Ann. Surg.* **174,** 91–100.

Cryer, P. E., Coran, A. G., Keenan, B. S., and Sode, J. (1972a). Cessation of growth hormone secretion associated with acute elevation of the serum-free fatty acid concentration. *Metab., Clin. Exp.* **21,** 867–873.

Cryer, P. E., Coran, A. G., Sode, J., Herman, C. M., and Horwitz, D. L. (1972b). Lethal *Escherichia coli* septicemia in the baboon: Alpha-adrenergic inhibition of insulin secretion and its relationship to the duration of survival. *J. Lab. Clin. Med.* **79,** 622–638.

Davidson, I. W. F., and Blackwell, W. L. (1968). Changes in carbohydrate metabolism of squirrel monkeys with chromium dietary supplementation. *Proc. Soc. Exp. Biol. Med.* **127,** 66–70.

Davidson, I. W. F., Lang, C. M., and Blackwell, W. L. (1967). Impairment of carbohydrate metabolism of the squirrel monkey. *Diabetes* **16,** 395–401.

DiGiacomo, R. F., Myers, R. E., and Rivera Baez, L. (1971). Diabetes mellitus in a rhesus monkey (*Macaca mulatta*): A case report and literature review. *Lab. Anim. Sci.* **21,** 572–574.

Dunn, J. S., Sheehan, H. L., and McLetchie, N. G. B. (1943). Necrosis of islets of Langerhans produced experimentally. *Lancet* **1,** 484–487.

Fiser, R. H., Denniston, J. C., and Beisel, W. R. (1972). Infection with *Diplococcus pneumoniae* and *Salmonella typhimurium* in monkeys: Changes in plasma lipids and lipoproteins. *J. Infec. Dis.* **125,** 54–60.

Fiser, R. H., Denniston, J. C., and Beisel, W. R. (1974). Endotoxemia in the rhesus monkey: Alterations in host lipid and carbohydrate metabolism. *Pediat. Res.* **8,** 13–17.

Fröhner, E. (1892). Ueber Zuckerharnruhr beim Hunde. *Monatsh. Prakt. Tierheilk.* **3,** 149–163.

George, D. T., Rayfield, E. J., and Wannemacher, R. W., Jr. (1974). Altered glucoregulatory hormones during acute pneumococcal sepsis in the rhesus monkey. *Diabetes* **23,** 544–549.

Gibbs, G. E., Wilson, R. B., and Gifford, H. (1966). Glomerulosclerosis in the long-term alloxan diabetic monkey. *Diabetes* **15,** 258–261.

Gibbs, G. E., Wilson, R. B., and Ho, C.-K. (1969). Experimental diabetes in the monkey. *Proc. Int. Congr. Primatol., 2nd, 1968* Vol. 3, pp. 169–173.

Gilbert, C., and Gillman, J. (1960). Structural modifications in the coronary artery of the baboon (*Papio ursinus*) with special reference to age and endocrine status. *S. Afr. J. Med. Sci.* **25,** 59–70.

Gilbert, C., Gillman, J., and Savage, N. (1960a). Persistence of the hyperglycaemia and reduction in the lipaemia and ketonaemia of diabetic baboons (*Papio ursinus*) following bilateral adrenalectomy. *S. Afr. J. Med. Sci.* **25,** 77–80.

Gilbert, C., Gillman, J., and Savage, N. (1960b). Lipaemic but non-ketogenic effects of hydrocortisone and cortisone and the non-lipaemic effect of desoxycorticosterone in depancreatised-adrenalectomised baboons (*Papio ursinus*). *S. Afr. J. Med. Sci.* **25,** 133–140.

Gillman, J., and Gilbert, C. (1958). Fatty liver of endocrine origin. With special reference to fatty liver of malnourished African infants. *Brit. Med. J.* **1,** 57–63.

Gillman, J., and Gilbert, C. (1959a). Arrest of body growth in depancreatised baboons. *S. Afr. J. Med. Sci.* **24,** 142–143.

Gillman, J., and Gilbert, C. (1959b). The dependence of the fatty liver of depancreatised baboons on adrenocortical activity. *S. Afr. J. Med. Sci.* **24**, 150–151.

Gillman, J., and Gilbert, C. (1970). Some aspects of the endocrine control of the serum lipids, blood ketones and blood sugar in fed and fasted baboons, and of the mechanism of fuel control in fasting, with special reference to diabetes and lipaemia. *Exp. Med. Surg.* **28**, 45–121.

Gillman, J., Gilbert, C., and Allan, J. C. (1958a). The relationship of hyperglycaemia to hyperlipaemia and ketonaemia in depancreatized baboons *(Papio ursinus). J. Endocrinol.* **17**, 349–362.

Gillman, J., Gilbert, C., Epstein, E., and Allan, J. C. (1958b). Endocrine control of blood sugar, lipaemia, and ketonaemia in diabetic baboons. *Brit. Med. J.* **2**, 1260 - 1263.

Gillman, J., Gilbert, C., Epstein, E., and Allan, J. C. (1958c). Uncoupling of the disorder of carbohydrate metabolism from fat metabolism in experimentally-produced diabetes in baboons *(Papio ursinus). Experientia* **14**, 79–80.

Goldner, M. G., and Gomori, G. (1944). Alloxan diabetes. *Proc. Amer. Diabetes Ass.* **4**, 89–106.

Grant, A. M., Basabe, J. C., Lopez, N. L., Krees, S. V., and Wolff, F. W. (1970). Mode of action of a diazoxide analog (AO25). Its effects on insulin secretion. *Diabetes* **19**, 630–639.

Gray, C. W., Mikolajczyk, E. E., and Schneider, T. G. (1972). "Pseudodiabetes—Rhesus Monkey *(Macaca mulatta),*" 1970 Annual Report, p. 59. National Zoological Park, Smithsonian Institution, Smithsonian Institution Press, Washington, D. C.

Greep, R. O., Knobil, E., Hofmann, F. G., and Jones, T. L. (1952). Adrenal cortical insufficiency in the rhesus monkey. *Endocrinology* **50**, 664–676.

Groenewald, J. H., and Louw, G. C. J. (1973). Beta cell cytolytic drugs and pancreatic islet cell grafting in vervet monkeys. *S. Afr. J. Surg.* **11**, 136–137.

Gupta, A. N., Sarkar, A. K., and Chakravarti, R. N. (1967). Lipid-protein interrelationship in pregnancy. *Amer. J. Med. Sci.* **253**, 469–472.

Hamerton, A. E., and Rewell, R. E. (1947). Report of the pathologist for the year 1946. *Proc. Zool. Soc. London* **117**, 663–672.

Hamilton, C. L. (1972). An observation of long-term experimental obesity and diabetes mellitus in the monkey. *J. Med. Primatol.* **1**, 247–255.

Hamilton, C. L., and Brobeck, J. R. (1963). Diabetes mellitus in hyperphagic monkeys. *Endocrinology* **73**, 512–515.

Hamilton, C. L., and Brobeck, J. R. (1965). Control of food intake in normal and obese monkeys. *Ann. N. Y. Acad. Sci.* **131**, 583–592.

Hamilton, C. L., and Kuo, P. (1974). Social interaction and hyperinsulinemia in the monkey. *Fed. Proc., Fed. Amer. Soc. Exp. Biol.* **33**, 464.

Hamilton, C. L., and Lewis, D. (1975). Feeding behavior in monkeys with spontaneous diabetes mellitus. *J. Med. Primatol.* **4**, 145–153.

Hamilton, C. L., Kuo, P. T., and Feng, L. Y. (1972). Experimental production of syndrome of obesity, hyperinsulinemia and hyperlipidemia in monkeys. *Proc. Soc. Exp. Biol. Med.* **140**, 1005–1008.

Hiebert, J. M., and Egdahl, R. H. (1972). Cortisol responses to normotensive and hypotensive oligemia in unanesthetized primates. *Surg. Forum* **23**, 69–72.

Hiebert, J. M., McCormigh, J. M., and Egdahl, R. H. (1972). Direct measurement of insulin secretory rate. Studies in shocked primates and postoperative patients. *Ann. Surg.* **176**, 296–303.

Hiebert, J. M., Celik, Z., Soeldner, J. S., and Egdahl, R. H. (1973a). Insulin response to hemorrhagic shock in the intact and adrenalectomized primate. *Amer. J. Surg.* **125**, 501–507.

Hiebert, J. M., Sixt, N., Soeldner, J. S., and Egdahl, R. H. (1973b). Altered insulin and

glucose metabolism produced by epinephrine during hemorrhagic shock in the
adrenalectomized primate. *Surgery* **74**, 223–234.

Hill, W. C. O. (1951). Report of the Society's prosector for the year 1950. *Proc. Zool. Soc.
London* **121**, 641–650.

Hill, W. C. O. (1957). Report of the Society's prosector for the years 1955 and 1956. *Proc.
Zool. Soc. London* **129**, 431–446.

Hofmann, F. G., Knobil, E., and Greep, R. O. (1954). Effects of saline on the adrenalectomized rhesus monkey. *Amer. J. Physiol.* **178**, 361–366.

Houssay, B. A. (1936). Carbohydrate metabolism. *N. Engl. J. Med.* **214**, 971–986.

Houssay, B. A. (1937). Diabetes as a disturbance of endocrine regulation. *Amer. J. Med.
Sci.* **193**, 581–606.

Howard, C. F., Jr. (1972a). Streptozotocin-induced diabetes mellitus by direct pancreatic infusion in *Macaca nemestrina*. *Diabetes* **21**, 138–142.

Howard, C. F., Jr. (1972b). Spontaneous diabetes in *Macaca nigra*. *Diabetes* **21**,
1077–1090.

Howard, C. F., Jr. (1973a). Atherosclerosis in spontaneously diabetic monekys. *Circulation* **48**, IV–41.

Howard, C. F., Jr. (1973b). Lipogenesis from [2-^{14}C]glucose in squirrel monkeys. *Proc.
Soc. Exp. Biol. Med.* **142**, 660–665.

Howard, C. F., Jr. (1974a). Correlations of serum triglyceride and prebetalipoprotein
levels to the severity of spontaneous diabetes in *Macaca nigra. J. Clin. Endocrinol.
Metab.* **38**, 856–860.

Howard, C. F., Jr. (1974b). Diabetes in *Macaca nigra:* Metabolic and histologic changes.
Diabetologia **10**, 671–677.

Howard, C. F., Jr. (1975a). Basement membrane thickness in muscle capillaries of normal and spontaneously diabetic *Macaca nigra*. *Diabetes* **24**, 201–206.

Howard, C. F., Jr. (1975b). The relationship of diet and atherosclerosis in diabetic
Macaca nigra. In "Diet and Atherosclerosis" (C. Sirtori, G. Ricci, and S. Gorini,
eds.) (*Advan. Exp. Med. Biol.* **60**, 13–31), Plenum, New York.

Howard, C. F., Jr., and Palotay, J. L. (1975). Spontaneous diabetes mellitus in *Macaca
cyclopis* and *Mandrillus leucophaeus:* Case reports. *Lab. Anim. Sci.* **25**, 191–196.

Howard, C. F., Jr., and Peterson, L. H. (1973). Cataract development in streptozotocin-
diabetic monkeys (*Macaca nemestrina*). *Lab. Anim. Sci.* **23**, 366–369.

Jacobs, H. R. (1937). Hypoglycemic action of alloxan. *Proc. Soc. Exp. Biol. Med.* **37**,
407–409.

Jersky, J. (1972). Pancreatic allotransplantation in the non-human primate. *S. Afr. Med.
J.* **46**, 1006.

Johnson, B., Viktora, J., and Wolff, F. (1969). The efficacy of oral mannoheptulose in
monkey and man. *Diabetes* **18**, Suppl. 1, 360.

Jones, S. M. (1974). Spontaneous diabetes in monkeys. *Lab. Anim. (London)* **8**, 161–166.

Kanfor, I. S. (1962). The role of distant meaningful stimuli in the regulation of carbohydrate metabolism in monkeys. *Byull. Eksp. Biol. Med.* **52**, 1110–1113.

Kemp, C. B., Groenewald, J. H., and Van Zyl, J. J. W. (1972). Transplantation of the
distal pancreas in the baboon. *S. Afr. Med. J.* **46**, 1006.

Kennard, M. A., Hampel, C. W., and Willner, M. D. (1947). Effect of frontal lobectomy
on blood sugars of normal cats and monkeys and adrenal denervated cats. *Amer, J.
Physiol.* **149**, 246–253.

Kirk, J. H., Casey, H. W., and Harwell, J. F., Jr. (1972). Diabetes mellitus in two rhesus
monkeys. *Lab. Anim. Sci.* **22**, 245–248.

Knobil, E., Hofmann, F. G., and Greep, R. O. (1954). Effects of cortisone acetate and 17-

hydroxycorticosterone acetate on the adrenalectomized rhesus monkey. *Amer. J. Physiol.* **178**, 351–360.

Knobil, E., Best, G. R., and Goodman, H. M. (1961). The hypoglycemic action of simian and bovine growth hormone in hypophysectomized rhesus monkeys. *Endocrinology* **68**, 723–725.

Knopp, R. H., Warth, M. R., and Carrol, C. J. (1973). Lipid metabolism in pregnancy. I. Changes in lipoprotein triglyceride and cholesterol in normal pregnancy and the effects of diabetes mellitus. *J. Reprod. Med.* **10**, 95–101.

Koerker, D. J., Ruch, W., Chideckel, E., Palmer, J., Goodner, C. J., Ensinck, J. W., and Gale, C. C. (1974a). Somatostatin and regulation of glucose production in baboon. *Fed. Proc., Fed. Amer. Soc. Exp. Biol.* **33**, 264.

Koerker, D. J., Ruch, W., Chideckel, E., Palmer, J., Goodner, C. J., Ensinck, J., and Gale, C. C. (1974b). Somatostatin: Hypothalamic inhibitor of the endocrine pancreas. *Science* **184**, 482–484.

Kris, A. O., Miller, R. E., Wherry, R. E., and Mason, J. W. (1966). Inhibition of insulin secretion by infused epinephrine in rhesus monkeys. *Endocrinology* **78**, 87–97.

Lang, C. M. (1966). Impaired glucose tolerance in the squirrel monkey (*Saimiri sciureus*). *Proc. Soc. Exp. Biol. Med.* **122**, 84–86.

Lang, C. M., and Barthel, C. H. (1972). Effects of simple and complex carbohydrates on serum lipids and atherosclerosis in nonhuman primates. *Amer. J. Clin. Nutr.* **25**, 470–475.

Lehner, N. D. M., Clarkson, T. B., and Lofland, H. B. (1971). The effect of insulin deficiency, hypothyroidism, and hypertension on atherosclerosis in the squirrel monkey. *Exp. Mol. Pathol.* **15**, 230–244.

Lehner, N. D. M., Clarkson, T. B., Bell, F. P., St. Clair, R. W., and Lofland, H. B. (1972). Effects of insulin deficiency, hypothyroidism, and hypertension on cholesterol metabolism in the squirrel monkey. *Exp. Mol. Pathol.* **16**, 109–123.

Lewis, H. P., King, L. R., Ramirez, R., Brielmaeir, J., and McLaurin, R. L. (1969). Glucose intolerance in monkeys following head injury. *Ann. Surg.* **170**, 1025–1028.

Like, A. A., and Chick, W. L. (1974). Pancreatic beta cell replication induced by glucocorticoids in subhuman primates. *Amer. J. Pathol.* **75**, 329–348.

Lipman, R. L., Raskin, P., Love, T., Triebwasser, J., Lecocq, F. R., and Schnure, J. J. (1972). Glucose intolerance during decreased physical activity in man. *Diabetes* **21**, 101–107.

Luft, R., and Cerasi, E. (1967). Human growth hormone as a regulator of blood glucose concentration and as a diabetogenic substance. *Acta Endocrinol. (Copenhagen), Suppl.* **124**, 9–16.

Lundbaek, K. (1962). Intravenous glucose tolerance as a tool in definition and diagnosis of diabetes mellitus. *Brit. Med. J.* **2**, 1507–1513.

Maller, O., and Hamilton, C. L. (1968). Sucrose and caloric intake by normal and diabetic monkeys. *J. Comp. Physiol. Psychol.* **66**, 444–449.

Mann, G. V., and Crofford, O. B. (1970). Insulin levels in primates by immunoassay. *Science* **169**, 1312–1313.

Martin, D. E., Wolf, R. C., and Meyer, R. K. (1971). Plasma lipid levels during pregnancy in the rhesus monkey (*Macaca mulatta*). *Proc. Soc. Exp. Biol. Med.* **138**, 638–641.

Martin, J. E., Kroe, D. J., Bostrom, R. E., Johnson, D. J., and Whitney, R. A., Jr. (1969). Rhino-orbital phycomycosis in a rhesus monkey (*Macaca mulatta*). *J. Amer. Vet. Med. Ass.* **155**, 1253–1257.

Merimee, T. J., and Rabin, D. (1973). A survey of growth hormone secretion and action. *Metab., Clin. Exp.* **22**, 1235–1251.

Middleton, C. C., Clarkson, T. B., Lofland, H. B., and Prichard, R. W. (1964). Atherosclerosis in the squirrel monkey. *Arch. Pathol.* **78**, 16–23.

Miller, R. E., and Soeldner, J. S. (1969). Suppression of portal venous insulin concentration by epinephrine in the conscious monkey. *Diabetologia* **5**, 179–182.

Miller, R. E., Wherry, F. E., and Mason, J. W. (1966). Effect of tolbutamide on plasma insulin, glucose and corticosteroid levels in the rhesus monkey. *Endocrinology* **79**, 207–211.

Mintz, D. H., Chez, R. A., and Hutchinson, D. L. (1972). Subhuman primate pregnancy complicated by streptozotocin-induced diabetes mellitus. *J. Clin. Invest.* **51**, 837–847.

Mirsky, I. A., Nelson, N., and Elgart, S. (1941). Diabetic acidosis and coma in the monkey. *Science* **93**, 576.

Mirsky, I. A., Nelson, N., Grayman, I., and Elgart, S. (1942). Pancreatic diabetes in the monkey. *Endocrinology* **31**, 264–270.

Moloney, P. J., and Goldsmith, L. (1957). On the antigenicity of insulin. *Can. J. Biochem. Physiol.* **35**, 79–92.

Moss, G. S., Cerchio, G. M., Siegel, D. C., Popovich, P. A., and Butler, E. (1970). Serum insulin response in hemorrhagic shock in baboons. *Surgery* **68**, 34–39.

Moss, G. S., Cerchio, G., Siegel, D. C., Reed, P. C., Cochin, A., and Fresquez, V. (1972). Decline in pancreatic insulin release during hemorrhagic shock in the baboon. *Ann. Surg.* **175**, 210–213.

Napier, J. R., and Napier, P. H. (1967). "A Handbook of Living Primates." Academic Press, New York.

Natelson, B. H., Smith, G. P., Stokes, P. E., and Root, A. W. (1973). Changes of plasma glucose and insulin during defense reactions in monkeys. *Amer. J. Physiol.* **224**, 1454–1462.

Nelson, W. O., and Overholser, M. D. (1934). Effect of oestrin injections upon experimental pancreatic diabetes in the monkey. *Proc. Soc. Exp. Biol. Med.* **32**, 150–151.

Nelson, W. O., and Overholser, M. D. (1936). The effect of oestrogenic hormone on experimental pancreatic diabetes in the monkey. *Endocrinology* **20**, 473–480.

Peterson, E. N., Hutchinson, D. L., Sabbagha, R. E., Royal, J. S., and Levitt, M. J. (1972). Sonography and amniocentesis as predictors of gestational age and fetal growth in the rhesus monkey. *Amer. J. Obstet. Gynecol.* **114**, 883–889.

Pitkin, R. M., and Reynolds, W. A. (1970). Diabetogenic effects of streptozotocin in rhesus monkeys. *Diabetes* **19**, 85–90.

Pitkin, R. M., Van Orden, D. E., and Reynolds, W. A. (1970). Plasma insulin response and glucose tolerance in pregnant rhesus monkeys. *Endocrinology* **86**, 435–437.

Poirier, L. J., Ayotte, R. A., Lemire, A., Gauthier, C., and Cordeau, J. P. (1955). Influence of immobilization on the metabolic and hematological blood picture of the normal rhesus monkey. *Rev. Can. Biol.* **14**, 129–143.

Polikarpova, L. I., and Shulyatikova, A. Ya. (1962). Some changes in carbohydrate metabolism of monkeys with acute radiation sickness. *Radiobiologiya* **2**, 390–394.

Rabb, G. B., Getty, R. E., Williamson, W. M., and Lombard, L. S. (1966). Spontaneous diabetes mellitus in tree shrews, *Urogale everetti. Diabetes* **15**, 327–330.

Rakieten, N. (1965). "Studies on Streptozotocin, NSC 85998, and Zedalan, NSC 85680," Parts 1, 2, and 3, Report to CCNSC. South Shore Analytical and Research Lab., Inc., Islip, N. Y.

Rakieten, N. (1969). "Studies on Prolonged Diabetes in Rhesus Monkeys (*Macaca mulatta*) Following Single Intravenous Doses of Streptozotocin, NSC 85998," Report to CCNSC. South Shore Analytical and Research Lab., Inc., Islip, N. Y.

Ramfjord, S. (1952). Clinical and histologic effects of alloxan in rhesus monkeys. *Amer. J. Clin. Pathol.* **22**, 745–754.

Randle, P. J., Garland, P. B., Hales, C. N., and Newsholme, E. A. (1963). The glucose fatty-acid cycle. Its role in insulin sensitivity and the metabolic disturbances of diabetes mellitus. *Lancet* **1**, 785–789.

Ranson, S. W., Fisher, C., and Ingram, W. R. (1938). Adiposity and diabetes mellitus in a monkey with hypothalamic lesions. *Endocrinology* **23**, 175–181.

Reuther, R. T. (1967). Primate notes from the San Francisco Zoological Gardens. *Lab. Primate Newslett.* **6**(3), 19.

Rivière, M., and Combescot, C. (1954). Sur le conditionnement de certaines transformations langerhansiennes chez le Singe. *C. R. Soc. Biol.* **148**, 93–95.

Rose, H. P., Glenn, J. S., and Kuna, A. (1967). High blood sugar levels in rhesus monkeys. *J. Dent. Res.* **46**, 1105.

Salazar, H., Chez, R. A., and Pardo, M. (1973). Absence of ultrastructural changes in the basement membrane of muscle capillaries in streptozotocin-induced carbohydrate intolerance in rhesus monkeys. (1973). *Amer, J. Pathol.* **71**, 437–446.

Savage, N., Gilbert, C., and Gillman, J. (1959). The fat content of the livers of depancreatised baboons with and without insulin therapy. *S. Afr. J. Med. Sci.* **24**, 143–144.

Savage, N., Gillman, J., and Gilbert, C. (1960a). Unimpaired synthesis of fatty acids and altered synthesis of glycerol of triglycerides in diabetic baboons (*P. ursinus*). *S. Afr. J. Med. Sci.* **25**, 19–32.

Savage, N., Gillman, J., and Gilbert, C. (1960b). Influence of insulin on the incorporation of 2-^{14}C-sodium pyruvate into glyceride glycerol in diabetic and normal baboons. *Nature (London)* **165**, 168–169.

Savage, N., Gillman, J., and Gilbert, C. (1960c). Unimpaired synthesis of cholesterol from 2-^{14}C sodium pyruvate in diabetic baboons (*Papio ursinus*). *S. Afr. J. Med. Sci.* **25**, 71–75.

Savage, N., Gillman, J., and Gilbert, C. (1960d). Increased synthesis of phospholipid fatty acid from 2-^{14}C sodium pyruvate in the diabetic baboon (*Papio ursinus*). *S. Afr. J. Med. Sci.* **25**, 81–87.

Scharp, D. W., Kemp, C. B., Knight, M. J., Murphy, J. J., Newton, W. T., Ballinger, W. F., and Lacy, P. E. (1974). Long term results of portal vein islet isografts and allografts in the treatment of streptozotocin-induced diabetes. *Diabetes* **23**, Suppl. 1, 359.

Schein, P. S., Rakieten, N., Cooney, D. A., Davis, R., and Vernon, M. L. (1973). Streptozotocin diabetes in monkeys and dogs, and its prevention by nicotinamide. *Proc. Soc. Exp. Biol. Med.* **143**, 514–518.

Schwaier, A. (1973). Tupaias—low-cost laboratory primates. *In* "The Laboratory Animal in Drug Testing; 5th Symposium of the International Committee on Laboratory Animals, Hannover, 1972" (A. Spiegel, ed.), pp. 193–196. G. Fischer, Verlag, Stuttgart.

Sheldon, W. G., and Gleiser, C. A. (1971). Amyloidosis of the islets of Langerhans in a crab-eating monkey (*Macaca fascicularis*). *Vet. Pathol.* **8**, 16–18.

Siegel, D. C., Moss, G. S., Reed, P. C., Cochin, A., and Fresquez, V. (1972). Decline in pancreatic insulin release during hemorrhagic shock in the baboon. *Rev. Surg.* **29**, 144–145.

Siliprandi, N. (1947). Ricerche sul diabete allossanico. VIII. Il diabete allossanico nella scimmia. *Boll. Soc. Ital. Biol. Sper.* **23**, 225–227.

Simon, E., Frenkel, G., and Kraicer, P. F. (1972). Blockade of insulin secretion by mannoheptulose. *Isr. J. Med. Sci.* **8**, 743–752.

Siperstein, M. D., Raskin, P., and Burns, H. (1972). Electron microscopic quantification of diabetic microangiopathy. *Diabetes* **22**, 514–527.

Smith, G. P., Gibbs, J., Strohmayer, A. J., and Stokes, P. E. (1972). Threshold doses of 2-deoxy-D-glucose for hyperglycemia and feeding in rats and monkeys. *Amer. J. Physiol.* **222**, 77–81.

Smith, G. P., Gibbs, J., Strohmayer, A. J., Root, A. W., and Stokes, P. E. (1973). Effect of 2-deoxy-D-glucose on insulin response to glucose in intact and adrenalectomized monkeys. *Endocrinology* **92**, 750–754.

Smith, P. E., Dotti, L., Tyndale, H. H., and Engle, E. T. (1936a). Effect of hypophysectomy on blood sugar of rhesus monkeys. *Proc. Soc. Exp. Biol. Med.* **34**, 247–249.

Smith, P. E., Tyndale, H. H., Dotti, L., and Engle, E. T. (1936b). Response of normal and hypophysectomized rhesus monkeys to insulin. *Proc. Soc. Exp. Biol. Med.* **34**, 250–251.

Sokoloverova, I. M. (1960). *In* "Theoretical and Practical Problems of Medicine and Biology in Experiments on Monkeys" (I. A. Utkin, ed.), pp. 171–183. Pergamon, Oxford.

Srinivasan, S. R., McBride, J. R., Jr., Radhakrishnamurthy, B., and Berenson, G. S. (1974). Comparative studies on serum lipoprotein and lipid profiles in subhuman primates. *Comp. Biochem. Physiol. B* **47**, 711–716.

Tashjian, A. H., Jr., Levine, L., and Wilhelmi, A. E. (1965). Immunochemical relatedness of porcine, bovine, ovine and primate pituitary growth hormones. *Endocrinology* **77**, 563–573.

Taylor, J. F., New, A. E., Chang, C.-P., and Chiang, H.-S. (1973). Baseline blood determinations of the Taiwan macaque (*Macaca cyclopis*). *Lab. Anim. Sci.* **23**, 582–587.

Trant, H. (1967). Death of a monkey. *Afr. Wild Life* **21**, 67–70.

Tseng, C. H. (1972). Experimental diabetes mellitus in baboons. Ph.D. Thesis, University of Oklahoma, Stillwater.

Tseng, C. H., Spargo, B. H., Porch, J., Stout, C., and Kimmelstiel, P. (1972). Experimental diabetes in baboons. Early glomerular changes. *Diabetes* **21**, Suppl. 1, 338.

Valerio, D. A., Miller, R. L., Innes, J. R. M., Courtney, K. D., Pallotta, A. J., and Guttmacher, R. M. (1969). Miscellaneous diseases of adults. "Macaca mulatta: Management of a Laboratory Breeding Colony" pp. 101–102. Academic Press, New York.

Valerio, D. A., Valerio, M. G., Ulland, B. M., and Innes, J. R. M. (1971). Clinical conditions and diseases encountered in a large simian colony. *Proc. Int. Congr. Primatol., 3rd, 1970*, Vol. 2, pp. 205–212.

Viktora, J. F., Johnson, B. F., Penhos, J. C., Rosenberg, C. A., and Wolff, F. W. (1969). Effect of ingested mannoheptulose in animals and man. *Metab. Clin. Exp.* **18**, 87–102.

Vogin, E. E., and Oser, F. (1971). Comparative blood values in several species of nonhuman primates. *Lab. Anim. Sci.* **21**, 937–941.

Wakeman, A. M., and Morrell, C. A. (1931). Chemistry and metabolism in experimental yellow fever in *Macacus rhesus*. IV. Tolerance tests for dextrose. *Arch. Intern. Med.* **48**, 301–312.

Williamson, J. R., Vogler, N. J., and Kilo, C. (1969). Estimation of vascular basement membrane thickness. Theoretical and practical considerations. *Diabetes* **18**, 567–578.

Wilson, R. B., and Martin, J. M. (1970). Plasma insulin concentrations in dogs and monkeys after xylitol, glucose or tolbutamide infusion. *Diabetes* **19**, 17–22.

Wilson, R. B., Martin, J. M., and Kelly, H. (1970). Plasma and pancreatic insulin concentrations in squirrel and rhesus monkeys. *Diabetes* **19**, 405.

Wilson, R. B., Martin, J. M., Kelly, H., and Newberne, P. M. (1971). Plasma and pancreatic insulin concentrations in adult squirrel and rhesus monkeys. *Diabetes* **20**, 151–155.

Wolff, F., Grant, A., Wales, J., and Viktora, J. (1968). Experimental diabetes due to insulin inhibition. *Lancet* **1**, 818.

Biliary Lipids and Cholesterol
Gallstone Formation

OSCAR W. PORTMAN

Department of Nutrition and Metabolic Diseases, Oregon Regional
Primate Research Center, Beaverton, Oregon, and Department
of Biochemistry, University of Oregon
Medical School, Portland, Oregon

TOSHIAKI OSUGA[1]

Department of Medicine, University of Tokyo School of Medicine,
Tokyo, Japan

AND

NAOMI TANAKA

Department of Nutrition and Metabolic Diseases, Oregon Regional
Primate Research Center, Beaverton, Oregon

[1] Present address: Department of Medicine, University of Tsukuba School of Medicine, Sakura-mura, Niihari-gun, Ibaraki-ken 300-31, Japan.

I. Introduction

Until recently, the amount of research devoted to exploring the pathogenesis of gallstones was exceedingly limited relative to the medical importance of the problem. In many parts of the world, including the United States and Western Europe, cholesterol gallstones are extremely common. Since this form of cholelithiasis shares with atherosclerosis the common manifestation of ectopic crystalline cholesterol, there have been numerous studies of the relationship between the two conditions and the populations that are afflicted with them. And yet, we know much less about the epidemiology of human cholelithiasis than of atherosclerosis and its sequelae. One fact clearly emerges: gallstones are extremely prevalent in those geographic populations afflicted with a high incidence of events related to atherosclerosis.

In at least two groups, however, cholesterol gallstones are more prevalent than the incidence of those clinical events related to atherosclerosis would lead us to expect. First, the prevalence of gallstones is at least twice as high in women as in men, whereas the rate of myocardial infarction is much greater in men than in women. In a series of 1600 autopsies in Malmo, Sweden, Sternby (1968) confirmed the greater incidence of gallstones in women (Fig. 1) but found in both men and women that the severity of atherosclerosis in all of the arteries examined was the same for subjects with and without gall-

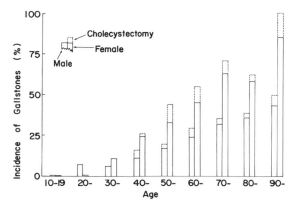

FIG. 1. The incidence of gallstones and cholecystectomy according to age and sex in the autopsy series of Sternby (1968) in Malmo, Sweden.

stones (Fig. 2). A second population with an unusually high frequency of gallstones but with low plasma cholesterol levels and presumably reduced atherosclerosis is certain American Indians, particularly females (e.g., Sampliner *et al.*, 1970; Small and Rapo, 1970; Thistle *et al.*, 1971; Grundy and Metzger, 1972). The Indians of Southwestern United States have been most extensively studied in this respect. Sex-related differences and the susceptibility of Indians to gallstone formation suggest that such formation results from the very factors that provide protection from atherosclerosis. In one study (Sturdevant *et al.*, 1973; Hofmann, 1973) a dietary regimen designed to lower plasma

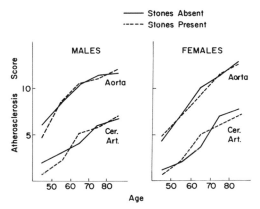

FIG. 2. The severity of atherosclerosis in the aorta and cerebral arteries (cer. art. on figure) of men and women with and without gallstones. From the autopsy series of Sternby (1968) in Malmo, Sweden.

lipid levels and perhaps to act as a preventive measure against the sequelae of atherosclerosis may actually have caused an increase in the incidence of gallstones. Any attempt to alter the concentration of cholesterol in the blood by diet or drugs can also alter the frequency of gallstones. Of even greater importance, any medical approach to the treatment of gallstones can elevate the blood lipids and thus hasten the development of atherosclerosis. This important possibility of an antagonistic effect between the factors that favor the development of gallstones and atherosclerosis, together with the need to understand the fundamental mechanisms of development of both conditions, makes imperative an experimental animal model which is susceptible to both diseases.

In this review, we will describe the development of cholesterol gallstones in several species of experimental animals, but with particular emphasis on nonhuman primates. Because of our experience with squirrel monkeys (*Saimiri sciureus*) and because of their particular suitability for studies of atherosclerosis (review of Portman, 1970; Portman and Illingworth, 1974c) and gallstones, we will emphasize the studies in this species. The following sections will deal with species and individual predispositions to gallstones, morphogenesis, relationships of gallstones to plasma and biliary lipids, nutritional and pharmacologic effects, physiological factors such as pools and turnovers, and the factors other than biliary lipid that determine gallstone formation. Where possible, we will emphasize the similarities and differences between squirrel monkeys and other experimental animals or man, but we have aimed for completeness only in the studies on nonhuman primates.

II. Species and Individual Susceptibilities to Cholesterol Gallstones

A. SPONTANEOUS AND INDUCED GALLSTONES IN NONHUMAN PRIMATES

Despite the relatively small number of species and individuals that have been examined, it can be stated that spontaneous gallstones are probably infrequent in nonhuman primates. Hamerton's (1932) report of gallstones in a marmoset was one of the first. A number of years later Lapin and Yakovleva (1963) reported gallstones in two more marmosets. The stones contained 77% cholesterol and 0.28% calcium. Gallstones occur relatively frequently in baboons (*Papio anubis* and *P. cynochealus*) (Lapin and Yakovleva, 1963). Ruch (1967) also reported that Osman Hill had received several gallstones which East African natives had removed from anubis baboons. Glenn and McSherry (1969, 1970) and McSherry *et al.* (1971a,b, 1972) reported that 6 of 35 adult female baboons had gallstones whose cholesterol contents varied from 86 to 97%.

Anver *et al.* (1972) reported cholesterol gallstones in 3 female owl monkeys (*Aotus trivirgatus*): of these, 2 had gallstones that were almost completely cholesterol, the third had gallstones that were 50% cholesterol and 50% of undetermined composition. The single occurrences of gallstones in an orangutan (*Pongo pygmaeus*) reported by Fox (1930) and in a rhesus monkey reported by Martin *et al.* (1972) complete the history of spontaneous gallstones in nonhuman primates. Lorentz (1966) found no gallstones in 300 vervet monkeys (*Cercopithecus aethiops*); we found no spontaneous gallstones in squirrel (*Saimiri sciureus*) monkeys (e.g., Osuga and Portman, 1971); and Dowling *et al.* (1971) found none in rhesus monkeys.

Except for Mann's (1970) report of gallstones induced in 2 cebus monkeys (*Cebus albifrons*) by a cholesterol-rich diet, the only other reports of nutritionally induced gallstones dealt with squirrel monkeys (Osuga and Portman, 1971, 1972; Melchior *et al.*, 1972, 1974; Lofland *et al.*, 1975; Portman *et al.*, 1975; Osuga *et al.*, 1974a; Tanaka and Portman, 1974). Table I shows the incidence and mean weights of cholesterol gallstones from squirrel monkeys in our laboratory which had been fed diets associated with low, intermediate, and high rates of stone formation for 6 months or longer.

Table I

INCIDENCE AND MEAN WEIGHTS OF CHOLESTEROL GALLSTONES
IN SQUIRREL MONKEYS FED THREE DIFFERENT DIETS FOR 6
MONTHS OR LONGER: ONE RESULTED IN NO STONES, ONE IN
A LOW, AND ONE IN A HIGH INCIDENCE OF STONES[a]

Diet	Females	Males
Commercial chow	0/16[b]	0/21[b]
Semipurified diet—corn oil—15% of cal.	6/27 (21.0)[c]	3/9 (21.1)
Semipurified diet—butter—45% of cal + cholesterol	23/44 (79.8)	7/12 (133.9)

[a] Modified from Portman *et al.* (1975).

[b] Number of animals with stones/number of animals in group.

[c] Numbers in parentheses indicate mean weight of stones (mg) in those animals with stones.

Individual susceptibility and resistance to gallstones in this species are illustrated by an experiment in which the gallbladders of squirrel monkeys with and without gallstones from the high butter plus cholesterol group were emptied at laparotomy. Afterwards they were put back on the same diets; from 4 to 9 months later, 9 monkeys that had been initially free of gallstones remained free, whereas 12 of 15 monkeys that had initially had gallstones removed suffered a recurrence of the disease.

B. Spontaneous and Induced Gallstones in Nonprimates

Biliary calculi are quite rare in most domestic animals (Rains, 1964). Even in the ox, gallstones are composed mainly of bile pigment and calcium.

Many of the preparations used to induce alimentary cholelithiasis in nonprimates do not result in cholesterol gallstones and presumably are not directly pertinent to the mechanisms of cholesterol crystal growth and assembly. Cholesterol gallstones have been formed by means of special diets in hamsters (Dam and Christensen, 1952; Dam, 1971), mice (Tepperman et al., 1964), dogs (Englert et al., 1969), rabbits (Borgman, 1965), and prairie dogs (Patton et al., 1961; Brenneman et al., 1972; Chang et al., 1973; den Besten et al., 1974). High cholesterol diets produced calcium phosphate stones in guinea pigs (Okey, 1942), cholestanol produced glycoallodeoxycholic acid stones in rabbits (Bevans and Mosbach, 1956; Hofmann and Mosbach, 1964) and guinea pigs (Caira et al., 1957), and diets high in casein and oleic acid produced glycoallodeoxycholic acid stones in rabbits (Kyd and Bouchier, 1971, 1972). Low protein diets with lithocholic acid were associated with lithocholic acid stones in rats (Palmer and Hruban, 1966).

III. Morphogenesis of Cholesterol Gallstones in Nonhuman Primates and Man

As we shall develop subsequently, much of what is known about the formation of cholesterol gallstones in man and experimental animals was learned from studies of the composition and metabolism of the three principal lipid constituents of bile: cholesterol, phospholipid, and bile salts. The reasons for crystal growth and aggregation and crystal dissolution in gallstones are not completely understood, however. In particular, how the many varied and peculiarly shaped structures are assembled into the mature gallstone remains a mystery.

Luckily, phase contrast microscopy, scanning electron microscopy, and X-ray crystallography, together with highly sensitive chromatographic techniques, now make it possible to determine the composition and structure not only of the whole gallstone but of isolated areas in it as well. In this section, we will compare microscopic particulates in bile and in different gallstones from man and squirrel monkeys in order to determine how gallstones are put together and whether the squirrel monkey is a relevant animal model of human gallstones.

A. GALLSTONE COMPOSITION

Gallstones, largely cholesterol, have been induced experimentally in squirrel monkeys (Osuga and Portman, 1971, 1972) which have then been used in studies to compare the morphological aspects of gallstone formation in monkeys (Osuga *et al.*, 1974a) and in man (Osuga *et al.*, 1974b).

The three major components of human gallstones are: (1) cholesterol (Bogren, 1964; Russell *et al.*, 1968; Nakayama and van der Linden, 1970; Carlisle and Tasman-Jones, 1973); (2) calcium (Sutor and Wooley, 1969, 1973); (3) a group of bile pigments (Miyake and Johnston, 1968; Hwang, 1970). The calcium, in turn, is found in (1) three forms of calcium carbonate: valerite, aragonite, and calcite; (2) calcium palmitate; (3) bilirubinate; (4) two forms of phosphate: apatite and whitlockite. Other minor components include fatty acid, triglyceride, polysaccharide, protein, bile acids, and miscellaneous minerals. Analyses have been performed chemically, by X-ray diffraction, infrared analysis, and histochemically.

Bogren and Larsson (1963) claimed that cholesterol monohydrate is the only form in which cholesterol crystallizes *in vivo*. However, in an X-ray crystallographic study of gallstones from eight countries, Sutor and Wooley (1969) found that cholesterol accounted for 71% of crystalline material: 52.3% anhydrous cholesterol, 16% cholesterol monohydrate, and 2.7% of a form called cholesterol II. The latter is probably another form of anhydrous cholesterol.

Miyake and Johnston (1968) found that more than 90% of a series of gallstones from Asia, Japan, and the United States could conveniently be classified as cholesterol (more than 70% cholesterol by weight) or pigment (less than 30% cholesterol) stones. In Asia, most stones are pigment; in the West, cholesterol stones predominate. In Japan, there has been a shift from pigment stones, which were most prevalent in the past, to a predominance of cholesterol stones, probably as a result of a changed life style (Nakayama and Miyake, 1970; Kameda, 1964).

In the following section (III,B), using considerations of crystal structure as a basis, we will describe the similarity between cholesterol gallstones in human and nonhuman primates.

B. ASSEMBLY AND GROWTH OF CRYSTALS AND GALLSTONES

Gallstones (Fig. 3) produced by nutritional procedures in squirrel monkeys can be classified into four categories which are similar to their counterparts in man: sandlike grains and simple round, multilobar, and mulberry stones. Faceting of stones is observed in both squirrel monkeys and man whereas size is one of the major species differences.

Three months on a lithogenic diet were required to form sandlike gallstones in squirrel monkeys. After longer periods, the number of animals with stones increased as did the mass and number of stones and the variation in stone size. Presumably these evidences of slow and continuous stone growth have their counterpart in the delayed

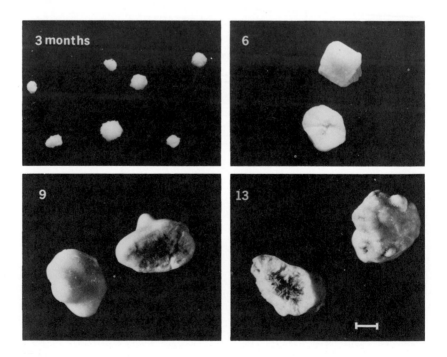

FIG. 3. The typical appearance of gallstones in squirrel monkeys after 3 (sandlike), 6 (simple round), 9 (multilobar), and 13 months (mulberry) on a lithogenic diet. Stones at 6, 9, and 13 months have been fractured; the fracture and external surfaces are shown. Line = 1 mm. From Osuga *et al.*, (1974a).

onset of cholelithiasis in man. After 6 months, simple round stones were observed in susceptible squirrel monkeys. The more complex forms of gallstones generally did not form until 9 months or more on the lithogenic diets. In a few squirrel monkeys, all of the numerous gallstones present were equal in size, an indication of multiple nucleation at one time. This phenomenon is also sometimes observed in human cholelithiasis.

The structures of particulate materials isolated by centrifugation from hepatic and gallbladder bile and of gallstones from human subjects and squirrel monkeys were examined by phase contrast and scanning electron microscopy (Osuga *et al.*, 1974a,b).

Frequently, euhedral crystals in the shape of parallelograms were seen in the hepatic and gallbladder bile, particularly of monkeys with gallstones. Polygonal or irregular growth layers, which probably resulted from two-dimensional nucleation, were often seen on the surface of these crystals. The second form of crystal growth results from an aggregation of crystals of various sizes and shapes (Fig. 4). Regard-

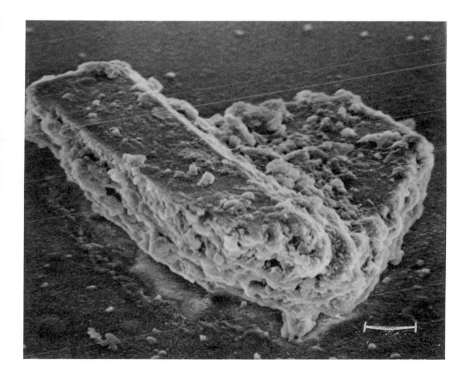

FIG. 4. Overlapped crystal plates resulting from aggregation in the gallbladder bile of a squirrel monkey. Line = 3μ.

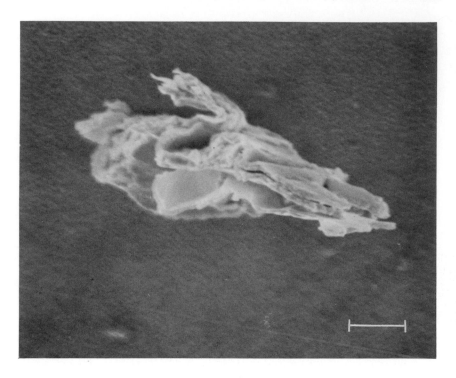

FIG. 5.   Layers composed of platy band units which are the basic structural constituents of larger concrements. Line = 2μ. From Osuga et al. (1974a).

less of the mechanism of growth, the next most mature structure is the platy band (Fig. 5) which contains subparallel laminations and is the basic unit of microliths. Figure 6 shows one of the many forms of microliths which were found in squirrel monkey bile. A third type of small concrement found in hepatic and gallbladder bile in monkeys with gallstones is shown in Fig. 7. It has a rounded amorphous appearance and is composed of tiny, irregular fragmented crystals. This form is probably the same as that designated "wagon wheels" by us when we saw a characteristic axle and spoke configuration with phase contrast microscopy.

We frequently found single or aggregated crystals entrapped in mucous substances, an observation that supported Womack's (1971) findings in human bile and perhaps his hypothesis about the importance of mucus in the formation of microliths.

Probably any of the three mechanisms of cholesterol concrement growth—layer growth, crystal aggregation, and amorphous assembly

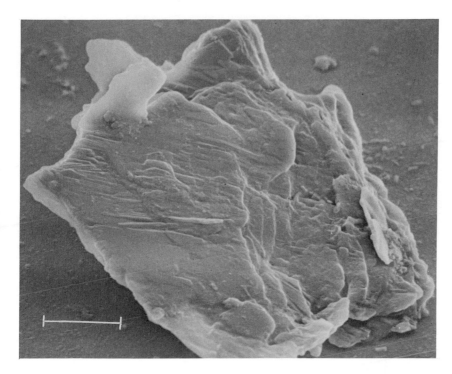

FIG. 6. A microlith which is composed of platy band units of crystals in the hepatic bile of a squirrel monkey. Line = 10μ. From Osuga *et al.* (1974a).

of fragmented crystals—can lead to the appearance of the smallest macroscopic forms, the sandlike stone (Fig. 8), which appears in squirrel monkeys after about 3 months on the lithogenic diets. The irregular arrangement of subunits is a characteristic feature of this stone.

The medium sized simple round stone (Fig. 9) has a much smoother external surface than the sandlike stone. Examination of the fracture surface shows the more regular arrangement of platy units radiating from a center which consists of a tiny crater. Crystals appear to be arranged according to a geometrical selection. Because of this radial arrangement and the logical assumption that stone growth begins from the center, it is important that no foreign body or unusual cholesterol crystalline structure was found at the center (Fig. 10) as a nidus for initiation of stone growth. Globules, which were assumed to be bilirubin because similar forms were observed in human pigment stones (Wolpers, 1968; Wolpers and Blaschke, 1971; Ogata and Murata,

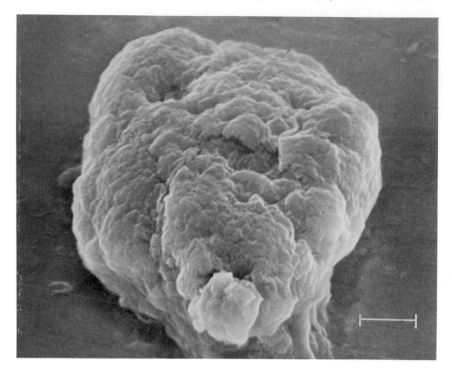

FIG. 7.   A microlith in squirrel monkey bile. Line $= 2\mu$. From Osuga *et al.* (1974a).

1971), were sometimes found in the central zone but not as a central core of squirrel monkey gallstones (Fig. 10). Thus although heterogeneous nucleation around some inorganic calcium salt or trace of protein could not be ruled out, homogeneous nucleation secondary to supersaturation of the bile seems the most likely mechanism of gallstone formation in squirrel monkeys.

Another result of the radial arrangement of crystals in gallstones is their arrangement perpendicular to the stone surface. Although the surfaces tend to become smooth because of intermittent dissolution or mechanical polishing of one stone by another, these perpendicular crystals (Fig. 11) may be important as a mechanism of the mechanical linking of the surfaces of adjacent stones and thus of the formation of multilobar stones. A special case of fusion of simple stones to form more complex ones is the mulberry stones (Fig. 12). In this type of stone, which is seen both in human subjects and in squirrel monkeys, several simple or multilobar stones form a mass held together by some cementing material. The fracture surface of the mulberry stone in Fig.

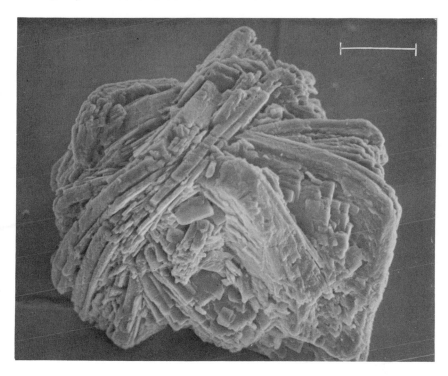

Fig. 8. The irregular external surface of a sandlike stone formed in a squirrel monkey after 3 months on the lithogenic diet. There is random (subparallel) aggregation of smaller units. Line = 100μ. From Osuga *et al.* (1974a).

13 shows several such adhering multilobar stones. Each of these in turn was probably formed by the aggregation of two or more simple stones. There was, however, no foreign cementing substance between the domes of multilobar stones, and the crystals were intermingled at the hypothetical fusion lines.

Figure 14 summarizes the mechanisms involved in gallstone formation in the squirrel monkey. One aspect of stone morphogenesis which is not illustrated in this diagram is the continuing growth and dissolution that occurs. Evans and Cussler (1974) have described this dynamic process from the theoretical viewpoint. The microscopic evidences of crystal dissolution, which are particularly apparent in some of the human specimens discussed in the following section, can be explained by long-term and diurnal changes in the extent to which bile is saturated or supersaturated with cholesterol. These diurnal variations in bile composition, which are related to nutritional status,

FIG. 9. Fracture surface through the approximate center of a medium sized radial stone formed after 6 months on a lithogenic diet. Note the radial crystalline arrangement. Line = 250μ. From Osuga *et al.* (1974a).

have been frequently described (e.g., McSherry *et al.*, 1971a,b; Small *et al.*, 1972; Smallwood *et al.*, 1972; Metzger *et al.*, 1973). One evidence for longer term variations in bile composition is the finding by Sutor (1974) of sequential deposition of compounds. For example, a gallstone that has a nucleus of cholesterol and a surface layer of calcium carbonate may indicate a change in bile composition.

C. Comparisons with the Morphology of Human Gallstones

Despite a more varied composition in human cholesterol gallstones than in those of squirrel monkeys, the two species share many similarities in the basic mechanism of gallstone morphogenesis. Crystals of various sizes and shapes are found in the gallbladder and common bile duct of human subjects with cholelithiasis. Most

FIG. 10.   The central cavity of a medium sized radial stone from a squirrel monkey. There are no foreign structures in the core. Line = 20µ. From Osuga *et al.* (1974a).

frequently, these crystals are thin and rhombic (Fig. 15) and have a surface layering which suggests growth by two-dimensional nucleation (see Stevenson and Stevenson, 1973).

A second form of crystal growth in human bile is a random aggregation of crystals to form clusters of various sizes (Fig. 16). The platy band units, which consist of subparallel laminations and are formed by either of the two mechanisms just described, are the same basic units of macroscopic stones in squirrel monkeys. Figures 17 and 18 show microliths in human bile which are about the size of red blood cells. Beside the euhedral crystals, tiny fragmented crystals are combined into concrements (Fig. 19) which are also somewhat similar to forms isolated from monkey bile.

Despite similarities between the microscopic forms (composed largely of cholesterol) in the bile of man and the squirrel monkey, human gallstones have much more variety. Because of geometrical selection, crystal plates are radially arranged (Fig. 20) although amor-

FIG. 11.   Bilirubin globules found near, but not actually in, the central cavity of a radial stone from a squirrel monkey. Line = 5μ. From Osuga *et al.* (1974a).

phous (organic) materials are sometimes observed. The outer crystals are perpendicular to the surface (Fig. 21). This radial growth from the center was also observed by Matsukura *et al.* (1968) and Ogata and Murata (1971). The element of crystal dissolution (Fig. 22) is another factor shared by both species.

Differences between the two species include the greater frequency of hexagonal (Fig. 23) crystals in human bile and the greater prevalence of fragmented crystals in squirrel monkey bile. The center of the human gallstone is likely to have an amorphous substance containing randomly arranged crystal plates thus differing from the simple gallstone of the squirrel monkey which has a microscopic hole in the center. The core of the human gallstone contains pigment (Bogren, 1964) and glycoprotein (Womack *et al.*, 1963) or is enriched with calcium phosphate (Sutor and Wooley, 1971).

Another unique feature of human gallstones is the concentric layer or ring formation. Microscopically, this ring is formed by a groove or

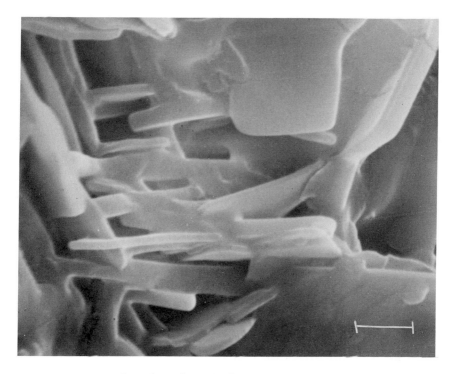

F IG. 12.   Outer surface of a medium sized stone showing that crystals are sometimes arranged perpendicular to the surface in a position that would facilitate intermeshing with neighboring stones. Line = 3μ. From Osuga *et al.* (1974a).

space which separates two layers of cholesterol crystals which have different axial orientations (Fig. 24). Lonsdale (1968a,b) regards these concentric rings in urinary stones and in gallstones as indicating temporary cessations in stone growth. Liesegang's phenomenon, a mineralogical term describing the periodic precipitation of crystals in gels, has been invoked to explain the ring phenomenon. The periodicity of crystal deposition in human gallstones may also be related to changes in the degree of cholesterol saturation of bile. Diurnal changes in this saturation are presumably characteristic of all species with gallstones; however, the day-to-day composition of bile from squirrel monkeys fed an unvarying diet is probably quite constant. The hypothetical periodic interruption of gallstone growth in man could be the basis for a reorientation of crystal direction when growth is resumed. Other potential influences on the orientation of crystal growth are the doping effect of minerals (Henisch, 1970) and the changes in cholesterol satu-

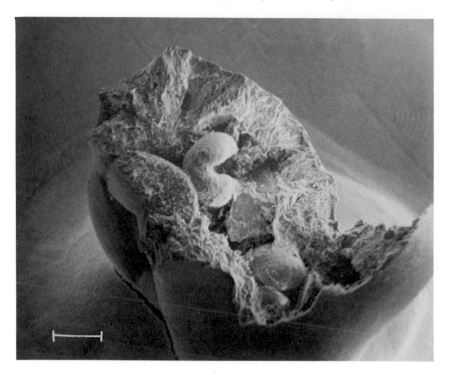

FIG. 13.   The fracture surface of a mulberry stone in which constituent stones retain their identity. Some smaller stones (e.g., the horseshoe-shaped stone in the center) appear to have formed originally from the fusion of yet smaller stones in a squirrel monkey. Line = 400μ. From Osuga *et al.* (1974a).

ration secondary to convection currents generated by cholesterol consumption around a growing concrement.

Yet another morphological difference between human and squirrel monkey gallstones is the way in which the domes or lobes of the multilobar stones form. In the monkey, this phenomenon results from the aggregation of smaller stones; in man the domes are composed of fanlike arrays of crystals originating from foci that are often at or near a concentric ring. Thus the domes of human gallstones may also be related to new growth from various epicenters on the periphery of smaller stones.

In summary, the formation of crystals and microliths from bile is similar in man and the squirrel monkey, but the later stages in the growth of gallstones are quite different. These species differences are probably the result of differences in the time required for stone growth (a few months for the monkey versus years for man) and the

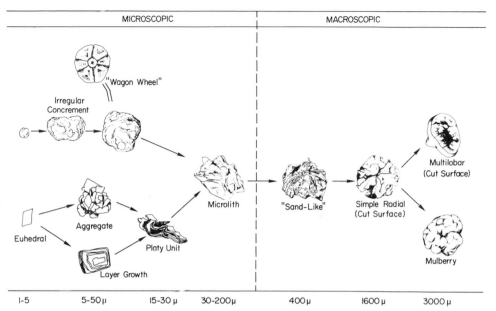

FIG. 14. A hypothetical sequence of cholesterol gallstone formation in the squirrel monkey, based on the structures in hepatic and gallbladder bile. From Osuga *et al.* (1974a).

kind of bile composition (unvarying in monkeys on constant lithogenic diets versus varied in man).

IV. Relationships of Biliary Lipids to Cholesterol Gallstone Formation

A. Theoretical Considerations of Cholesterol Solubility in Bile

Almost as soon as the presence of cholesterol in gallstones and in soluble form in bile was established, it became apparent that gallstones probably result from excess cholesterol or a destabilization of the cholesterol in bile. Since the quantity of protein was smaller in bile than in blood plasma, it seemed unlikely that a lipoprotein could be involved in cholesterol stabilization. Much of the early effort to explain this was devoted to elucidating the role of bile salts, including the kind of bile salts, in stabilizing cholesterol (Isaksson, 1954a;

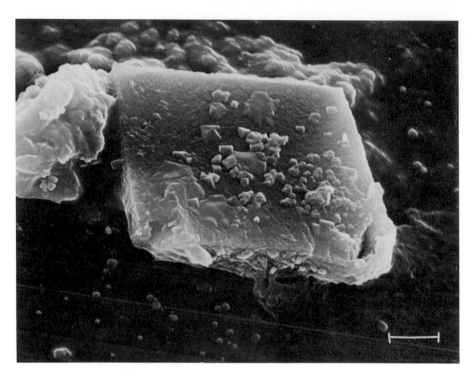

FIG. 15. A euhedral crystal in the bile of a patient with gallstones. Line = 3μ. From Osuga *et al.* (1974b).

Sjövall, 1960). It was clear, however (e.g., Polonovski and Bourillon, 1952; Isaksson, 1954b), that lecithin plays an important part in solubilizing biliary cholesterol, and Isaksson proposed that a molar ratio of bile salts plus lecithin to cholesterol of at least 11:1 was necessary to stabilize the cholesterol in bile.

Within the last decade, a great deal of progress has been made in defining the limits of the apparent solubility of cholesterol with different concentrations of the three major lipid constituents of bile. Hofmann and Small (1967), Tamesue and Juniper (1967), and Small and associates (1966a,b; Bourges *et al.*, 1967) proposed that bile is a micellar solution. Mixed liquid crystals of cholesterol and phospholipid were converted into mixed micelles by the action of bile salts. The origin of such a micelle is obscure, but Small (1970) has suggested that bile salts form the micelle from the cholesterol and lecithin of the bile canalicular membrane, and Bouchier (1971) has postulated vesicle formation. Wheeler and King (1972) have investigated in detail the

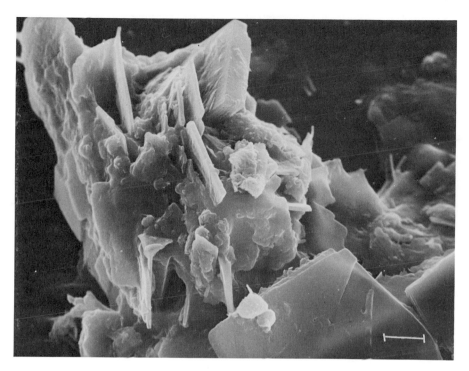

FIG. 16. A cluster of crystals aggregated at random in human bile. Note the thicknesses of different crystalline plates which illustrate various degrees of growth. Line = 5µ. From Osuga *et al.* (1974b).

relationship between cholesterol and phospholipid excretion. All physiological bile salt concentrations are above the critical micellar concentration (Tamesue and Juniper, 1967).

Admirand and Small's (1968) application to bile of specific criteria for determining the quantities of cholesterol that are stabilized in mixed micelles with various combinations of cholesterol, phospholipid, bile salts, and water was, perhaps, the single most important stimulus of recent years to research on the pathogenesis of gallstones. These workers showed that the absolute concentrations of total lipids were much less important than the relative proportions of the three major ingredients. They also demonstrated that a three-dimensional plot of the relative molar concentrations of cholesterol, phospholipid, and total bile salts (where the sum of the concentrations = 100) could conveniently be used to describe the compositions that would result in the formation of crystalline cholesterol and those that would not.

FIG. 17.   A typical microlith that illustrates radial growth found in gallbladder bile of man. Line = 2μ. From Osuga *et al.* (1974b).

The limits established by this method were used to accurately separate the gallbladder biles of people with gallstones from those without.

Several investigators, however, soon pointed out that supersaturated bile can be secreted by people who have no evidence of gallstones (Dam *et al.*, 1971; Nakayama and van der Linden, 1971; Thistle *et al.*, 1971; Vlahcevic *et al.*, 1971; Danziger *et al.*, 1971). These differences among investigators about the relationship between gallstones and bile composition can be explained by diurnal variations in bile composition which are related to fasting and eating (see Section VI). There is also some disagreement about the precise limits of cholesterol solubility. Several investigators (Neiderhiser and Roth, 1968; Dam, 1971; Dam and Hegardt, 1971; Hegardt and Dam, 1971; Hozlbach *et al.*, 1971, 1973; Mufson *et al.*, 1972; Tamesue *et al.*, 1973) have suggested solubility limits for cholesterol in bile which differ from those of Admirand and Small (1968). A reduction in solubility cri-

FIG. 18. A microlith with rounded and flattened surface (partial dissolution is indicated). Line = 3μ. From Osuga *et al.* (1974b).

teria would, of course, increase the number of individuals with supersaturated bile and of those purported to have gallstones. There have also been numerous suggestions that the criteria of Admirand and Small (1968) for expressing the lithogenic potential or cholesterol saturation of bile be simplified (Metzger *et al.*, 1972; Thomas and Hofmann, 1973; Swell *et al.*, 1974).

The fact that laboratories differ considerably about the limits of cholesterol solubility may well be due to the methodology of preparing and analyzing bile samples. Whether crystals are included in the bile or are removed by filtration or centrifugation and how bile is stored (temperature, time, freezing) before sampling are important in determining its composition. Mufson *et al.* (1972) and Evans and Cussler (1974) have pointed out that cholesterol solubility in artificial systems can differ enormously in the period immediately after preparation of the mixtures as a result of different experimental techniques. The eventual equilibrium solubilities, however, would be the same regardless of the history of the samples.

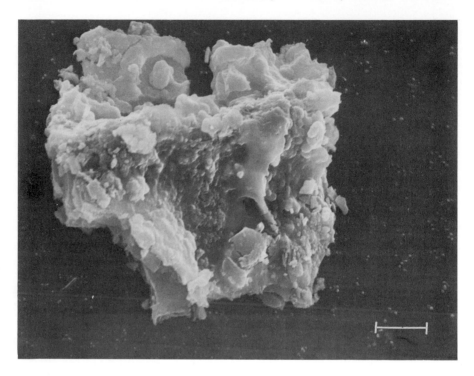

FIG. 19.   A concrement composed of many irregular smaller concrements in human bile. Line = 4μ. From Osuga *et al.* (1974b).

Differences in sample handling also explain, at least partly, disagreements over whether crystals occur in hepatic bile that is supersaturated with cholesterol. We have consistently found crystals in the hepatic bile of squirrel monkeys (Osuga and Portman, 1971, 1972; Osuga *et al.*, 1974a) and human subjects (Osuga *et al.*, 1974b) with gallstones (see Section III,B). Small and Rapo (1970), however, found hepatic bile from a group of American Indians with gallstones to be optically clear, and Chang *et al.* (1973) found no crystals in the hepatic bile of prairie dogs which had been fed a lithogenic diet and had gallstones. Cahlin *et al.* (1972) found microcrystals in the hepatic bile of 50% of their patients with saturated or supersaturated bile and with cholesterol gallstones.

Holzbach *et al.* (1973) and Mufson *et al.* (1972) wondered why bile that is supersaturated with cholesterol does not form crystals and questioned whether some forgotten water-soluble component was responsible. Olszewski *et al.* (1973) suggested that cholesterol exists

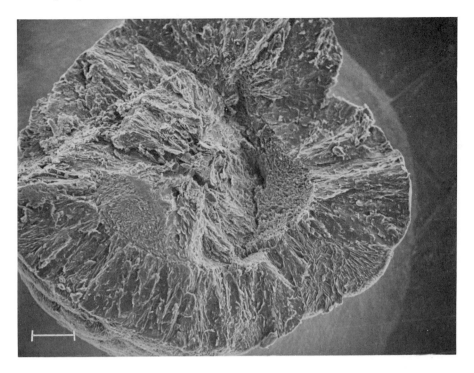

FIG. 20. The fractured surface of a human multilobar stone which reveals a nucleus and two concentric layers. Note the fanlike pattern of crystals in the outer layer (lower right) which corresponds with a dome-shaped protrusion on the external surface of the stone. Line = 300μ. From Osuga *et al.* (1974b).

in the form of liquid crystals, a hypothesis that is supported by the extremely high cholesterol content (25 mole%) in the hepatic bile of hamsters fed hyodeoxycholic acid (Wheeler, 1973), in spite of the protection provided by hyodeoxycholate against cholesterol gallstones (Dam and Christensen, 1962).

B. MECHANISMS OF CHOLESTEROL CRYSTALLIZATION FROM BILE

The thermodynamic factors controlling cholesterol crystallization from bile are very unclear. The physical reality of a critical nucleus (an embryo of cholesterol molecules of a size sufficient to resist dissolution) appears certain, but such nuclei are too small to measure directly. Their size has been calculated to be about 10 Å (quoted from Henisch, 1970). The probability of homogeneous nucleation is, of course, enhanced by increased concentrations of cholesterol in bile.

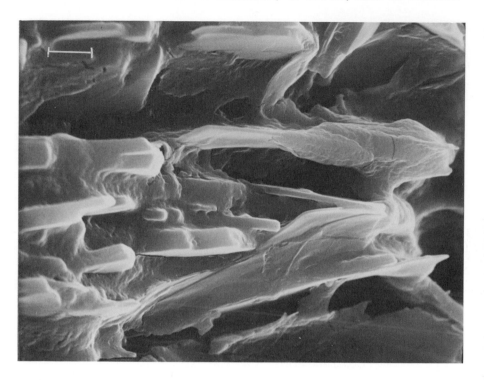

FIG. 21. Surface of a human gallstone. Crystal plates are perpendicular to the surface and dissolution patterns are apparent on the ridges of crystals and between crystals. Line = 3μ. From Osuga *et al.* (1974b).

Heterogeneous nucleation, in which cholesterol crystallizes around a foreign nidus such as calcium salt, unconjugated bilirubin, unconjugated bile acid, sequestered cells from the gallbladder wall, bacteria, or parasite eggs, can probably occur at a lower level of cholesterol supersaturation than homogeneous nucleation. As we observed in Section III,B, squirrel monkey gallstones appear to form by homogeneous nucleation, whereas human stones usually formed with a solid, partly amorphous, core that may have contained calcium bilirubinate (Maki and Suzuki, 1964) or mucopolysaccharide (Womack *et al.*, 1963).

Since temperature and pressure are practically constant in the gallbladder, crystal growth depends mainly on the concentrations of solutes and other physiological considerations. The first step is the separation of cholesterol molecules from the mixed micelle; the second, the sedimentation of cholesterol molecules on the surface of a nucleus

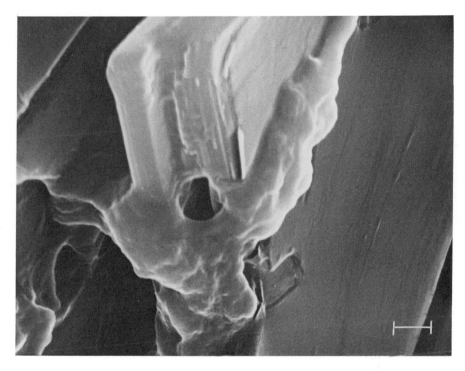

FIG. 22. A plate composed of laminated crystals which show evidence of dissolution. Line = 1μ. From Osuga *et al.* (1974b).

or growing crystal; and finally, the movement of the donor micelle away from the growing crystal. Evans and Cussler (1974) discussed the first and third steps; we will discuss the second step briefly here.

The way in which growth by molecular attachment occurs depends on the nature of the crystal surface. Rough crystals full of molecular "steps" provide logical points of attachment for new molecules. If the attachment is to smooth crystal surfaces, the new molecules must either attach to a new two-dimensional nucleus or grow by attachment to the existing crystal in a screwlike dislocation, a mechanism that is called spiral growth. Chang *et al.* (1973) observed this spiral growth in prairie dogs fed a lithogenic diet; Ogata and Murata (1971) made a similar observation in man. Layer growth by two-dimensional nucleation predominated in the squirrel monkey. (Osuga *et al.*, 1974a).

Freston *et al.* (1969) suggested that mucous substances such as mucopolysaccharides are large molecules with many faces that could provide a wide area of epitaxial contact and crystal deposit. Lonsdale

FIG. 23.   Hexagonal and other polygonal crystals which probably develop into parallelograms. Line = 1μ. From Osuga *et al.* (1974b).

(1968a,b,c) described the importance of epitaxis (the growth of one crystal on the structure of another which has a close geometrical fit) in crystal development. Foreign organic molecules may also act as cementing or embedding media for the large biliary concrements as in the spaces between the lobes of mulberry stones.

C. COMPOSITION OF BILE FROM NONHUMAN PRIMATES

The relative concentrations of cholesterol, phospholipid, and bile salts in bile have proved to be useful criteria for predicting the predisposition of different nonhuman primates to cholesterol gallstones. Two species of macaques (rhesus and stumptails), baboons, squirrel monkeys, and African green monkeys have been used to compare the relations between bile composition and gallstone formation. These studies show clearly that the higher the concentration of cholesterol (compared with bile salts and phospholipid) in bile, the higher is the

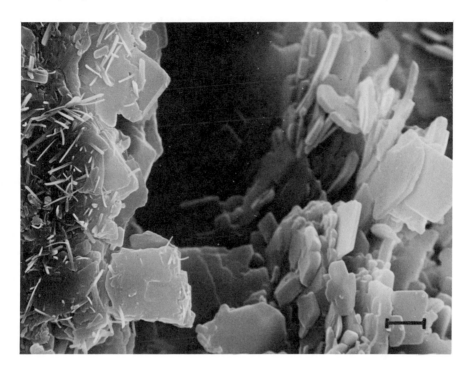

FIG. 24.   The groove between 8 concentric layers in a human gallstone. The general orientations of crystals are different in the two layers. Line = 5μ. From Osuga *et al.* (1974b).

likelihood that cholesterol gallstones are present. As in a great many other biological variables, species differences in bile composition are almost as great among the various members of the Order Primates as among the whole range of mammals (Portman, 1962; Wiggins and Wooton, 1958; Haslewood, 1967).

The relative concentrations of cholesterol in the gallbladder and hepatic bile of the rhesus monkey are extremely low even when it is fasting (a condition which, as we shall see in the following section, increases the relative cholesterol concentration of bile). The series of Campbell *et al.* (1971) showed the highest mean relative cholesterol value for rhesus monkeys (6%), but others (e.g., Redinger *et al.*, 1973) have reported 2% or less. Only after continuous interruption of the enterohepatic circulation for 4 hours or more did Dowling *et al.* (1971) observe hepatic bile that was supersaturated with cholesterol (about 10% relative concentration). In the single reported case of gallstones in a rhesus monkey, the bile was saturated with cholesterol (Martin *et al.*, 1973). That monkey had recently delivered an infant, but in another series of rhesus monkeys, Martin *et al.* (1972) did not observe that pregnancy affected biliary composition. Lynn *et al.* (1973) caused rhesus monkey bile, which was normally highly unsaturated with cholesterol, to become saturated by administering estrogens, particularly estriol. These workers utilized the data of Small (1970) to define the criteria for saturation of the dilute hepatic bile that was observed. As Admirand and Small (1968) pointed out in the original paper, the relative percentage of cholesterol that results in saturation is somewhat less in more dilute (e.g., hepatic) than in concentrated (e.g., gallbladder) bile. The reduced solubility of cholesterol in bile which is very dilute in total lipid must be considered in determining the degree of saturation with cholesterol. In further support of the nonlithogenic nature of rhesus bile, Nakayama and Johnston (1960) observed that human gallstones implanted in rhesus monkey gallbladders were somewhat reduced in size; the results were even more striking in other species. Rapid dissolution of human gallstones exposed to flowing rhesus monkey bile was associated with (1) high cholesterol content of the gallstone, (2) bile undersaturated with cholesterol, and (3) high surface area/weight ratio for the gallstone (Bell *et al.*, 1972a).

Gallbladder bile from the baboon, which is susceptible to spontaneous gallstones (Glenn and McSherry, 1970; Lapin and Yakovleva, 1963), contained a much higher concentration of cholesterol than bile from the rhesus monkey (McSherry *et al.*, 1971a,b, 1972) and was near the saturation level. The cholesterol concentration was higher in those baboons that had gallstones or were pregnant than in those that had no gallstones and those that were not pregnant (McSherry *et al.*, 1972). In agreement with the findings of Small and Rapo (1970) on human subjects, McSherry *et al.* (1972) found that hepatic bile was more likely to be saturated or supersaturated with cholesterol than gallbladder bile. Because the hepatic bile was nearly always supersaturated, it was only tenuously related to the incidence of gallstones in individual animals. These workers showed that the supersaturated bile was a result of the animals being fasted; this, in turn, resulted in a partial interruption of the enterohepatic circulation (see Section VI).

We (Osuga and Portman, 1971, 1972; Portman *et al.*, 1975; Osuga *et al.*, 1974a; Tanaka and Portman, 1974) and Melchior and associates (1972, 1974; Lofland *et al.*, 1975) have described the composition of bile in normal squirrel monkeys and in those on a lithogenic diet. We sampled hepatic and gallbladder bile from monkeys which had been fasted overnight. Aliquots were taken within 1 hour after bile collections; samples were stirred, and all microcrystals that were aspirated with bile into a micropipette were included. As Fig. 25 shows, the composition of gallbladder bile differed between groups and between those with and those without gallstones from the same group. Monkeys that had been fed a diet based on a commercial monkey chow and that had never had gallstones showed a mean relative cholesterol concentration of less than 2 mole%. Corresponding mean values for monkeys fed a lithogenic diet that had resulted in slightly more than a 50% incidence of gallstones after 6 months were 11.6% for animals with and 5.5% for those without gallstones. The differences between hepatic and gallbladder bile composition were of borderline statistical significance and were not nearly as striking as those observed for the baboon by McSherry *et al.* (1971a,b, 1972). Perhaps interruption of the enterohepatic circulation of bile salts with fasting was less complete in the squirrel monkey than in the baboon or man (Smallwood *et al.*, 1972). All bile salts in the bile of squirrel monkeys

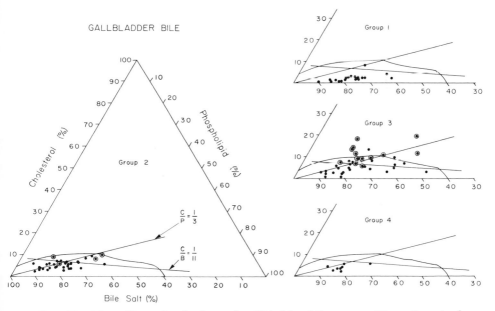

FIG. 25. Three-dimensional plots of gallbladder bile composition of squirrel monkeys from four experimental diet groups. Molar concentrations of cholesterol, phospholipid, and total bile acids are on the three axes. The encircled points are for animals with cholesterol gallstones. The irregular lines in the lower corner of each triangle are the boundaries between bile compositions in which cholesterol exists as a mixed micelle (lower area) and compositions in which cholesterol exists partially in the crystalline form (Admirand and Small, 1968). From Osuga and Portman (1972).

were conjugated with taurine, but, depending on their diet, there were significant differences in the composition of the steroid components. The fact that deoxycholic acid was low in the bile of monkeys fed the monkey chow diet is consistent with a slow turnover of a large pool of cholic acid (see Section VI) and minimal exposure to the action of bacterial flora; on the other hand, deoxycholic acid was also very low in those animals that had gallstones and a low cholic acid pool. The chenodeoxycholic–cholic ratio was high in the monkey chow group and in monkeys fed the lithogenic diet but without gallstones.

By applying the criteria of Admirand and Small (1968) to the composition of gallbladder bile, Lofland *et al.* (1975) could distinguish between squirrel monkeys fed a control diet and those fed a lithogenic diet but on that basis could not tell which animals from the latter group had stones. These workers found that stumptail macaques had gallbladder bile unsaturated with cholesterol and did not have stones. On the other hand, 1 of 10 African green monkeys had gallstones (1 of 7 on a lithogenic test diet), and this was the only monkey from that group with supersaturated (lithogenic) bile.

V. Nutritional and Pharmacological Effects on Gallstone Formation in Nonhuman Primates

A. GENERAL

How diet and drugs affect the development or regression of human cholesterol gallstones is not well understood. Dietary factors clearly affect plasma and biliary lipid composition, but the relationship of the latter to gallstone formation is exceedingly complex. Nutritional factors exert dramatic effects on biliary composition and are crucial in the induction of gallstones in experimental animals. One of these, the squirrel monkey, is the only primate species to have been used fairly extensively to evaluate the effect of diet and drugs on the incidence of gallstones. We will compare the results of experiments on this species with those on the hamster, the prairie dog, and man. In Section VI, we will discuss the effects of diet and fasting on biliary composition and physiology in rhesus monkeys and baboons.

B. NUTRITIONAL FACTORS AND GALLSTONES IN SQUIRREL MONKEYS

The nutritional factors that influence gallstone formation in squirrel monkeys have not been completely defined. Dietary cholesterol and

the level and type of fat are factors which influence the plasma cholesterol level and also are related to gallstone formation, but there is no
obvious relationship between plasma cholesterol level and the incidence of gallstones either in the diet group or in individuals within
the different groups. Table II shows the incidence and mean weight
of gallstones for squirrel monkeys which had been maintained on a
lithogenic diet for 6 months or longer according to their mean plasma
cholesterol levels. The only groups free of gallstones are those fed
Purina monkey chow without added fat and cholesterol and those fed
semipurified diets without cholesterol but with 45% of the calories as
fat. Animals fed semipurified diets with 15% of calories as fat had
cholesterol gallstones. Semipurified diets high in butterfat or safflower oil and with cholesterol (0.1 gm/100 kcal) were associated with
a high incidence (>50%). High butter and cholesterol supplements to
Purina monkey chow or to semipurified diets, which included corn-
starch in lieu of sucrose or had added cellulose (Alphacel), were also
associated with gallstones. The experiments of Melchior and associates (1972, 1974) as well as our own (Tanaka and Portman, 1974)
indicate that a diet with safflower oil, a highly unsaturated fat, and
cholesterol is at least as lithogenic as one with butter plus cholesterol.
Monkeys fed 45% of calories as fat, regardless of its unsaturation, did
not form cholesterol gallstones unless cholesterol was included in the
diet, whereas a significant number did form stones on a cholesterol-
free diet with 15% of calories from an unsaturated fat. Thus, although
dietary cholesterol is the most lithogenic factor for squirrel monkeys
that we have tested so far, it is not a requirement for gallstone forma-

Table II

RELATIONSHIP OF MEAN PLASMA CHOLESTEROL TO GALLSTONE
INCIDENCE, MEAN WEIGHT OF GALLSTONES IN ANIMALS WITH GALLSTONES,
AND CHOLESTEROL CONCENTRATION IN THE AORTIC INTIMA + INNER MEDIA[a,b]

Mean plasma cholesterol	Gallstone incidence[c]	Mean weight of gallstones (mg)	Intima + inner media cholesterol (mg/gm)
< 300 mg%	9/20	104.8	13.0
> 300 mg%	12/20	72.6	21.8
	r, plasma cholesterol versus arterial cholesterol = 0.349,		
$P = 0.03$.			
	r, plasma cholesterol versus weight of gallstones = -0.020		

[a] From Portman *et al.* (1975).

[b] Squirrel monkeys were on a single hyperlipemia-inducing diet containing butter
and cholesterol for 6 or more months; 20 monkeys had a mean plasma cholesterol
less than 300 mg% and 20 had values greater than 300 mg%.

[c] Number of monkeys with stones/number of monkeys in group.

tion. Perhaps even when used in conjunction with cholesterol-free diets, very low levels of fat would favor gallstones in the squirrel monkey. This would be consistent with Dam's findings in hamsters (Dam, 1971). Redinger *et al.* (1971, 1973) reported that relative bile composition in the rhesus monkey was not affected by the type of fat infused intraduodenally.

C. Dietary Factors Influencing Gallstone Formation in Man and Nonprimates

Dietary cholesterol is also important in the induction of cholesterol gallstones in prairie dogs (Patton *et al.*, 1961; Brenneman *et al.*, 1972; Chang *et al.*, 1973; den Besten *et al.*, 1974) but is not lithogenic in hamsters, the most widely used nonprimate species for gallstone studies (Dam, 1971). Dam (1971) and his associates, as well as others (e.g., Robins and Fasulo, 1973), have established that a low level of polyunsaturated fatty acids plus glucose or sucrose, as the source of carbohydrate, are essential to gallstone induction in hamsters. The type of carbohydrate and the level of roughage exert some influence on bile salt excretion (Portman, 1960, 1962) but have no demonstrable effect on gallstones in squirrel monkeys. We have no clear proof that nutrition plays a role in the etiology of cholesterol gallstones in man. Sturdevant *et al.* (1973) found a significant increase in the incidence of gallstones in a group of men whose diet had been changed to one high in unsaturated fat, and numerous reports indicate a high degree of association between obesity and the incidence of cholesterol gallstones (e.g., Friedman *et al.*, 1966).

D. Drugs Influencing Gallstone Formation

Several drugs used to reduce blood lipids may influence the formation of cholesterol gallstones. Conversely, chenodeoxycholic acid (Danziger *et al.*, 1972; Bell *et al.*, 1972b) or other agents that will be developed to treat gallstones may have side effects on blood lipids. We (Tanaka and Portman, 1974) found that chenodeoxycholic acid substantially expanded the total bile acid pool, particularly the pool of chenodeoxycholic acid, in squirrel monkeys but had no effect on the incidence of gallstones (Table III). Danziger *et al.* (1973) reported that in patients given chenodeoxycholic acid, 1 to 4 gm per day, the bile became unsaturated with cholesterol and the bile acid pool expanded. Mok *et al.* (1974) found that 0.5 gm per day also reduced cholesterol saturation in bile without side effects. Chenodeoxycholic

Table III

THE EFFECT OF TYPE OF FAT (45% OF CALORIES), CHOLESTEROL (0.1 gm/100
CALORIES), AND CHENODEOXYCHOLIC ACID (CDC) (0.1%) ON THE PLASMA
CHOLESTEROL LEVEL AND THE INCIDENCE AND WEIGHT OF GALLSTONES
IN SQUIRREL MONKEYS FED SEMIPURIFIED DIETS FOR 12 MONTHS[a]

Diet	Mean plasma cholesterol (mg/100 ml)	Incidence of stones[b]	Mean weight of gallstones (mg)
Butter	237	0/6	—
Safflower	163	0/6	—
Butter—cholesterol	420	5/6	76.6
Safflower—cholesterol	241	5/6	78.6
Butter—cholesterol—CDC	286	4/6	39.5
Safflower—cholesterol—CDC	210	6/6	102.2

[a] From Tanaka and Portman (1974).
[b] Number of monkeys with stones/number of monkeys in group.

acid (0.1%) in the diet of squirrel monkeys did not produce toxicity
but it was associated with some increase in the serum transaminase
activities of rhesus monkeys (Webster *et al.*, 1973). In squirrel
monkeys on a diet which included chenodeoxycholic acid, the plasma
cholesterol level was significantly lowered. The serum triglyceride
concentration was reduced in patients receiving chenodeoxycholic
acid (Bell *et al.*, 1972b).

The failure of dietary chenodeoxycholic acid to protect against
cholesterol gallstone formation in squirrel monkeys has its parallel in
the studies of Dam and Christensen (1962), Dam *et al.* (1972a), and
Prange *et al.* (1973) in hamsters. These workers found that chenodeoxycholic acid as well as lithocholic acid at 0.1% not only increased the
production of gallstones in diet groups which formed stones when not
treated with bile acids but also induced gallstones in some groups that
had otherwise been free of stones. Hyodeoxycholic acid ($3\alpha,6\alpha$-
dihydroxycholanic acid) greatly inhibited gallstone formation. Cholic,
dehydrocholic, and deoxycholic acids added to the diet had little effect.

Although there is no information about how gallstone production in
nonhuman primates is affected by drugs that are used to lower the
plasma cholesterol level in man, Dam *et al.* (1972b) found that 2-(*p*-
chlorophenoxy)-isobutyric acid ethyl ester (Clofibrate) inhibited cholesterol gallstones in hamsters. On the other hand, Pertsemlidis *et al.*
(1974) found that Clofibrate tended to increase the lithogenicity of
bile in man.

Despite the difficulty of establishing with certainty a relationship between diet and gallstones in man, the nutritional induction of gallstones in experimental animals, together with similarities between the biliary composition and physiology of man and some animals, suggest that nutritional factors play an etiologic role in man.

VI. Biliary Physiology and Gallstones in Nonhuman Primates

A. GENERAL

Insofar as the initiation and growth of cholesterol gallstones depend upon the secretion of bile which is supersaturated with cholesterol, the etiology of gallstones can be understood only when we know the factors that determine the secretion of the three constituents of the mixed micelle: cholesterol, phospholipid, and bile salts. Much recent insight into the factors that control bile composition has been gained from studies on nonhuman primates, particularly those of Small, Dowling, and their associates on the rhesus monkey and of McSherry and his colleagues on the baboon.

The metabolism of the three major lipid constituents is extremely complex; as a consequence, many studies have suffered from a misinterpretation of the results and an oversimplification of the experimental design. For example, only recently have the effects of inserting a catheter into the common bile duct to collect bile been understood. The introduction of a procedure to study the quantity and composition of bile while the major quantity was being returned to the duodenum (Dowling et al., 1968) was extremely important, but even this preparation excluded the gallbladder and its ability to store and intermittently discharge bile into the duodenum. Perhaps even less appreciated was the role of the sphincter of Oddi in controlling direct access of hepatic bile to the duodenum even when the gallbladder did not contract. The development by Thorbjarnarson et al. (1972) of methods to sample the gallbladder bile of the baboon without interfering with the function of the gallbladder or sphincter of Oddi was a very important advance. With this preparation, Shaffer et al. (1974) (see also O'Brien et al., 1974) brilliantly demonstrated that the gallbladder of the baboon does not contract during fasting but that over half the hepatic bile passes the sphincter of Oddi and enters the duodenum directly without entering the gallbladder. Thus fasting does not completely interrupt the enterohepatic circulation of bile salts. Such factors as secretory volume and pressure probably determine what proportions of hepatic bile are stored and what go directly to the gut; the distribution of bile between these two pathways could be one of the most important determinants of an individual's ability to continuously produce unsaturated bile. We consider the amount of bile salt outside the gallbladder in the fasting state to be the most crucial determinant of cholesterol unsaturation of hepatic bile in squirrel monkeys (see Section VI, B).

Another important advance in learning about bile kinetics by noninvasive techniques is the use of multiple intubations of the human duodenum (Grundy and Metzger, 1972; Danziger *et al.*, 1973). By simultaneously infusing a reference material, one can quantify the secretion of biliary constituents in the samples that are withdrawn. Results can be applied to typical physiological conditions with only one limitation: the intubation procedure is best with a continuous nutrient infusion, which presumably induces a constant cholecystokinin stimulus for gallbladder contraction.

B. BILE SALTS

There is a very imperfect relationship between the rates of secretion of the three major constituents, but bile salts clearly have the greatest acute influence on the secretion of the other two. One of us (Portman, 1962) reviewed certain aspects of bile salt metabolism in nonhuman primates, and more recently Small *et al.* (1972) published an up-to-date review. We will, therefore, limit our discussion only to those recently investigated aspects that are particularly relevant to the formation of lithogenic bile and gallstones.

Figure 26 is an idealized diagram of approximate mean pool sizes and 24-hour rates for bile salts. The total pool of bile salts is concentrated largely in the gallbladder and the gut, with very much smaller concentrations usually present in the liver and portal vein. B and C represent the almost equal amounts of hepatic bile salts going to the gallbladder and directly to the duodenum. Since bile salts circulate several times a day and are efficiently absorbed into the portal circulation, new synthesis (A) and fecal excretion (F) of them are much smaller than the 24-hour rate for bile salt absorption (E). The factor that enormously complicates our understanding of bile salt metabolism is the periodicity of the indicated rates. Contraction of the gallbladder greatly increases the short-term rate (D and E). On the other hand, such factors as fasting, which block D, or surgical interruption of the common duct, which blocks B + C, or gastrointestinal

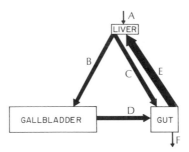

FIG. 26. Idealized diagram representing the average distribution of the bile salt pool throughout a 24-hour period. Arrows are proportional to 24-hour rates. A = bile salt synthesis; B = hepatic secretion and passage to the gallbladder; C = hepatic secretion and passage directly to the duodenum (Shaffer *et al.*, 1974); D = passage from gallbladder to duodenum with gallbladder contraction; E = absorption of bile salts and transfer via the portal vein to the liver; F = fecal excretion.

tract disease, which interferes with bile salt return via the portal vein, all reduce the rate of E. Since most of the bile salt that is newly secreted has just been reabsorbed, reducing the rate of bile salt return to the liver reduces the rate of secretion. Dowling *et al.* (1970) showed that rhesus monkey liver has only a limited ability to replace bile salts that are diverted by a common duct fistula. Thus a chronic loss of 20% or more of bile salts from each enterohepatic circulation decreases the total secretion of bile salts. In other words, the ability of the rhesus monkey to maintain constant bile salt secretion by new synthesis is equivalent to less than 20% of hepatic secretory rate. Furthermore, new synthesis of bile salt does not begin immediately with a blockade of the negative feedback signal to the liver (bile salts in the portal circulation). As we indicate below, the diet and individual predisposition to gallstones of squirrel monkeys seem to be related to the rapidity with which new bile salt synthesis begins and to the continued secretion of preexisting bile salts after interruption of the enterohepatic circulation.

The size of the body pool of bile salts is not *a priori* determined by the rates of new synthesis or the excretion of bile salts in the steady state. There is, moreover, no inevitable relationship between the size of the pools and hepatic secretory rates of bile salts since, regardless of size, the bile salt pool can circulate many times or only a few times per day. In general, squirrel monkeys on experimental diets which were associated with large bile salt pools also had greater total rates of bile secretion and new bile acid production but fewer circulations of the pool per day. The demonstration by Vlahcevic and associates (1970) that cholesterol gallstones in man are associated with a low bile salt pool has made determination of the latter particularly desirable. Grundy and Metzger (1972) and Schwartz *et al.* (1974) have described techniques based on duodenal intubation for measuring pool sizes and secretory rates in man. Chronic intubations of the gut are difficult to maintain in nonhuman primates or other animal species, but surgical procedures enable one to continuously or intermittently sample the hepatic and gallbladder bile. Dowling *et al.* (1970) have determined the total bile salt pool by measuring all of the bile salts draining from a total bile fistula. We have observed that different groups of squirrel monkeys differ in the time it takes for new bile salt synthesis to increase after a fistula has been established and in the extent of that increase. We have therefore used an isotope dilution technique to determine the size of the bile salt pool. Originally we used a single sample technique (Osuga and Portman, 1972). But more recently (Fig. 27) we have measured bile acid pool size, turnover, and synthesis rates by injecting intravenously labeled cholic and chenodeoxycholic acids and determining their specific activities in gallbladder and common duct bile after 18 hours and 7¾ days. Within a few hours, the specific activities of gallbladder and common duct bile were equal except in monkeys with nonfunctioning gallbladders or with gallbladders containing an unusually large mass of stones. The mean values for the cholic and chenodeoxycholic acid pool sizes of 700-gm squirrel monkeys fed a commercial monkey chow were 86.0

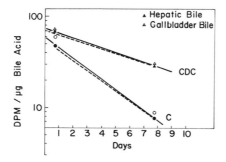

FIG. 27. The method for determining bile salt pool sizes and fractional turnovers in squirrel monkeys. Labeled cholic and chenodeoxycholic acids were injected at time zero. Common duct bile and gallbladder bile samples were obtained at 18 hours and 7¾ days after injection. Theoretical specific activities at zero time were determined from the solid lines connecting hepatic bile specific activities. Biological half-lives were based on the dashed line (which included a correction for radioactivity on samples withdrawn at 18 hours).

and 29.6 mg per kilogram of body weight respectively. This is equivalent to about 0.29 mmoles of bile salts per kilogram and concurs with a mean value of about 0.20 mmoles per kilogram for a 5-kg rhesus monkey (Dowling *et al.*, 1970). The same squirrel monkeys had mean half-lives for cholic and chenodeoxycholic acid of 4.18 and 2.50 days and mean synthesis rates of 15.1 and 7.6 mg per kilogram per day respectively. Vlahcevic *et al.* (1970) reported a slower turnover of chenodeoxycholic acid than of cholic acid, which was also true in some experimental groups of squirrel monkeys.

C. CHOLESTEROL

Cholesterol secretion into the bile is much more constant than that of bile salts. One way this constancy is manifested is the patterns of change in bile composition as a function of time after interruption of the enterohepatic circulation with a total fistula. In man (Scherstén, 1973), baboons (McSherry *et al.*, 1972), and rhesus monkeys (Dowling *et al.*, 1971), the absolute concentrations of cholesterol dropped much less rapidly than did those of bile salts; instead the rate of decline was even less than that of phospholipid. The continuous infusion of bile salts into rhesus monkeys (Small *et al.*, 1972) which had been depleted of bile salts by a fistula resulted in a maximum 10-fold increase in bile salt secretion which contrasted with the 3-fold increase in total bile flow, cholesterol, and phospholipid secretions. McSherry *et al.* (1971b) made similar observations on the effects of bile salt repletion in the baboon, i.e., bile that had become lithogenic was rendered nonlithogenic by the infusion of bile into the gut. The absolute concentrations of cholesterol were constant, and the relative concentrations increased during the 180 minutes after the enterohepatic circulation of squirrel monkeys had been interrupted. This was true whether the animals were fed diets that promoted bile that was highly unsaturated with respect to cholesterol or bile that was nearly saturated (Figs. 28A and 28B and 29A and 29B).

Whereas the quantity of bile salts is quite small (each molecule is absorbed and reexcreted at least 5 times daily) and the pool of bile salts is very restricted anatomically, cholesterol is distributed to every cell of the body and is particularly rich in the plasma membrane. In the latter cellular subfraction, the molar ratio of cholesterol to total phospholipid is often slightly less than 1, whereas the ratio to lecithin is about 2. The lipoproteins of plasma are also cholesterol-rich structures which rapidly exchange their free cholesterol with tissue membranes,

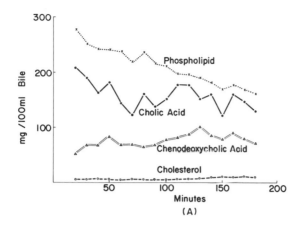

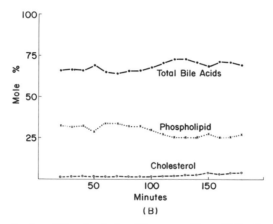

FIG. 28. The absolute (A) and relative (B) composition of bile, from a common duct fistula in a squirrel monkey fed monkey chow (without gallstones), as a function of time after introduction of a cannula.

particularly plasma membranes. There is, therefore, little likelihood that a given cholesterol molecule secreted into the bile will be immediately reabsorbed and reexcreted because it will have been so completely randomized in a large pool. However, the theory, once proposed, that biliary cholesterol is only newly synthesized hepatic cholesterol is probably incorrect. In rats (Portman and Mann, 1955; Portman *et al.*, 1955) and squirrel monkeys (Osuga and Portman, 1972), cholesterol feeding causes increased concentrations of biliary cholesterol and of bile salts in the body pool. How cholesterol is secreted into the bile is difficult to understand. Under certain condi-

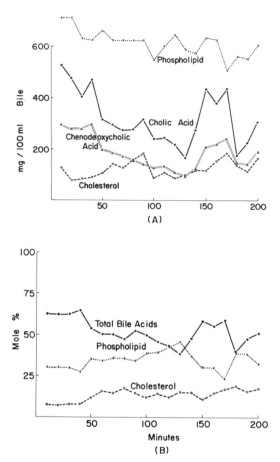

FIG. 29. The absolute (A) and relative (B) composition of bile from a common duct fistula in a squirrel monkey fed a lithogenic diet as a function of time after introduction of a cannula.

tions, the relative concentration of cholesterol in the bile of squirrel monkeys sometimes reaches 20 mole%, which represents marked supersaturation. Even under these conditions, a cholesterol–lecithin ratio of 2:1, which obtains for the plasma membrane and presumably for the canalicular membrane, is not seen in bile. Thus micellization of the canalicular membrane by bile salts suggested by Small (1970) seem implausible to us. Selective micellization of parts of the membrane is possible, however, since lecithin has been selectively micellized from biological membranes relative to sphingomyelin by deoxycholate *in vitro* (O. W. Portman, unpublished). Gregory *et al.* (1974) believe that hepatic microsomes are the primary source of biliary phospholipid and cholesterol and that bile salts promote the transport of those lipids as a macromolecular complex to the bile. Scherstén (1973) has pointed out that extrapolation of the curves that relate the biliary secretion of cholesterol to that of bile salts or to lecithin suggests that cholesterol could be secreted without bile salts or lecithin.

D. Phospholipids

In several species (e.g., Eriksson, 1957; Wheeler and Ramos, 1960; Kay and Entenman, 1961; Thureborn, 1962; Swell *et al.*, 1968; Nilsson and Scherstén, 1969), including the rhesus monkey (Dowling *et al.*, 1968), bile salts are a major determinant of phospholipid concentrations in bile and perhaps a requirement for phospholipid synthesis (Balint *et al.*, 1971; Cahlin *et al.*, 1972) and secretion. Although the importance of the different pathways of biliary lecithin synthesis is uncertain, that component is predominantly of the linoleoyl–palmitoyl type. It is undoubtedly true that biliary lecithin is derived from a much smaller pool than total plasma and liver lecithin (Zilversmit and van Handel, 1958; Stein and Stein, 1969). Balint *et al.* (1971) showed that bile salts increased the synthesis of labeled lecithin from $^{32}PO_4$, methionine-methyl-^{14}C, and choline-methyl-^{3}H. Circulation of intact lecithin in the enterohepatic circulation is negligible.

Plasma lysolecithin, generated in part from the plasma lecithin–cholesterol acyl transferase (LCAT) reaction, is a major source of lecithin in many tissues of the squirrel monkey (Portman *et al.*, 1970; Portman and Illingworth, 1974a,b). Like free fatty acids, lysolecithin is not present in plasma in high concentrations, but it has a very rapid turnover rate. When lysolecithin labeled with [1-^{14}C]-palmitate and [^{3}H]-choline was injected into squirrel monkeys, lecithin in bile had a ^{3}H–^{14}C ratio which was similar to that of lysolecithin in plasma (Fig. 30). Furthermore, the specific activities of bile lecithin exceeded those of plasma and liver. The quantity of labeled lecithin in animals with high lecithin secretory rates was greater than in those with low lecithin secretion (the specific activities for the two groups were similar).

E. Values of Different Kinetic Parameters in the Prediction of Gallstone Formation

The composition of random samples of bile is not a reliable indicator that gallstones are present. Using baboons and rhesus monkeys, McSherry *et al.* (1971a,b) and Small *et al.* (1972) showed

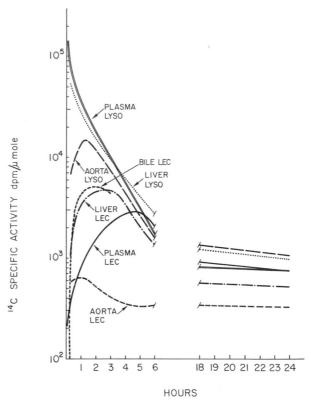

FIG. 30. The specific activity of ¹⁴C-lecithin in bile and other tissues of a squirrel monkey as a function of time after the intravenous injection of lysolecithin containing [1-¹⁴C]-palmitate at the 1-position of glycerol. When lysolecithin labeled with [Me-³H]-choline was also injected, the ³H–¹⁴C ratio of biliary lecithin and plasma lysolecithin were the same. From Portman *et al.* (1970) and Portman and Illingworth (1975).

that this variability depended partly on whether the samples were from fasted animals. The increase with fasting in the percentage of lipids as cholesterol is particularly characteristic of hepatic bile in the baboon. The relative cholesterol concentration of bile from the fasting gallbladder had some predictive value for gallstones in squirrel monkeys.

Diet affected the mean values of pool size, fractional turnover, and bile salt synthesis in squirrel monkeys (Figs. 31, 32, and 33). The animals in Group A (on laboratory chow) which had never had gallstones had nearly 4 times as much cholic acid and twice as much chenodeoxycholic acid in the total bile salt pool as the animals from

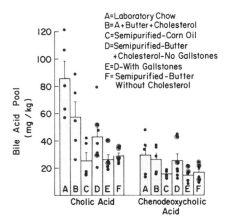

FIG. 31. The pool sizes of cholic and chenodeoxycholic acids in squirrel monkeys from different dietary groups.

Group C which were fed a semipurified diet without cholesterol and sometimes had gallstones. Of particular interest is the finding that monkeys on a lithogenic diet which did not form gallstones had almost twice as large a cholic and chenodeoxycholic acid pool as animals from the same group with gallstones. This finding is consistent with the observations of Vlahcevic and others (1970) on the reduction of the size of the bile salt pool associated with gallstone disease in man. In general, the larger the pool size in squirrel monkeys, the longer the half-life. Northfield and Hofmann (1973) made similar observations on human patients. Therefore, bile acid production (synthesis) was

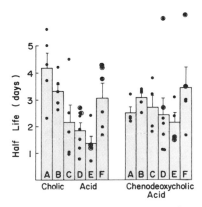

FIG. 32. The biological half-lives of cholic and chenodeoxycholic acids in squirrel monkeys from different dietary groups. (See Fig. 31.)

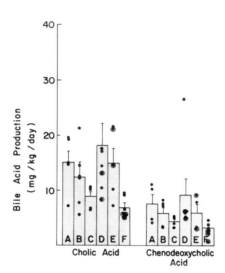

FIG. 33. Daily synthesis of new cholic and chenodeoxycholic acids in squirrel monkeys from different dietary groups. (See Fig. 31.)

not affected by diet as much as the other two parameters. Nevertheless, it was higher in monkeys on the lithogenic diet, but without gallstones, than in those from the same group with stones.

Depending on the length of the diet and on the presence or absence of gallstones, there were also pronounced differences in the responses of squirrel monkeys to interruptions of the enterohepatic circulation. After an overnight fast and insertion of a biliary catheter, the absolute concentration of cholesterol was constant or rose whereas the bile salt declined (Figs. 28 and 29). Thus the bile became progressively more saturated with cholesterol, much more so in monkeys on a lithogenic diet and with gallstones. Figure 34 shows the rise in mole% cholesterol resulting from the 180-minute interruption of the enterohepatic circulation in monkeys with gallstones. Depending on whether or not animals had gallstones, there was also a striking difference in the decline in the mole percentage of bile salts during that 180 minutes. This tendency in animals with gallstones (but not in controls) for the biliary secretion of bile salts to rapidly decrease after interruption of the enterohepatic circulation, was not due to a failure of the former group to initiate new bile salt synthesis. Table IV shows that during the 3-hour period when the total biliary fistula was maintained there

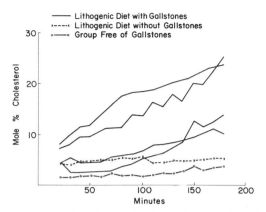

FIG. 34. Relative mole% of cholesterol (where cholesterol + phospholipid + bile salt molar concentrations = 100) in hepatic bile as a function of time after introduction of a cannula into the common bile duct. Monkeys with gallstones showed a particularly rapid rise.

was much more active dilution of the labeled cholic and chenodeoxy-cholic acid pools in monkeys fed semipurified diets than of the much larger pools of bile salts in the monkeys fed the control commercial diet.

The rapid decline in bile salt secretion, in spite of the very active synthesis of bile salts, which was characteristic of the monkeys with gallstones when their common bile ducts were cannulated (in this procedure, the gallbladders were removed at the same time the fistulas were made), is consistent with their small body pools of bile salts and with the disproportionately large amount of that pool in the gallbladder during fasting.

If a large body pool of bile salts confers protection against gallstones in man (Vlahcevic *et al.*, 1970) and squirrel monkeys, we propose as a reason the large quantity of bile salts in the gastrointestinal tract and its return to the liver via the portal vein even during fasting. How this high concentration of bile salts is maintained in the enterohepatic

Table IV

NEW BILE ACID SYNTHESIS DURING FASTING AND SURGICAL INTERRUPTION OF THE
ENTEROHEPATIC CIRCULATION FOR 3 HOURS (% OF POOL AT TIME ZERO)

Diet	Cholic acid	Chenodeoxycholic acid
Control diet	3.8	27.0
Semipurified diet	64.0	106.0

circulation even during fasting can be explained in several ways. The most likely explanation appears to be that animals with large bile salt pools divert a larger proportion of the bile salts (and presumably total bile) secreted by the liver directly to the intestine during fasting. This hypothesis is possible in view of the demonstration by Shaffer *et al.* (1974) in the baboon that during fasting half of the newly secreted bile enters the duodenum directly. Our squirrel monkeys with large bile salt pools have larger gallbladders and greater amounts of hepatic secretion. It is likely, therefore, that the concentrating capacity of the gallbladder is not unlimited and that secretory pressure (Strasberg *et al.*, 1971) is increased in the monkeys with large bile salt pools. Such a difference in secretory pressure between animals on lithogenic and those on nonlithogenic diets, and perhaps even between those on lithogenic diets with and without gallstones, could influence the amount of bile entering the duodenum directly without entering the gallbladder during fasting. This theory is illustrated by Fig. 35.

Squirrel monkeys fed a commercial monkey chow with added cholesterol and butter are not protected against gallstones by a large bile salt pool. Presumably the excretion of exogenous cholesterol is crucial. In such a group, the secretory rates of bile and the total gallbladder volumes were even greater than in animals fed commercial chow alone. We suspect that incomplete gallbladder emptying at each contraction results from abnormally high bile secretion rates and gallbladder distention.

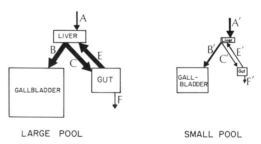

LARGE POOL   SMALL POOL

FIG. 35. A theory to explain the way in which the size of the bile salt pool influences the distribution of bile salts and hepatic secretion (B and C) of bile salts during fasting. With a large pool of bile salts, there is increased hepatic secretion of bile salts. A greater proportion of those bile salts that are secreted enter the duodenum without entering the gallbladder (C). Thus with a large bile salt pool, fasting does not reduce the enterohepatic circulation nearly as completely as is the case for the monkey with a small pool (CE versus C'E'). Bile salt synthesis (A and A') has a limited short-term capability to replace bile salts diverted to the gallbladder during fasting.

VII. Factors Other than Biliary Lipids Which Influence Gallstone Formation

A. ROLE OF THE GALLBLADDER

Since cholesterol gallstones form in the gallbladder rather than in the other parts of the biliary tree, removal of the gallbladder usually prevents the recurrence of gallstones (Glenn, 1972). The gallbladder probably plays three roles in gallstone formation. First, it provides an environment favorable to crystal growth; second, the absorptive function of the gallbladder wall alters the composition of bile (even if this involves only the concentration of solutes); last, through its influence on the enterohepatic circulation of bile salts, the gallbladder affects the relative composition of bile.

The gallbladder provides a place where cholesterol crystals can grow without passing immediately into the duodenum. Besides the increasing weight of a concrement in the gallbladder which might reduce the likelihood of discharge with each contraction, the viscosity of gallbladder bile may favor the retention of gallstones. Bile is not homogeneous in the gallbladder. Tera (1961) has shown that the density of bile is lowest in the upper part of the bladder. Bile also tends to stratify in the gallbladder (Freston *et al.*, 1969) as a result of the removal of water and electrolytes by the gallbladder epithelium (Cussler *et al.*, 1970). The concentrating power of the gallbladder is particularly apparent in the niches formed by the folds of gallbladder epithelium where a gel-like material develops and provides a favorable site for the growth and trapping of crystals (Hultén, 1968a,b). Henisch (1970) has described such a gel as a "three-dimensional crucible" for supporting crystals. Crystallization is also enhanced by the slowing of molecular movements in gels. Cussler *et al.* (1970) believe that the finding of gallstones in only one of the two limbs of a double gallbladder is evidence that bile composition alone does not determine the presence of gallstones. Simendinger *et al.* (1971), however, reported the presence of gallstones in each part of a double gallbladder. The gallbladder also provides a milieu for gallstone dissolution when the conditions are favorable.

The efficient emptying of the gallbladder is another important factor affecting gallstone formation. Even under physiological conditions, some residual bile always remains after each gallbladder contraction. By reducing the gallbladder's ability to empty itself, dyskinesia, vagotomy, or cystic duct syndrome favor the retention of growing stones. Crystals or microliths are generally flushed out, and recently gallstones were found in the feces of 34 of 36 patients with pancreatitis and gallstones (Acosta and Ledesma, 1974). Spontaneous disappearance of gallstones may often be attributed to mechanical excretion from the gallbladder (Rains, 1964; Wolpers, 1968).

There is still considerable uncertainty about how much the composition of hepatic bile is altered in the gallbladder. The passive movement of water from the gallbladder is generally thought to be coupled to active anion–cation transport; the fact that dinitrophenol blocks the process (Dietschy, 1964; Diamond, 1964) is evidence for this theory. If only water and electrolytes were absorbed, the relative composition of the three major biliary lipids would not undergo change, and this concentrating action would therefore have little effect on cholesterol solubility. Actually, the higher concentration of total lipid in gallbladder bile results in a slightly higher solubility limit in terms of relative concentration of cholesterol. According to this view, the concentrating power of the gallbladder *per se* is not a factor in gallstone formation.

Several reports indicate that under certain conditions bile salts and lecithin may be absorbed from the gallbladder (Caldwell *et al.*, 1965; Ostrow, 1967, 1969; Caldwell and Levitsky, 1967; Neiderhiser *et al.*, 1973). To examine this question of absorption from the gallbladder, it has been necessary to tie the cystic duct which causes a marked decline in gallbladder volume and abnormally high solute concentrations. Under such experimental conditions, bile salts, particularly unconjugated bile salts, are removed from the gallbladder and the relative concentration of cholesterol is increased.

Actually under most conditions (e.g., the work of McSherry *et al.*, 1971b, on baboons), the relative concentrations of cholesterol in hepatic bile are greater than those in gallbladder bile. Such a result cannot be explained by selective absorption of bile salts by the gallbladder.

The most likely explanation for differences in the relative lipid compositions of gallbladder and hepatic bile is the diurnal variation in hepatic bile which results from the intermittent discharge of bile salts from the gallbladder. The secretion of cholesterol by the liver is relatively constant whereas the secretion of bile salts is reduced by fasting and the consequent accumulation of bile salts in the gallbladder (see Section VI). Thus the liver may produce bile saturated with cholesterol during fasting, whereas the gallbladder may contain unsaturated bile which reflects bile secreted during an earlier period after feeding. Although Shaffer *et al.* (1974) have shown that fasting does not completely interrupt the circulation of bile salts, fasting does resemble a partial (and perhaps variably active) bile fistula which results in the formation of lithogenic bile (Small *et al.*, 1972; Dowling *et al.*, 1971).

Some investigators have reported that cholecystectomy converts saturated hepatic bile to unsaturated (Shaffer *et al.*, 1972; Simmons *et al.*, 1972; Malagelada *et al.*, 1973; Hepner *et al.*, 1973; Nakayama and van der Linden, 1974), but there have also been negative reports (Almond *et al.*, 1973; Adler *et al.*, 1974). Hepner *et al.* (1973) found that the size of the bile acid pool was greater in cholecystectomized patients than in those with gallstones and equal to that in normal people. McSherry *et al.* (1971b) have emphasized that the composition of hepatic bile in the baboon varies when the gallbladder is present (including intermittent cholesterol supersaturation) and is constant (invariably unsaturated) when the gallbladder is absent.

The use of cholecystokinen did not prevent the formation of gallstones in rabbits fed dihydrocholesterol (Lindelöf and van der Linden, 1965; Scott *et al.*, 1972). Although the use of drugs that promote gallbladder contraction would be expected to result in a bile unsaturated with cholesterol, the rabbit which forms allodeoxycholic acid stones (Hofmann and Mosbach, 1964) is probably not the ideal test animal.

B. Estrogen

Besides their effect on bile lipid composition, estrogens may also affect gallstone formation. Studies with nonhuman primates have shown such an effect. Estriol, the significant estrogen in human pregnancy, increased the lithogenicity of rhesus monkey bile, and pregnancy, *per se*, had a similar effect on the bile of baboons (McSherry *et al.*, 1972). Cholesterol gallstones have been induced in rabbits by the administration of estrogen and progesterone (Imamoglu *et al.*, 1960). Although it is difficult to tie pregnancy *per se* to gallstone disease (van der Linden, 1961), parity is a factor in the incidence of gallstones (Nilsson, 1966). Oral contraceptives and postmenopausal estrogen therapy are associated with relative risks of gallstones of 2.0 and 2.5 respectively (Boston Collaborative Drug Surveillance Program, 1973, 1974).

Numerous reports document the greater prevalence of gallstones in women (Sternby, 1968; Wheeler *et al.*, 1970), but so far no sex differences have been seen in the incidence of induced gallstones or bile composition in squirrel monkeys. Holzbach *et al.* (1971) likewise found no sex difference in human bile composition.

Estrogens may, however, reduce gallbladder motility. Potter (1936) found that the otherwise normal gallbladders of pregnant women were often large, atonic, globular, and distended and that there was obvious biliary stasis. A reduction in gallbladder motility may explain the slow turnover of bile salts in the pregnant baboon (McSherry *et al.*, 1973a,b). Nilsson and Stattin (1967) also found decreased emptying of the gallbladder after cholecystokinen administration during the progesterone phase of the normal menstrual cycle in women.

Forker (1969) observed reduced bile flow, and BSP (sulfobromophthalein) clearance in rats treated with estrone, and Cumusio and Valdivieso (1971) found that ethyl estradiol impaired bile flow and bile salt secretion. Javitt and Harkavy (1969) also found that estrogen decreases the maximum rate of hepatic transfer of bile salts. Johnson and Kalant (1972) showed no differences in the relative or absolute concentrations of gallbladder and hepatic bile in pregnant and control rabbits.

In summary, estrogens may exert a direct effect on the hepatic cell (there are also many reports of effects on cholesterol and phospholipid synthesis) or may influence biliary metabolism in some other way such as through gallbladder motility.

C. MUCIN

We previously discussed the ways in which mucin acts to trap cholesterol crystals, to act as a nidus for cholesterol crystals through providing an area of epitaxial contact, to serve as a gel in which crystallization is favored, and to act as a cement between larger concrements. Whether abnormalities in mucin production determine susceptibility to gallstones is not yet known. Experiments with nonhuman primates have so far provided no satisfactory answer to this question.

In most of the experimental models, gallstones are associated with increased glycoproteins in the bile or biliary tract tissue (Freston *et al.*, 1969). Increased secretion of glycoprotein often precedes gallstone formation (Womack, 1971). In man, the level of mucus also increases in gallbladders with stones (Bouchier *et al.*, 1965; Lev and Spicer, 1965; Easterly and Spicer, 1968).

Bouchier and Clamp (1971) found no difference between normal and abnormal bile in the carbohydrate or amino acid components of glycoprotein, but Matsushiro *et al.* (1970) found an appreciable amount of acidic glycosaminoglycans in abnormal bile. Probably an increased quantity of mucin is the major cause of increased viscosity. The origin of biliary glycoprotein is uncertain, but Bouchier and

Clamp (1971) have proposed that glycoprotein buds off from the plasma membrane during the process of bile formation.

The claim that the center of most gallstones contains glycoprotein laid down in a laminated structure (Womack *et al.*, 1963; Nagamitsu, 1956) suggests that glycoproteins are important in the etiology of gallstones.

D. OTHER FACTORS

A great many other factors besides biliary lipids and those mentioned in the three preceding subsections of Section VII may influence gallstone formation. Vagotomy may increase the incidence of gallstones (Clave and Gaspar, 1969; Fletcher and Clark, 1968). Cholecystokinin and pancreozymin doubtless are paramount in gallbladder contractility, but the tonicity of the gallbladder depends on the control of the autonomic nervous system. The minimum volume after gallbladder contraction is increased after vagotomy (Parkin *et al.*, 1973) which may trigger the increased propensity to gallstone formation. After vagotomy, dogs are less able to dissolve human gallstones inserted into their gallbladders (Barnett and Hilbun, 1966; Sheen, 1971).

Other bile factors which have been incriminated in the etiology of gallstones but on which there have been no experiments with nonhuman primates are bilirubin (including the state of conjugation), electrolytes, protein, desquamated cells, unconjugated bile salts, stasis, and infection.

VIII. Conclusions

Nonhuman primates have proved extremely useful in studies of various aspects of bile chemistry, physiology, and pathology. Many of the conditions that are applicable to man can be duplicated in these models. Some of the similarities between species include the response of bile composition to fasting and surgical fistula of the common duct, the occurrence of gallstones in subjects with bile that is saturated with cholesterol, the mechanisms of crystal and gallstone growth evidenced by the microscopic examination of solids in bile, and the existence of individuals who are particularly susceptible or resistant to gallstone formation.

In the last decade or so, several important studies on the relationships between bile chemistry and physiology on the one hand and gallstone formation on the other have been made in nonhuman primates. One of the most important advances has been the use of theoretical limits of cholesterol stability in biles containing different proportions of the major bile lipids to predict the formation of gallstones. Another is the correlation of several kinetic parameters of bile acid metabolism to nutritional status, drugs, or individual predisposition to gallstone formation. Among these parameters are pool size, fractional turnover, daily synthesis and excretion, and hepatic secretory rates. The effects of fasting and surgical fistulas on biliary physiology have provided important insights into the way intermittent changes in bile composition may occur.

A crucial recent advance with nonhuman primates has been the use of preparations for determining hepatic and gallbladder bile composition without interfering with the function of the gallbladder or sphincter of Oddi. We now realize that part of the newly secreted hepatic bile goes directly to the duodenum and part to the gallbladder even during fasting. Probably the secretory volume (indirectly, perhaps, the size of the bile salt pool) determines the proportion of bile salts that enters the duodenum during fasting. The extent to which bile salts continue to circulate during fasting may determine the resistance to intermittent formation of lithogenic bile.

The most important future uses of nonhuman models for studies of biliary lipids and gallstone formation will probably be in determining the effects of nutritional and drug therapies to reduce blood lipids and lipoproteins in the treatment of atherosclerosis and of other or similar treatments to prevent the formation of cholesterol gallstones. Theoretically, at least, treatments aimed at reducing plasma lipoproteins and at gallstone prevention or dissolution may operate to alleviate one condition and accentuate the other. Two such current problems are the possible accentuation of gallstone formation by the feeding of polyunsaturated fats and the possible side effects of chenodeoxycholic acid therapy for gallstones. Solutions to these problems clearly indicate the use of nonhuman primates as experimental models.

ACKNOWLEDGMENTS

Some of the research carried out in the authors' laboratories was supported by grants-in-aid from the National Institutes of Health (HL09744). This work is publication No. 744 from the Oregon Regional Primate Research Center, which is supported in part by grant RR00163 from the National Institutes of Health, United States Public Health Service.

We wish to acknowledge the collaboration of the following colleagues at various stages of our work: Dr. Keiji Mitamura of the Department of Medicine, University of Tokyo School of Medicine; Mr. Keiji Matsumoto, Nissei Sangyo Co. (Tokyo); and Mr. Manfred Alexander and Ms. Patricia Soltys of the Oregon Regional Primate Research Center. We deeply appreciate the editorial help of Ms. Margaret Shetler and Ms. Margaret Barss.

References

Acosta, J. M., and Ledesma, C. L. (1974). *N. Engl. J. Med.* **290**, 484.

Adler, R. D., Metzger, A. L., and Grundy, S. M. (1974). *Gastroenterology* **66**, 1212.

Admirand, W. H., and Small, D. M. (1968). *J. Clin. Invest.* **47**, 1043.

Almond, H. R., Vlahcevic, Z. R., Bell, C. C., Jr., Gregory, D. H., and Swell, L. (1973). *N. Engl. J. Med.* **285**, 1213.

Anver, M. R., Hunt, R. D., and Chalifoux, L. V. (1972). *J. Med. Primatol.* **1**, 241.

Balint, J. A., Beeler, D. A., Kyriakides, E. C., and Treble, D. A. (1971). *J. Lab. Clin. Med.* **77**, 122.

Barnett, W. O., and Hilbun, G. R. (1966). *Surgery* **60**, 840.

Bell, G. D., Sutor, D. J., Whitney, B., and Dowling, R. (1972a). *Gut* **13**, 836.

Bell, G. D., Whitney, B., and Dowling, R. H. (1972b). *Lancet* **2**, 1213.

Bevans, M., and Mosbach, E. H. (1956). *Arch. Pathol.* **62**, 112.

Bogren, H. (1964). *Acta Radiol., Suppl.* **226**, 1.

Bogren, H., and Larsson, K. (1963). *Scand. J. Clin. Lab. Invest.* **15**, 557.

Borgman, R. F. (1965). *Amer. J. Vet. Res.* **26**, 1167.

Boston Collaborative Drug Surveillance Program. (1973). *Lancet* **1**, 1399.

Boston Collaborative Drug Surveillance Program. (1974). *N. Engl. J. Med.* **290**, 15.

Bouchier, I.A.D. (1971). *Lancet* **1**, 71.

Bouchier, I. A. D., and Clamp, J. R. (1971). *Clin. Chim. Acta* **35**, 219.

Bouchier, I. A. D., Cooperband, S. R., and el Kodsi, B. M. (1965). *Gastroenterology* **49**, 343.

Bourges, M., Small, D. M., and Dervichian, D. G. (1967). *Biochim. Biophys. Acta* **144**, 189.

Brenneman, D. E., Connor, W. E., Forker, E. L., and den Besten, L. (1972). *J. Clin. Invest.* **51**, 1495.

Cahlin, E., Jönsson, J., Nilsson, S., and Scherstén, T. (1972). *Scand. J. Clin. Lab. Invest.* **29**, 109.

Caira, E. G., Skoryna, S. C., Ritchie, A. C., and Webster, D. R. (1957). *Surg. Forum* **8**, 222.

Caldwell, F. T., and Levitsky, K. (1967). *Ann. Surg.* **166**, 753.

Caldwell, F. T., Levitsky, K., and Rosenberg, B. (1965). *Amer. J. Physiol.* **209**, 473.

Campbell, C. B., Burgess, P., Roberts, S. A., and Dowling, R. H. (1971). *Aust. N.Z. J. Med.* **1**, 49.

Carlisle, V. F., and Tasman-Jones, C. (1973). *Amer. J. Surg.* **126**, 403.

Chang, S. H., Ho, K. J., and Taylor, C. B. (1973). *Arch. Pathol.* **96**, 417.

Clave, R. A., and Gaspar, M. R. (1969). *Amer. J. Surg.* **118**, 169.

Cumusio, J. J., and Valdivieso, V. D. (1971). *Gastroenterology* **61**, 339.

Cussler, E. L., Evans, D. F., and DePalma, R. G. (1970). *Proc. Nat. Acad. Sci. U. S.* **67**, 400.

Dam, H. (1971). *Amer. J. Med.* **51**, 596.

Dam, H., and Christensen, F. (1952). *Acta Pathol. Microbiol. Scand.* **30**, 236.

Dam, H., and Christensen, F. (1962). *Z. Ernaehrungswiss.* **2**, 154.

Dam, H., and Hegardt, F. G. (1971). *Z. Ernaehrungswiss.* **10**, 239.

Dam, H., Kruse, I., Prange, I., Kallenhauge, H. D., Fenger, H. J., and Jensen, K. (1971). *Z. Ernaehrungswiss.* **10**, 160.

Dam, H., Prange, I., and Søndergaard, E. (1972a). *Z. Ernaehrungswiss.* **11**, 80.

Dam, H., Prange, I., and Søndergaard, E. (1972b). *Z. Ernaehrungswiss.* **11**, 95.

Danziger, R. G., Gordon, H., Schoenfield, L. J., and Thistle, J. L. (1971). *Gastroenterology* **60**, 652.

Danziger, R. G., Hofmann, A. F., Schoenfield, L. J., and Thistle, J. L. (1972). *N. Engl. J. Med.* **286**, 1.
Danziger, R. G., Hofmann, A. F., Thistle, J. L., and Schoenfield, L. J. (1973). *J. Clin. Invest.* **52**, 2809.
den Besten, L., Safie-Shirazi, S., Connor, W. E., and Bell, S. (1974). *Gastroenterology* **66**, 1036.
Diamond, J. M. (1964). *J. Gen. Physiol.* **48**, 1.
Dietschy, J. M. (1964). *Gastroenterology* **47**, 395.
Dowling, R. H., Mack, E., Picott, J., Berger, J., and Small, D. M. (1968). *J. Lab. Clin. Med.* **72**, 169.
Dowling, R. H., Mack, E., and Small, D. M. (1970). *J. Clin. Invest.* **49**, 232.
Dowling, R. H., Mack, E., and Small, D. M. (1971). *J. Clin. Invest.* **50**, 1917.
Easterly, J. R., and Spicer, S. S. (1968). *J. Nat. Cancer Inst.* **40**, 1.
Englert, E., Jr., Harman, C. G., and Wales, E. E., Jr. (1969). *Nature (London)* **224**, 280.
Eriksson, S. (1957). *Proc. Soc. Exp. Biol. Med.* **94**, 578.
Evans, D. F., and Cussler, E. L. (1974). *Hosp. Pract.* **9**(2), 133.
Fletcher, D. M., and Clark, C. G. (1968). *Brit. J. Surg.* **55**, 895.
Forker, E. L. (1969). *J. Clin. Invest.* **48**, 654.
Fox, H. (1930). *Rep. Lab. Comp. Pathol.* pp. 12-22 (quoted by Ruch, 1967).
Freston, J. W., Bouchier, I. A. D., and Newman, J. (1969). *Gastroenterology* **57**, 670.
Friedman, G. D., Kannel, W. B., and Dawber, T. R. (1966). *J. Chron. Dis.* **19**, 273.
Glenn, F. (1972). *Surg., Gynecol. Obstet.* **134**, 249.
Glenn, F., and McSherry, C. K. (1969). *Ann. Surg.* **169**, 712.
Glenn, F., and McSherry, C. K. (1970). *Arch. Surg. (Chicago)* **100**, 105.
Gregory, D. H., Vlahcevic, Z. R., Schatzki, P., and Swell, L. (1974). *Gastroenterology* **66**, 705.
Grundy, S. M., and Metzger, A. L. (1972). *Gastroenterology* **62**, 1200.
Hamerton, A. E., (1932). *Proc. Zool. Soc. London* **102**, 613.
Haslewood, G. A. D. (1967). "Bile Salts" (monograph). Methuen, London.
Hegardt, F. G., and Dam, H. (1971). *Z. Ernaehrungswiss.* **10**, 223.
Henisch, H. K. (1970). "Crystal Growth in Gels." Pennsylvania State Univ. Press, University Park.
Hepner, G. W., Hofmann, A. F., and Klein, P. E. (1973). *Gastroenterology* **64**, 165.
Hofmann, A. F. (1973). *N. Engl. J. Med.* **228**, 46.
Hofmann, A. F., and Mosbach, E. H. (1964). *J. Biol. Chem.* **239**, 2813.
Hofmann, A. F., and Small, D. M. (1967). *Annu. Rev. Med.* **18**, 333.
Holzbach, R. T., Marsh, M. E., and Hallberg, M. C. (1971). *Gastroenterology* **60**, 288.
Holzbach, R. T., Marsh, M., Olszewski, M., and Holan, K. (1973). *J. Clin. Invest.* **52**, 1467.
Hultén, O. (1968a). *Acta Chir. Scand.* **134**, 125.
Hultén, O. (1968b). *Acta Chir. Scand.* **134**, 557.
Hwang, W. S. (1970). *Gut* **11**, 141 and 148.
Imamoglu, K., Wangensteen, S. L., Root, H. D., Salmon, P. A., Griffen, W. O., Jr., and Wangensteen, O. H. (1960). *Surg. Forum* **10**, 246.
Isaksson, B. (1954a). *Acta Soc. Med. Upsal.* **59**, 296.
Isaksson, B. (1954b). *Acta Soc. Med. Upsal.* **59**, 307.
Javitt, N. B., and Harkavy, M. (1969). *Gastroenterology* **56**, 400.
Johnson, J., and Kalant, N. (1972). *Amer. J. Dig. Dis.* **17**, 1.
Kameda, H. (1964). *Gastroenterology* **46**, 109.
Kay, R. E., and Entenman, C. (1961). *Amer. J. Physiol.* **200**, 855.
Kyd, P. A., and Bouchier, I. A. D. (1971). *Gastroenterology* **61**, 723.

Kyd, P. A., and Bouchier, I. A. D. (1972). *Biochem. J.* **128**, 80P.

Lapin, B. A., and Yakovleva, L. A. (1963). "Comparative Pathology in Monkeys," p. 236. Thomas, Springfield, Illinois.

Lev, R., and Spicer, S. S. (1965). *Amer. J. Pathol.* **46**, 23.

Lindelöf, G., and van der Linden, W. (1965). *Acta Chir. Scand.* **130**, 494.

Lofland, H. B., Clarkson, T. B., and Melchior, G. W. (1975). *Proc. Int. Symp. Atheroscler., 3rd, 1973* (in press).

Lonsdale, K. (1968a). *Science* **159**, 1199.

Lonsdale, K. (1968b). *Sci. Amer.* **219**, 104.

Lonsdale, K. (1968c). *Nature (London)* **217**, 56.

Lorentz, T. G. (1966). *Brit. J. Surg.* **53**, 503.

Lynn, J., Williams, L., O'Brien, J., Wittenberg, J., and Egdahl, R. H. (1973). *Ann. Surg.* **178**, 514.

McSherry, C. K., Javitt, N. B., de Carvalho, J. M., and Glenn, F. (1971a). *Ann. Surg.* **173**, 569.

McSherry, C. K., Glenn, F., and Javitt, N. B. (1971b). *Proc. Nat. Acad. Sci. U. S.* **68**, 1564.

McSherry, C. K., Morrissey, K. P., Javitt, N. B., and Glenn, F. (1972). "Medical Primatology," *Proc. Conf. Exp. Med. Surg. Primates, 3rd, 1972.* Part II, pp. 16–28.

McSherry, C. K., Morrissey, K., May, P., Javitt, N. B., and Glenn, F. (1973a). *Gastroenterology* **64**, 163.

McSherry, C. K., Morrissey, K. P., Javitt, N. B., and Glenn, F. (1973b). *Ann. Surg.* **178**, 669.

Maki, T., and Suzuki, N. (1964). *Tohoku J. Exp. Med.* **84**, 259.

Malagelada, J. R., Go, V. L. W., Gamble, W. S., and Summerskill, W. H. J. (1973). *Gastroenterology* **64**, 164.

Mann, G. V. (1970). *In* "Feeding and Nutrition of Nonhuman Primates" (R. S. Harris, ed.), pp. 143–158. Academic Press, New York.

Martin, D. E., Wolf, R. C., and Meyer, R. K. (1972). *Proc. Soc. Exp. Biol. Med.* **139**, 115.

Martin, D. E., Wolf, R. C., and Houser, W. D. (1973). *Amer. J. Vet. Res.* **34**, 971.

Matsukura, S., Tomita, K., and Matsunaga, M. (1968). *Clin. Surg. (Tokyo)* **23**, 1169.

Matsushiro, T., Nemoto, T., Endo, M., and Yoshizawa, Z. (1970). *Clin. Chim. Acta* **30**, 645.

Melchior, G. W., Clarkson, T. B., Bullock, B. C., and Lofland, H. B. (1972). *Circulation* **46**, II-19.

Melchior, G. W., Lofland, H. B., and Jones, D. C. (1974). *Fed. Proc., Fed. Amer. Soc. Exp. Biol.* **33**, 626.

Metzger, A. L., Heymsfield, S., and Grundy, S. M. (1972). *Gastroenterology* **62**, 499.

Metzger, A. L., Adler, R., Heymsfield, S., and Grundy, S. M. (1973). *N. Engl. J. Med.* **288**, 333.

Miyake, H., and Johnston, C. G. (1968). *Digestion* **1**, 219.

Mok, H. Y. I., Bell, G. D., and Dowling, R. H. (1974). *Lancet* **2**, 253.

Mufson, D., Meksuwan, K., Zarembo, J. E., and Ravin, L. J. (1972). *Science* **177**, 701.

Nagamitsu, S. (1956). *Jap. J. Stomatol. Soc.* **57**, 1546.

Nakayama, F., and Johnston, C. G. (1960). *Proc. Soc. Exp. Biol. Med.* **104**, 73.

Nakayama, F., and Miyake, H. (1970). *Amer. J. Surg.* **120**, 794.

Nakayama, F., and van der Linden, W. (1970). *Acta Chir. Scand.* **136**, 605.

Nakayama, F., and van der Linden W. (1971). *Amer. J. Surg.* **122**, 8.

Nakayama, F., and van der Linden, W. (1974). *Acta Chir. Scand.* **139**. 45.

Neiderhiser, D. H., and Roth, H. P. (1968). *Proc. Soc. Exp. Biol. Med.* **128**, 221.

Neiderhiser, D. H., Morningstar, W. A., and Roth, H. P. (1973). *J. Lab. Clin. Med.* **82**, 891.

Nilsson, S. (1966). *Acta Chir. Scand.* **132**, 275.

Nilsson, S., and Scherstén, T. (1969). *Gastroenterology* **57**, 525.
Nilsson, S., and Stattin, S. (1967). *Acta Chir. Scand.* **133**, 648.
Northfield, T. C., and Hofmann, A. F. (1973). *Lancet* **1**, 747.
O'Brien, J. J., Shaffer, E. A., Williams, L. F., Small, D. M., Lynn, J., and Wittenberg, J. (1974). *Gastroenterology* **67**, 119.
Ogata, T., and Murata, F. (1971). *Tohoku J. Exp. Med.* **104**, 25.
Okey, R. (1942). *Proc. Soc. Exp. Biol. Med.* **51**, 349.
Olszewski, M. F., Holzbach, R. T., Saupe, A., and Brown, G. H. (1973). *Nature (London)* **242**, 336.
Ostrow, J. D. (1967). *J. Clin. Invest.* **46**, 2035.
Ostrow, J. D. (1969). *J. Lab. Clin. Med.* **74**, 482.
Osuga, T., and Portman, O. W. (1971). *Proc. Soc. Exp. Biol. Med.* **136**, 722.
Osuga, T., and Portman, O. W. (1972). *Gastroenterology* **63**, 122.
Osuga, T., Portman, O. W., Mitamura, K., and Alexander, M. (1974a). *Lab. Invest.* **30**, 486.
Osuga, T., Mitamura, K., Miyagawa, S., Sato, N., Kintaka, S., and Portman, O. W. (1974b). *Lab. Invest.* **31**, 696.
Palmer, R. H., and Hruban, Z. J. (1966). *J. Clin. Invest.* **45**, 1255.
Parkin, G. J. S., Smith, R. B., and Johnston, D. (1973). *Ann. Surg.* **178**, 581.
Patton, D. E., Plotner, K., Cox, G. E., and Taylor, C. B. (1961). *Fed. Proc., Fed. Amer. Soc. Exp. Biol.* **20**, 248.
Pertsemlidis, D., Parveliwalla, D., and Ahrens, E. H., Jr. (1974). *Gastroenterology* **66**, 565.
Polonovski, M., and Bourillon, R. (1952). *Bull. Soc. Chim. Biol.* **34**, 712.
Portman, O. W. (1960). *Amer. J. Clin. Nutr.* **8**, 462.
Portman, O. W. (1962). *Fed. Proc., Fed. Amer. Soc. Exp. Biol.* **21**, 896.
Portman, O. W. (1970). *Advan. Lipid Res.* **11**, 41.
Portman, O. W., and Illingworth, D. R. (1974a). *Scand. J. Clin. Lab. Invest., Suppl.* **137**, 49.
Portman, O. W., and Illingworth, D. R. (1974b). *Biochim. Biophys. Acta* **348**, 136.
Portman, O. W., and Illingworth, D. R. (1975). In "Atherosclerosis in Primates" (J. P. Strong, ed.) (*Primates in Medicine* **9**, 1). Karger, Basel.
Portman, O. W., and Mann, G. V. (1955). *J. Biol. Chem.* **213**, 733.
Portman, O. W., Wysocki, A. P., and Mann, G. V. (1955). *Arch. Biochem. Biophys.* **59**, 224.
Portman, O. W., Soltys, P., Alexander, M., and Osuga, T. (1970). *J. Lipid Res.* **11**, 596.
Portman, O. W., Osuga, T., and Alexander, M. (1975). *Proc. Int. Symp. Atheroscler., 3rd, 1973* (in press).
Potter, M. G. (1936). *J. Amer. Med. Ass.* **106**, 1070.
Prange, I., Søndergaard, E., and Dam, H. (1973). *Z. Ernaehrungswiss.* **12**, 92.
Rains, A. J. H. (1964). "Gallstones. Causes and Treatment," p. 30. Thomas, Springfield, Illinois.
Redinger, R. N., Hermann, A. H., and Small, D. M. (1971). *Gastroenterology* **60**, 198.
Redinger, R. N., Hermann, A. H., and Small, D. M. (1973). *Gastroenterology* **64**, 610.
Robins, S. J., and Fasulo, J. (1973). *Gastroenterology* **65**, 104.
Ruch, T. C. (1967). "Diseases of Laboratory Primates", p. 265. Saunders, Philadelphia, Pennsylvania.
Russell, I. S., Wheeler, M. B., and Freak, R. (1968). *Brit. J. Surg.* **55**, 161.
Sampliner, R. E., Bennett, P. H., Comess, L. J., Rose, F. A., and Burch, T. A. (1970). *N. Engl. J. Med.* **283**, 1358.
Scherstén, T. (1973). *Digestion* **9**, 540.

Schwartz, C. C., Vlahcevic, Z. R., Gregory, D. H., Meek, J. B., and Swell, L. (1974). *Gastroenterology* **66**, 893.

Scott, V. F., Roth, H. P., Bellon, E. M., and Neiderhiser, D. H. (1972). *Gastroenterology* **63**, 851.

Shaffer, E. A., Braasch, J. W., and Small, D. M. (1972). *N. Engl. J. Med.* **287**, 1317.

Shaffer, E. A., Beaudoin, M., Small, D. M., O'Brien, J., and Williams, L. (1974). *Gastroenterology* **66**, 775.

Sheen, P. C. (1971). *Jap. J. Surg.* **1**, 19.

Simendinger, E. A., Krutky, T. A., and Reodica, R. E. (1971). *J. Amer. Med. Ass.* **215**, 1823.

Simmons, F., Ross, A. P. J., and Bouchier, I. A. D. (1972). *Gastroenterology* **63**, 466.

Sjövall, J. (1960). *Clin. Chim. Acta* **5**, 33.

Small, D. M. (1970). *Advan. Intern. Med.* **16**, 243.

Small, D. M., and Rapo, S. (1970). *N. Engl. J. Med.* **283**, 53.

Small, D. M., Bourges, M., and Dervichian, D. G. (1966a). *Biochim. Biophys. Acta* **125**, 563.

Small, D. M., Bourges, M., and Dervichian, D. G. (1966b). *Nature (London)* **211**, 816.

Small, D. M., Dowling, R. H., and Redinger, R. N. (1972). *Arch. Intern. Med.* **130**, 552.

Smallwood, R. A., Jablonski, P., and Watts, J. McK. (1972). *Brit. Med. J.* **4**, 263.

Stein, O., and Stein, Y. (1969). *J. Cell Biol.* **40**, 461.

Sternby, N. H. (1968). *Acta Pathol. Microbiol. Scand., Suppl.* **194**, 1.

Stevenson, J. S., and Stevenson, L. S. (1973). *Can. Mineral.* **11**, 985.

Strasberg, S. M., Dorn, B. C., Small, D. M., and Egdahl, R. H. (1971). *Surgery* **70**, 140.

Sturdevant, R. A. L., Pearce, M. L., and Dayton, S. (1973). *N. Engl. J. Med.* **288**, 24.

Sutor, D. J. (1974). *Gut* **15**, 130.

Sutor, D. J., and Woolcy, S. E. (1969). *Gut* **10**, 681.

Sutor, D. J., and Wooley, S. E. (1971). *Gut* **12**, 55.

Sutor, D. J., and Wooley S. E. (1973). *Gut* **14**, 215.

Swell, L., Bell, C. C., Jr., and Entenman, C. (1968). *Biochim. Biophys. Acta* **164**, 278.

Swell, L., Bell, C. C., Jr., Gregory, D. H., and Vlahcevic, Z. R. (1974). *Amer. J. Dig. Dis.* **19**, 261.

Tamesue, N., and Juniper, K. (1967). *Gastroenterology* **52**, 473.

Tamesue, N., Inoue, T., and Juniper, K., Jr. (1973). *Amer. J. Dig. Dis.* **18**, 670.

Tanaka, N., and Portman, O. W. (1974). *Circulation* **50**, III–271.

Tepperman, J., Caldwell, F. T., and Tepperman, H. M. (1964). *Amer. J. Physiol.* **206**, 628.

Tera, H. (1961). *Acta Chir. Scand.* **120**, 358.

Thistle, J. L., Eckhart, K. L., Jr., Nensel, R. E., Nobrega, F. T., Poehling, G. G., Reimer, M., and Schoenfield, L. J. (1971). *Mayo Clin. Proc.* **46**, 603.

Thomas, P. J., and Hofmann, A. F. (1973). *Gastroenterology* **65**, 698.

Thorbjarnarson, B., Gilder, H., and Morrissey, K. (1972). "Medical Primatology," *Proc. Conf. Exp. Med. Surg. Primates, 3rd, 1972* Part II, pp. 52–57.

Thureborn, E. (1962). *Acta Chir. Scand., Suppl.* **303**, 1.

van der Linden, W. (1961). *Acta Chir. Scand., Suppl.* **269**, 1.

Vlahcevic, Z. R., Bell, C. C., Jr., Buhac, I., Farrar, J. T., and Swell, L. (1970). *Gastroenterology* **59**, 165.

Vlahcevic, Z. R., Bell, C. C., Jr., Juttijadata, P., and Swell, L. (1971). *Amer. J. Dig. Dis.* **16**, 797.

Webster, R. H., Lancaster, M. C., Wease, D. F., Hofmann, A. F., and Baggenstoss, A. H. (1973). *Gastroenterology* **65**, 576.

Wheeler, H. O. (1973). *Gastroenterology* **65**, 92.

Wheeler, H. O., and King, K. K. (1972). *J. Clin. Invest.* **51**, 1337.
Wheeler, H. O., and Ramos, O. L. (1960). *J. Clin. Invest.* **39**, 161.
Wheeler, M., Hills, L. L., and Laby, B. (1970). *Gut* **11**, 430.
Wiggins, H. S., and Wootton, I. D. P. (1958). *Biochem. J.* **70**, 349.
Wolpers, C. (1968). *Deut. Med. Wochenschr.* **93**, 2525.
Wolpers, C., and Blaschke, R. (1971). *Proc. Electron Micros. Soc. Amer. 29th Annu. Meet.*
Womack, N. A. (1971). *Surg. Gynecol. Obstet.* **133**, 1.
Womack, N. A., Zeppa, R., and Irwin, I. G., III. (1963). *Ann. Surg.* **157**, 670.
Zilversmit, D. B., and van Handel, E. (1958). *Arch. Biochem. Biophys.* **72**, 224.

The Composition and Biosynthesis of Milk Fat[1]

STUART SMITH[2] AND S. ABRAHAM

Bruce Lyon Memorial Research Laboratory,
Children's Hospital Medical Center of
Northern California, Oakland, California

I. Growth and Development of the Mammary Gland

A feature which makes the mammary gland distinct among mammalian tissues is that it periodically undergoes changes of the most striking kind, both structurally and functionally. These changes are controlled by the actions of specific hormones and can generally be divided into four stages (Figs. 1A–C and 2A and B). The first is called cellular proliferation and occurs when the animal attains adulthood. During this period, development of the epithelia occurs which pro-

---

[1] Supported by grants AM 16073 and AM 17489 from the National Institute of Health and grant BMS 7412723 from the National Science Foundation.
[2] Established Investigator of the American Heart Association.

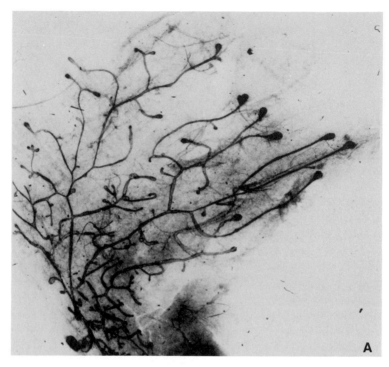

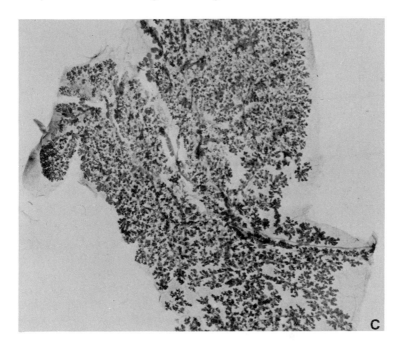

FIG. 1. Whole mounts of part of mammary gland from female C_3H/He Crgl mice at various stages of development. Stained with hematoxylin. Magnification: 6×. (A) Typical gland from an 8-to 10-week-old virgin. Numerous end buds and ducts are visible. (B) Gland from a mouse pregnant for 1 week. An increase in duct branching and the presence of a few small lobules can be seen. (C) Gland from a 2-week pregnant mouse showing highly developed lobules of alveoli. From Nandi (1959).

duces a structure characterized by the formation of small ducts, club-shaped terminal end buds, and finally, alveoli. This type of activity begins with puberty and is completed at the point of sexual maturity. The nature of accelerated duct growth, associated with the onset of puberty, depends upon the type of estrus cycle and ranges from a rapid extension and growth of the duct system to the development of a lobulo-alveolar system comparable to that occurring in late pregnancy (Figs. 1A–1C). If pregnancy does not occur, the gland shows some regression. The second stage is characterized by the morphological differentiation of the epithelia of the terminal ducts and alveoli into secretory cells. This change occurs during the late part of pregnancy and is completed immediately after parturition. The third stage begins not long after parturition and continues throughout the lactational period (Figs. 2A and 2B). During this time the epithelial cells are primarily concerned with milk synthesis, and cell growth diminishes

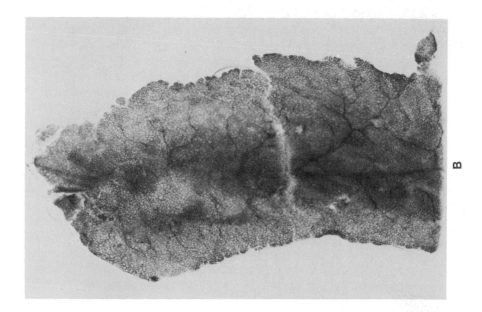

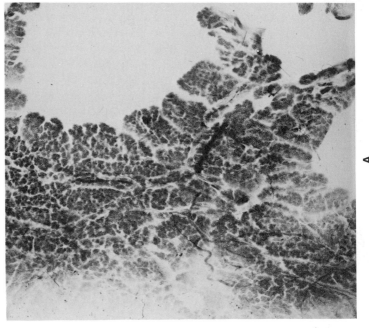

(Fig. 3). Involution is the fourth stage and although it starts in lactation, the process becomes most pronounced after extended lactation or cessation of suckling. Subsequently, the secreting cells disappear resulting in atrophy of the gland and thus, a return to the beginning of the rhythmic changes associated with the estrus cycle.

It is usual to regard milk secretion as being composed of two phases: the synthesis of milk by the epithelial cells of the alveoli and the movement of that milk from the cytoplasm of the cells into the alveolar lumen (Cowie *et al.*, 1951; Folley, 1947). Lactogenesis, or the initiation of milk secretion, is a different process from the one which maintains an established production, however, and as pointed out by Cowie and Tindall (1971) the features of each have not been clearly defined. The following is a brief account of some of the efforts made to investigate the effects of hormones on milk fat synthesis.

During the 1930s, Turner and his co-workers showed that the ovarian steroid hormones were not effective in stimulating growth of the mammary glands in the absence of the pituitary gland (Turner, 1939). Subsequently, Lyons and colleagues (Lyons and Johnson, 1958) were able to demonstrate the synergistic actions of hormones from the pituitary, ovaries, and adrenals in their experiments with replacement therapy in rats which had their pituitary, gonads, and adrenals removed. These workers were able to show that lobulo-alveolar growth could be developed in hypophysectomized-ovariectomized-adrenalectomized (triply operated) rats to a stage comparable to that occurring in late pregnancy by suitable injections of estrogen, progesterone, adrenal steroids, growth hormone, and prolactin. At this point, lactogenesis could occur if the rats received only prolactin and the adrenal steroids. Thus, in the rat, it was clearly demonstrated that growth hormone, estrogen, and progesterone were not needed for lactogenesis. In similar studies with triply operated mice, lactogenesis occurred when the ovarian steroids were withdrawn while injections of prolactin and adrenal steroids were continued (Nandi, 1959; Nandi and Bern, 1961; Wellings, 1969). Furthermore, in some strains of mice (Nandi, 1959) a mixture of growth hormone plus adrenal steroids was shown to be lactogenic, and indeed when growth hormone was added to those mice receiving prolactin and adrenal steroids the best lactogenic response was obtained. In studies with rats hypophysectomized during lactation, administration of prolactin plus ACTH

FIG. 2. Whole mounts of part of mammary gland from female C_3H/He Crgl mice at two stages of lactation. Stained with hematoxylin. Magnification: $5\frac{1}{4}\times$. (A) Three days postpartum. Alveoli are now considerably enlarged. (B) Twelve days postpartum. The gland is now considerably thicker than at 2 days postpartum. From Nandi (1959).

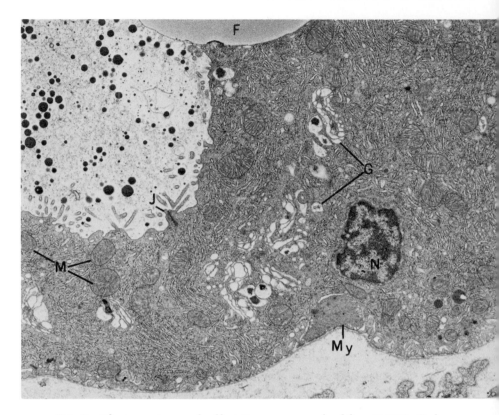

FIG. 3.   Electron micrograph of lactating mammary gland from C₃H/He Crgl mouse. Preparation was fixed in paraformaldehyde-glutaraldehyde, postfixed in osmium, embedded in Epon, thin-sectioned, and stained with uranyl acetate and lead citrate. The micrograph shows parts of two cells in an alveolus. Characteristically abundant, flattened cisternae of endoplasmic reticulum occupy most of the cytoplasm. G, Golgi bodies; M, mitochondria; N, nucleus sectioned superficially; My, myoepithelial process; F, edge of a large fat droplet at the cell apex; J. tight junction between cells. The luminal surfaces bear microvilli, while the basal surfaces exhibit the convolutions of the basal labyrinth, surrounded by a thin basal lamina. Magnification: 7360×. From Pitelka *et al.* (1969).

(adrenocorticotropic hormone) or prolactin plus adrenal steroids elicited a substantial restoration of the milk secretion (Bintarningsih *et al.*, 1957; Cowie, 1957; Cowie and Tindall, 1971). Thus, in mice and rats, the evidence points to the requirement of the hypophyseal hormones (prolactin and ACTH) for both the induction and maintenance of milk secretion.

Lactation can be maintained in hypophysectomized goats by the administration of sheep prolactin, bovine growth hormone, triiodothyronine, and adrenal steroids (Cowie, 1969). In the rabbit, only a single hormone, prolactin, appears to be required (Denamur, 1971). Information concerning the hormonal requirements for lactation in primates is limited and has been discussed by Forsyth (1971). The data suggest that whereas placental hormones induce mammary growth and milk secretion in the absence of the pituitary, growth hormone and chorionic somatomammotropin are both needed for the initiation of lactation.

II. Hormonal Requirements for Milk Fat Production

In 1960, Abraham (Abraham *et al.*, 1960) investigated the effects of various combinations of adenohypophyseal and adrenocortical hormones on the metabolism of rat mammary glands and their ability to maintain milk fat synthesis in hypophysectomized rats. These workers showed that when rats were hypophysectomized at mid-pregnancy, they could deliver their young normally but did not lactate. The minimum hormonal combination required for glandular development and lactation was shown to be prolactin and hydrocortisone. If the rats were supplied with these hormones at the time of parturition and maintained during the postpartum period, slices prepared from the glands displayed the same metabolic behavior as those from normal lactating rats. Metabolism was characterized by glucose utilization, via the Embden-Meyerhof and pentose phosphate pathways, as well as a great capacity for lipogenesis. Since that time, additional studies on the hormonal requirements for milk fat synthesis have focused on the use of tissue explants.

When mammary explants from pseudopregnant rabbits were cultured with insulin, corticosterone, and prolactin, Strong and co-workers (Strong *et al.*, 1972), could demonstrate a striking increase not only in the rate of fatty acid synthesis but also in the proportion of octanoate and decanoate synthesized from acetate. In a subsequent report, these same workers (Forsyth *et al.*, 1972) were able to show that the stimulus to mammary gland lipogenesis and the initiation of synthesis of these medium-chain fatty acids observed between days 16 and 23 of pregnancy in the rabbit could be obtained by the *in vitro* addition of prolactin alone. However, to obtain rates of lipogenesis similar to those seen in early lactation, culture of the pregnant rabbit glands with three hormones, insulin, corticosterone, and prolactin, was required. These results obtained with the rabbit differ somewhat from those observed with mouse tissues. In the mouse, synthesis of milk fatty acids could be induced by culture with insulin, corticosterone, and prolactin (Wang *et al.*, 1972). With this species lipogenesis could not be stimulated with prolactin alone, and, although insulin could increase fatty acid synthesis in explants from the mammary glands of pregnant mice (Moretti and Abraham, 1966), the types of fatty acids synthesized resembled those of the tissue rather than the milk lipid (Wang *et al.*, 1972).

In the rat the situation is again somewhat different. When explants prepared from the mammary glands of virgin or 10-day pregnant rats were cultured, Hallowes *et al.* (1973) showed that insulin, corticosterone, and prolactin increased the conversion of ^{14}C-acetate into octanoate, decanoate, and laurate. In this regard, growth hormone could substitute for prolactin but less efficiently. Since these workers showed that the growth hormone preparation used did not contain sufficient amounts of prolactin to produce this effect, they suggested that an independent effect of growth hormone on lipogenesis could not be excluded. In addition, whereas the majority of the saturated fatty acids synthesized by slices of lactating rat mammary glands are of the C_8 to C_{12} variety (about 70%; Abraham *et al.*, 1961), explants prepared from the glands of pregnant rats could only produce these medium-chain length fatty acids in the presence of insulin, corticosterone, and prolactin.

Thus it would appear that although the hormonal requirements vary somewhat from one species to another, the basic principles remain the same. Insulin increases the synthesis of fatty acids, and prolactin and a glucocorticoid are needed to produce the pattern of fatty acids characteristic of the gland during the lactational period.

III. Secretion of Milk Fat

Most of the lipid present in milk occurs as discrete droplets, surrounded by a lipid–protein membrane. The droplets, without their surrounding membrane, can also be seen inside the alveolar cell; usually the smaller droplets are close to the basal cytoplasm and the larger droplets nearer the apical region of the cell (Bargmann and Knoop, 1959; Wooding, 1971). The sequence of events which leads to formation of the milk fat globule is thought to proceed as follows: Chylomicrons passing through the mammary gland capillaries become attached to the endothelial cells where they are subject to the action of lipoprotein lipase. Thus the chylomicron triglyceride is partially hydrolyzed to a mixture of fatty acid and mono- and diglyceride (Scow *et al.*, 1974). The glycerides are taken up into microvesicles in the endothelial cells and the fatty acid is released into the blood. Within the endothelial microvesicles, the glycerides are further broken down to fatty acids and glycerol. The glycerol is released into the blood and the fatty acids transported into the alveolar cell. Inside the alveolar cell, on the endoplasmic reticulum, the fatty acids derived from the chylomicrons, along with the endogenously synthesized fatty acids, are converted to triglyceride. The molecular aspects of this process are dealt with later in this chapter. The resulting triglycerides assemble into droplet form and the droplets continue to increase in size and move toward the apical region of the cell. At the apical surface, the droplets are enveloped by the plasma membrane so

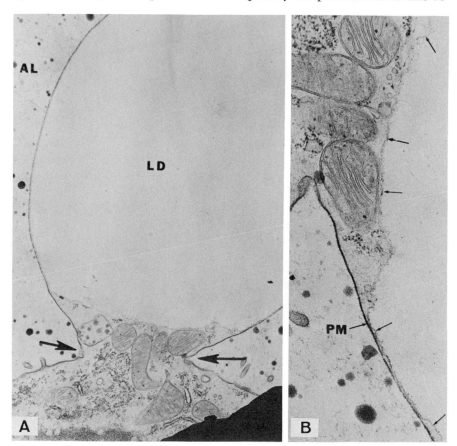

FIG. 4. Electron micrographs of a lipid droplet (LD) in the final stage of being secreted into the alveolar lumen (AL). On the basis of the location of the constriction of the plasma membrane shown by the arrows in Fig. 4A, it appears that cytoplasm containing mitochondria and a Golgi vacuole will be included in the secreted droplet. Figure 4B is a higher magnification micrograph of the base of the droplet. The milk fat globule membrane is shown by the arrows and the plasma membrane is indicated by PM. From Saacke and Heald (1974).

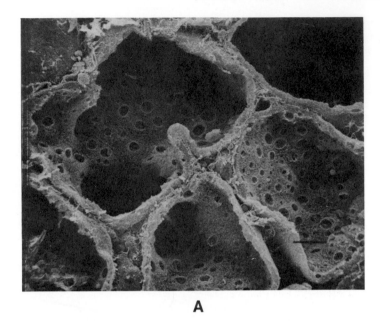

A

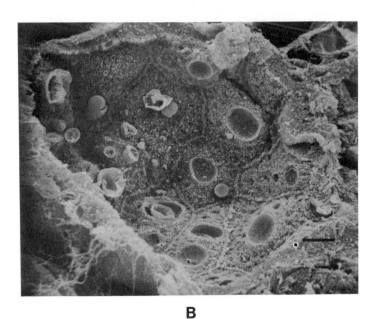

B

FIG. 5. Scanning electron micrographs of mammary gland from BALB/cCrgl mice 13 days postpartum. (A) On the luminal surface of the alveolar cells are numerous small craters left by extracted fat droplets. Between the alveoli are clumped connective tissue fibers and occasional red blood cells. Because the gland was engorged with milk after $1\frac{1}{2}$ hours without suckling, the alveolar walls are thin. During suckling, many alveoli

Table I

Comparison of Phospholipid Composition of Cow Milk Fat Globule Membrane with That of Cow Mammary Cell Plasma Membrane[a]

Phospholipid	Milk fat globule membrane	Plasma membrane
Sphingomyelin	21.9	24.5
Phosphatidylinositol	10.5	12.7
Phosphatidylserine	11.6	8.5
Phosphatidylcholine	28.7	29.0
Phosphatidylethanolamine	27.5	25.0

[a] Data from Keenan *et al.* (1970).

that they protrude into the alveolar lumen. Eventually, the droplets are pinched off by constriction of the plasma membrane (Figs. 4A and 4B). Mitochondria and other cytoplasmic constituents are sometimes included in the region pinched off by closure of the plasma membrane. With the aid of the scanning electron microscope, we can obtain an added dimension to our view of the process of milk fat secretion. Figures 5A and 5B show a view of the luminal surface of the alveolar cells. Numerous craters are in evidence which represent the space left by extracted lipid droplets. Some of the craters still contain collapsed remnants of the bulging plasma membrane, and occasionally small fat droplets persist.

Apart from the histological evidence which points to the plasma membrane as the precursor of the milk fat globule membrane, there is supporting evidence of a chemical nature. The milk fat globule membrane has a characteristic lipid–protein composition which closely resembles that of the plasma membrane (Table I).

IV. Coordination of Metabolic Pathways Related to Milk Fat Production

Glucose has long been regarded as one of the most important substrates for milk fat production by the mammary glands of nonruminant animals. The central role played by this sugar is emphasized by the fact that it can supply both the carbon skeleton and the reducing equivalents required for fatty acid production. Thus a great deal of

contract and the cells change shape and project into the lumen. Magnification: 440×. (B) Part of an alveolus showing a polygonal pattern of distinct cell boundaries marked by bands of densely set microvilli. The craters left by extracted fat droplets often contain collapsed membrane remnants, and occasionally small fat droplets persist. Magnification: 1020×. From Nemanic and Pitelka (1971).

attention has been given to a detailed study of its metabolism in this tissue, particularly the quantitative importance of the pentose phosphate cycle and the Embden-Meyerhof pathway. In general, two different approaches have been pursued. The first involves the measurement of individual enzyme activities concerned with the Embden-Meyerhof and the pentose phosphate cycle and the second with the isolation of isotopically labeled products or intermediates from specifically labeled carbon or tritium substrates. Pentose phosphate cycle enzymes with high activities have been demonstrated in rats (Baldwin and Milligan, 1966; Glock and McLean, 1954; Gul and Dils, 1969; Karlsson and Carlsson, 1968; McLean, 1958a,b; Novello and McLean, 1968), mice (Kopelovich et al., 1966), sows (Bauman et al., 1970), and rabbits (Mellenberger and Bauman, 1974), and the various intermediates of the pathway have been isolated from lactating rat mammary tissues (Gumaa et al., 1970; Peeters et al., 1957). In addition, both transaldolase and transketolase activities have been shown to be present in this tissue at high levels during lactation (Gumaa et al., 1970; Novello and McLean, 1968).

Since the early 1950s, when Glock and McLean (1954) first reported that lactating rat mammary gland tissue contained high levels of the hydrogenases that act on glucose 6-phosphate and 6-phosphogluconate in addition to the enzymes responsible for the breakdown of pentose phosphate, various investigators have attempted to calculate the relative participation of the Embden-Meyerhof and pentose phosphate pathways in this tissue taken from a variety of animals. One of the earliest of such attempts was made by Abraham et al. (1954) who showed that slices prepared from mammary glands of lactating rats were capable of converting the sixth carbon of glucose to fatty acids many times faster than the first carbon of this hexose. Additional studies with this same tissue (Abraham and Chaikoff, 1959) clearly showed that the pentose phosphate pathway was a major participant in the extensive lipogenesis during the lactating condition. However, during the prepartum period and the post-weaned condition, this pathway did not play a significant role. Such a correlation between high rates of lipogenesis and extensive operation of the pentose phosphate pathway, a mechanism for the production of NADPH (nicotinomide adenine dinucleotide phosphate, reduced form), has been subsequently noted by many workers in a variety of tissues. Indeed, this property, the production of NADPH from glucose via the pentose phosphate pathway has been invoked to explain the fact that the addition of glucose to the media results in a 40- to 150-fold stimulation of lipogenesis from acetate by lactating rat mammary gland slices (Abraham *et al.*, 1954; Abraham and Chaikoff, 1959; Balmain *et al.*, 1952; Bauman *et al.*, 1970, 1972).

Initial attempts to determine the origin of the hydrogen in fatty acids formed by lactating rat mammary glands were made by Abraham *et al.* (1963). These studies showed that the reductive hydrogen needed in fatty acid synthesis originated from the glucose molecule and was probably transferred during its metabolism via the pentose phosphate cycle by way of NADPH. Previously, Foster and Bloom (1963) had made a similar observation with rat liver preparations. Through the use of glucose labeled with ^{14}C in positions 1, 2, 3, and 6, as well as with tritium in all six positions, Katz and Wals (1972) investigated the production of reducing equivalents by lactating rat mammary gland slices. As a result of this intensive study, these workers concluded that during lactation, the pentose phosphate cycle activity was adequate enough to produce 80–100% of the NAPDH required for the lipogenesis observed. In addition, their calculations revealed that the formation of reducing equivalents in the cytoplasm, the intracellular site of fatty acid synthesis, indeed exceeds that required for the reductive biosynthesis occurring in this tissue. They propose, therefore, that the excess amount of reducing equivalents is transferred into the mitochondrion.

The enzymes involved in the conversion of glucose to pyruvate (whether via the pentose phosphate cycle or the Embden-Meyerhof pathway) are located in the soluble cytoplasm (cytosol) and those which oxidize pyruvate to acetyl-CoA are in the mitochondrion. In most tissues from nonruminant animals, it is generally agreed that citrate acts as the carrier for the transport of the acetyl-CoA across the mitochondrial barrier into the cytosol where the enzyme apparatus for the synthesis of saturated fatty acids is located. Through the action of citrate cleavage enzyme, the acetyl-CoA is generated together with an equal amount of oxaloacetate. Most workers in this field have accepted the theory that the oxaloacetate is reduced to malate, some of which can reenter the mitochondrion where it can supply the oxaloacetate to keep such a cycle operating, and some can be oxidized to pyruvate through the action of malic enzyme. This latter step can also supply NADPH. The relative proportion of the required reducing equivalents for fatty acid synthesis in the form of NADPH originating from the pentose phosphate cycle and the malic enzyme in mammary tissue is not known at this time.

In ruminants and perhaps in some nonruminant herbivores having enlarged hind guts, such as the rabbit, the products of microbial fermentation in the digestive tract play an important role as carbon

sources for metabolism in the tissues. Thus, acetate is a major precursor for fatty acid synthesis and propionate is an important carbon
source for gluconeogenesis (Annison and Lindsay, 1961; Bergman *et
al.*, 1966; Kleiber *et al.*, 1952; Leng *et al.*, 1967). This latter pathway is
of major importance to ruminants in view of the relatively small
amount of glucose available to the animal via the digestive tract. Thus
the metabolic pathways in the mammary gland of the ruminant, in
common with other tissues of these animals, reflect the evolutionary
adaptations which have taken place in the digestive tract. In particular, the enzymes concerned with the transport of acetyl units from the
mitochondria to the cytosol, the so-called pyruvate cycle or citrate
cleavage pathway, are very low in activity in the mammary glands of
ruminants (Bauman and Davis, 1974). Because of the low activity of ci-
trate-cleavage enzyme and malic enzyme in the mammary gland of
cow and sheep, the pyruvate cyle is thought to be unimportant in
these animals (Bauman and Davis, 1974). In view of both the lack of
glucose as a carbon source for fatty acid synthesis and the low activity
of the enzymes of the hexose monophosphate shunt (Bauman and
Davis, 1974), it is clear that in ruminant mammary gland, there must
be alternative supplies of both carbon and reducing equivalents for
lipogenesis. The absence of malic enzyme as a potential source of
reducing equivalents simply compounds the problem. Whereas acetate can clearly supply the carbon requirement, the source of reducing
equivalents is less clear. The most likely explanation seems to be that
citrate which diffuses into the cytosol, instead of being cleaved to
acetyl-CoA and oxaloacetate, is oxidized to α-ketoglutarate by the
NADP-dependent isocitrate dehydrogenase. In support of this idea is
the observation that the activity of this enzyme is about 20-fold higher
in the mammary gland of cow and sheep than in that of the rat
(Bauman *et al.*, 1970, 1973).

The citrate in turn, could be derived, at least in part, from acetate
which is converted to acetyl-CoA intramitochondrially. In this scheme
(Fig. 6), the citrate which flows to isocitrate and hence to ketoglutarate,
in the cytosol, could be returned to the mitochondria either by direct
diffusion as ketoglutarate (Chappell and Robinson, 1968) or indirectly
by a transamination sequence (Lardy *et al.*, 1965). Figure 6 shows the
pathways of fatty acid synthesis operative in ruminants and nonruminants. In ruminants and some nonruminant herbivores, the major
operative route is probably that which begins with the conversion of
acetate to both intra- and extramitochondrial acetyl-CoA. The extramitochondrial acetyl-CoA can be used directly for fatty acid synthesis
and the intramitochondrial acetyl-CoA for both generation of ATP and

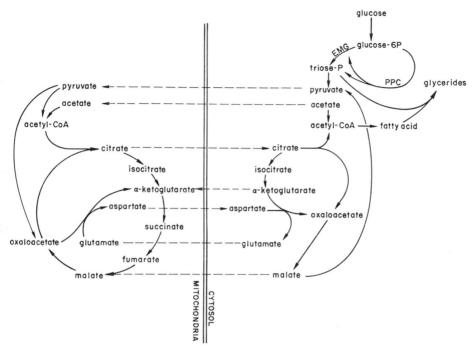

FIG. 6. Scheme for conversion of glucose and acetate to fatty acid by the lactating mammary gland.

supply of citrate for export to the cytosol. In nonruminants, the major route involves the initial conversion of glucose to pyruvate, which enters the mitochondria and begins the pyruvate cycle, pyruvate → acetyl-CoA → citrate → acetyl-CoA. The oxaloacetate formed by the extramitochondrial cleavage of citrate is then converted via the NAD-dependent malic dehydrogenase to malate. This metabolite can either return directly to the mitochondria or can be converted to pyruvate to complete the cycle. Whether in nonruminant mammary gland most of the carbon returns to the mitochondria as malate or as pyruvate has not been firmly established.

V. Milk Fat Composition

A. COMPOSITION OF THE MILK FAT GLOBULE

Milk fat globules, which average several microns in diameter are composed of a triglyceride core surrounded by a membrane approxi-

Table II
COMPOSITION OF COW MILK LIPIDS[a]

Lipid	Weight (%)
Hydrocarbons	Trace
Sterol esters	Trace
Triglycerides	97–98
Diglycerides	0.28–0.59
Monoglycerides	0.016–0.038
Free fatty acids	0.10–0.44
Free sterols	0.22–0.41
Phospholipids	0.2–1.0

[a] From Jensen (1973).

mately 90 Å thick (Patton, 1973). The milk fat globule membrane has a characteristic lipid–protein composition resembling that of the plasma membrane from which it is formed. Most of the minor components of milk fat, the glycerophospholipids and sphingolipids, are found in the globule membrane (Table I). In this review we will concern ourselves solely with the structure and biosynthesis of the major components of milk fat, the triglycerides, which account for about 98% of the milk fat (Table II).

B. FATTY ACID COMPOSITION OF THE MILK FAT TRIGLYCERIDE

The overall fatty acid composition of milk fats was first studied by Hilditch and co-workers (Hilditch and Williams, 1964) using the techniques of ester distillation and alkali isomerization. With the advent of gas–liquid chromatography, the number of species analyzed has grown to almost one hundred. The fatty acid components of milk triglyceride include straight-chain saturated acids of odd and even carbon number, iso and anteiso acids, multibranched acids, as well as positional and geometrical isomers of unsaturated acids (Garton, 1963). Thus as many as 64 different fatty acids have been identified in cow's milk (Herb et al., 1962), although 27 of these accounted for only a combined total of 1% of the milk fatty acids. In the following discussion we shall deal only with the major constituents of the milk fat triglycerides.

One of the most interesting features to emerge from the early analyses of the milk fat of a number of species was that the fatty acid composition differed from that of the corresponding depot fat inasmuch as significant amounts of short-(C_4 and C_6) and medium-chain (C_8 to C_{12}) fatty acids were present (Garton, 1963). At this time a sufficiently large number of species have been examined for us to recognize that many groups of mammals do not produce milk fat containing short- or medium-chain fatty acids. Thus the milk fats of monotremes, marsupials, and insectivores consist almost exclusively of fatty acids containing 16 and 18 carbon atoms (Glass *et al.*, 1967; Glass and Jennes, 1971). The milk fats of most primates contain 10–25% of the medium-chain fatty acids but that of the rodent shows considerable diversity. For example, the milk fats of the guinea pig (Cavidae family), golden hamster (Cricetidae family), and flying squirrel (Sciuridae family) have no medium-chain fatty acids; in fact the milk fat of the latter species contains as much as 69% oleic acid (Glass *et al.*, 1967; Glass and Jennes, 1971; Smith *et al.*, 1968). Rodents more commonly used in the laboratory such as rat and mouse, contain significant quantities of medium-chain acids, but the highest quantities of medium-chain acids are found in the milk of the orders Lagomorpha and Proboscidea. Thus, milk fats of the rabbit, jack rabbit, and cottontail contain large amounts of C_8 and C_{10} acids, often as high as 70%, while the milk fats of the Indian and African elephants contain prodigious amounts of C_8, C_{10}, and C_{12}, as high as 93% (Glass and Jennes, 1971; McCullagh *et al.*, 1969; Smith *et al.*, 1968).

The milk fats of most carnivores are characterized by the absence of significant amounts of medium-chain acids, in particular the milk fat of marine carnivores is characterized by a high proportion of $C_{16:1}$. Almost all of the many families of ruminants which have been studied produce milk fat containing significant amounts of the short-chain acids C_4 and C_6. The fatty acid composition of the milk fats of a selection of species representative of the groups of mammals referred to above, is presented in Table III.

Certain features of milk fat composition clearly reflect the dietary habits of some species. For example, the high proportion of palmitoleic acid found in the milk of the harp seal (Table III) and other marine mammals is probably dietary in origin since the plankton and fish consumed by these animals are rich in this fatty acid (Glass *et al.*, 1967). Similarly, in ruminant milk, the high content of butyric acid and the predominantly saturated nature of the long-chain fatty acids undoubtedly reflect the action of the intestinal flora in these animals. In the laboratory, the lineoleate content of mouse milk can be raised or lowered, simply by altering the amount of this fatty acid in the diet (Smith *et al.*, 1969). However, some features of milk fat composition remain unaltered by dietary manipulations. This is particularly evi-

Table III
Fatty Acid Composition of Milk Fats of Various Species

Fatty acid	Human[a]	Bottlenose dolphin[b]	Harp seal[b]	Jaguar[b]	Guinea pig[c]	Rabbit[c]	Rat[c]	Mouse[c]	Sheep[d]	Jersey cow[d]
4:0	0	0	0	0	0	0	0	0	10.3	9.8
6:0	0	0	0	0	0	0	0.4	0	3.4	5.0
8:0	0	0	0	0	0	44.9	7.6	0.5	2.3	2.4
10:0	1.9	0	0	0	0.1	23.4	20.3	8.3	3.4	4.8
12:0	7.4	0	0	0	0.1	1.1	13.0	13.2	1.8	4.1
14:0	8.4	5.1	6.1	2.6	1.9	0.8	10.2	16.4	5.0	11.8
16:0	24.0	23.3	17.7	22.8	36.4	8.6	26.3	33.1	20.9	36.5
16:1	2.1	4.9	20.4	8.4	1.6	0.9	1.6	2.7	1.2	1.1
18:0	5.7	6.0	1.9	5.7	4.2	1.4	3.3	1.8	15.5	8.6
18:1	29.4	24.9	28.9	42.8	30.0	8.4	12.6	15.7	27.2	13.0
18:2	15.3	1.8	1.9	14.0	22.3	9.3	4.8	8.3	2.9	0.4
18:3	0.6	0	0	0	3.3	0.5	0	0	2.4	0
Others	5.2	34.0	23.1	3.7	0	0	0	0	3.7	2.5

[a] From Breckenridge et al. (1969).
[b] From Glass and Jennes (1971).
[c] From Smith et al. (1968).
[d] From Breckenridge and Kuksis (1967).

dent in the instance of the rabbit and guinea pig milk fats reported by Smith *et al.* (1968). In these experiments both species were fed identical diets yet the fatty acids were predominantly medium chain (C_8 and C_{10}) in the rabbit, and long chain (C_{16} and C_{18}) in the guinea pig. Although the ultimate composition of milk fat can be influenced considerably by environmental and physiological factors such as diet and intestinal flora, certain broad phylogenetic differences are clearly recognizable.

C. Distribution of the Fatty Acids in Milk Fat Triglycerides

It can be calculated that in a milk fat containing 60 different fatty acids randomly distributed on the glycerol moiety, almost 0.25×10^6 triglyceride species would be possible. As it turns out, the distribution is not random so considerably fewer species can exist, probably only several hundred!

The early analyses of triglyceride species, again performed by Hilditch and colleagues (Hilditch and Williams, 1964), necessitated fractional crystallization, oxidative removal of unsaturated acids, and low temperature crystallization. In the last decade the invaluable tool of gas–liquid chromatography has been successfully adapted, primarily by Kuksis and co-workers, for the resolution of milk triglycerides into their component species. The high temperatures required for the analyses usually necessitate the use of the stable nonpolar stationary phases; these materials do not permit separation of positional isomers of triglycerides or of triglycerides of various degrees of unsaturation Thus the method is successful only in separating triglycerides which differ in their total number of carbon atoms. Recently Kuksis *et al.* (1973) have been able to separate short-chain triglycerides (<40 carbons in the acyl moieties) on the basis of carbon number, degree of unsaturation, and position of the acyl groups, using as stationary phase, EGSS-X, a copolymer of silicone and ethylene glycol succinate. Resolution of mixtures containing longer chain triglycerides awaits the development of polar stationary phases with better temperature stability characteristics.

Gas–liquid chromatographic analysis of intact milk fat triglycerides has revealed that the spectrum of triglyceride species differs considerably (Table IV) from that which would be expected from a random association of fatty acids from a single pool (Breach *et al.*, 1973; Breckenridge and Kuksis, 1967). That the distribution of fatty acids in milk triglycerides is nonrandom has also been demonstrated directly

Table IV

TRIGLYCERIDE COMPOSITIONS OF MILK FATS OF SEVERAL SPECIES

Triglyceride	Human[a]	Guinea pig[b]	Rabbit[b]	Rat[b]	Mouse[b]	Sheep[c]	Jersey cow[c]
24	0	0	3.5	0.1	0	0	0
26	0	0	14.8	0.7	0	0.3	0.1
28	0	0	11.5	1.8	0	0.5	0.5
30	0	0	5.9	4.6	0	1.0	1.0
32	0	0	6.8	7.2	0.7	1.6	2.2
34	0	0	15.5	9.2	1.2	2.8	7.3
36	0	0	11.5	9.5	2.5	6.3	14.4
38	0	0	4.8	10.2	5.4	13.0	13.7
40	0.4	0	5.0	10.3	8.9	12.1	9.3
42	1.3	0.5	9.9	9.8	13.2	5.5	7.0
44	2.8	0.6	7.2	7.9	14.3	4.5	6.7
46	5.5	1.5	1.1	6.6	14.0	4.1	7.2
48	9.0	4.9	0.4	7.2	12.0	5.0	8.2
50	17.6	25.9	0.8	7.4	11.7	9.6	8.2
52	39.0	59.7	1.2	6.2	12.4	13.5	5.1
54	16.4	6.9	0.3	1.2	3.7	10.5	1.0
56	3.6	0	0	0	0	0.5	0
Others	4.6	0	0	0	0	9.2	8.1

[a] From Breckenridge et al. (1969).
[b] From Smith et al. (1968).
[c] From Breckenridge and Kuksis (1967).

by stereochemical analysis. The procedure for the analysis of fatty acids in all three positions of the glycerol moiety developed by Brockerhoff (1965, 1973) is outlined in Fig. 7. Stereochemical analyses performed so far have been focused mainly on ruminant milk triglycerides and the most striking feature to emerge from these experiments is the predominant localization of butyrate and hexanoate in the sn-3-position (Table V). Although human milk triglycerides contain no butyrate or hexanoate, the small amount of decanoate and laurate present also appears to be localized mainly in the sn-3-position. Certain other fatty acids are localized in specific positions on the glycerol backbone in the milk fat of some species. For example, in human milk triglycerides, palmitate is found predominantly in the sn-2-position and oleate in the sn-1,3-positions. These stereospecific arrangements are not common to the milk triglycerides of the sheep or cow however, since, in these fats, palmitate is found largely in the sn-1,2-position while oleate is relatively evenly distributed.

Table V

POSITIONAL DISTRIBUTION OF FATTY ACIDS IN MILK
FAT TRIGLYCERIDES OF COW,[a] SHEEP,[b] AND GOAT[b]

	Position relative to sn-glycerol-3-phosphate								
	One			Two			Three		
	Mole %								
Fatty acid	Cow	Sheep	Goat	Cow	Sheep	Goat	Cow	Sheep	Goat
4:0	5.0	—	—	2.9	—	—	43.3	10.8	13.2
6:0	3.0	—	—	4.8	—	—	10.8	10.4	10.6
8:0	0.9	0.3	1.7	2.3	2.0	1.2	2.2	4.4	4.6
10:0	2.5	1.4	3.3	6.1	5.2	6.9	3.6	10.3	12.2
10:1	—	—	—	—	0.1	0.1	—	0.4	0.5
12:0	3.1	2.2	4.0	6.0	4.7	4.6	3.5	3.5	1.2
14:0	10.5	8.2	8.4	20.4	17.6	20.3	7.1	5.3	2.7
14:1	—	0.2	—	—	0.9	0.8	—	1.1	1.0
15:0	—	2.6	1.9	—	4.1	2.7	—	1.5	1.5
16:0	35.9	38.0	43.6	32.8	23.8	33.9	10.1	2.5	3.4
16:1	2.9	2.2	2.9	2.1	2.2	2.0	0.9	1.5	1.6
17:0	—	1.7	1.3	—	0.9	0.5	—	0.7	1.8
18:0	14.7	19.1	15.3	6.4	12.6	6.3	4.0	9.1	7.7
18:1	20.6	18.7	16.1	13.7	19.3	16.1	14.9	27.2	30.2
18:2	1.2	2.7	0.3	2.5	4.2	2.5	0.5	6.0	4.5
18:3	—	2.2	—	—	1.7	—	—	4.4	—
20:1	—	0.5	0.9	—	0.2	1.7	—	0.4	2.7
20:2	—	—	0.4	—	—	0.1	—	0.2	0.9

[a] Data from Pitas *et al.* (1967).
[b] Data from Kuksis *et al.* (1973).

Combination of thin layer chromatography and gas–liquid chromatography with stereochemical analysis provides a powerful tool for the determination of triglyceride structure. Classes of triglycerides can first be resolved according to their degree of unsaturation by chromatography on silica gel impregnated with silver nitrate. Each class of triglyceride can then be analyzed by gas–liquid chromatography of the intact triglycerides and the component fatty acids. Finally, the geometric distribution of the fatty acids can be determined by Brockerhoff's procedure (Fig. 7). Such a combination of techniques has been used by Breckenridge *et al.* (1969) to determine the major species of triglyceride present in human milk (Table VI).

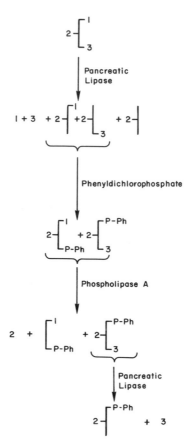

FIG. 7. Procedure for analysis of fatty acids in all three positions of the glycerol moiety, as outlined by Brockerhoff (1965, 1973).

VI. Biosynthesis of Milk Fat

Interest in the origin of milk fat dates back to at least 1850 when Liebig observed that lactating cows produced greater amounts of milk fat than could be accounted for by dietary intake. This led him to challenge the accepted hypothesis of that time, that animal fats were derived entirely from dietary sources. A century later, the experiments of Folley and co-workers with mammary gland slices demonstrated the ability of this tissue to synthesize fatty acids from labeled acetate (Folley and French, 1949; Folley et al., 1954; Popjak et al., 1950). Folley and French, in collaboration with Popjak, injected

Table VI

MAJOR TRIGLYCERIDE SPECIES OF HUMAN MILK FAT[a]

Triglyceride class	Percent	Positional distribution of fatty acids on glycerol moiety in major species		
		1	2	3
Saturated	6–8	18:0	16:0	14:0–18:0
Monoenes	25–27	18:1	16:0	12:0–18:0
Dienes	24–33	{18:0 18:1	18:1 16:0	18:1 18:1
Trienes	18–20	{18:1 18:1	18:1 16:0	18:1 18:2
Tetraenes	7–21	{18:1 16:0	18:1 18:2	18:2 18:2
Polyenes	~6	–	20:4	–

[a] Data from Breckenridge *et al.* (1969).

labeled acetate into lactating rabbits and showed that the short-chain fatty acids of the mammary gland were much more radioactive than the long-chain fatty acids of both the liver and mammary gland (Popjak *et al.*, 1950). Thus the short-chain fatty acids of the mammary gland could not have arisen directly from the liver fat, nor could they have been formed by degradation of long-chain fatty acids of the mammary gland fats. It was concluded that they had arisen by synthesis in the mammary gland itself, from acetate. In recent years, biochemists have sought an explanation at the enzyme level for the ability of the mammary gland of some species to synthesize these unique short- and medium-chain length acids, and insert them in a stereospecific manner into the glycerol moiety. The ability to synthesize these fatty acids does indeed appear to be confined to the mammary gland; the liver does not synthesize these acids (Table VII). It is not surprising, therefore, that a number of investigators, including ourselves, set about purifying and characterizing the enzyme responsible for the synthesis of fatty acids in the mammary gland via the fatty acid synthetase multienzyme complex. Somewhat to our disappointment we were unable to demonstrate any distinguishing features of the mammary gland fatty acid synthetase. In fact, for all the properties studied, the rat liver and rat mammary gland synthetase appeared to be identical.

In the following paragraphs we have summarized the evidence which suggests that the rat liver and rat mammary gland fatty acid synthetases are very similar, if not identical proteins.

Table VII

CHAIN LENGTH OF FATTY ACIDS SYNTHESIZED FROM [U-^{14}C] GLUCOSE
BY SLICES OF RAT LIVER AND LACTATING MAMMARY GLAND[a,b]

| Tissue | Glucose incorporated (nmoles/gm/hr) | Percentage distribution of radioactivity in fatty acids |||||||||||
| | | Chain length |||||||||||
		8:0	10:0	12:0	14:0	16:0	16:1	18:0	18:1	Others
Liver	789	0.7	1.7	0.6	8.7	44.6	6.4	19.0	15.8	2.5
Mammary	4070	5.7	28.8	29.2	18.6	15.5	0.5	0.8	0.5	0.4

[a] S. Smith and S. Abraham, unpublished data.
[b] Livers were obtained from young adult male rats which had been fasted 2 days and refed a fat-free, high glucose diet for 3 days. Mammary glands were obtained from lactating rats 8 days postpartum. Slices (100 mg) of tissue were incubated in 1 ml Krebs-Henseleit bicarbonate buffer, pH 7.3, containing [U-^{14}C]-glucose (25 mM) for 3 hours at 37° C with 95 % O_2, 5 % CO_2 as gas phase.

A. PROPERTIES OF THE FATTY ACID SYNTHETASE

1. *Size and Shape*

Both the rat liver and rat mammary enzymes are large ($M \simeq 480,000$), somewhat asymmetrical ($f/f_0 \simeq 1.6$) multienzyme complexes. The conversion of acetyl-CoA and malonyl-CoA to fatty acid involves the participation of several enzymic components in the complex, acetyl and malonyl transacylases, β-ketothioester synthetase, β-ketothioester reductase, β-hydroxyacylthioester dehydrase, enoylthioester reductase, and acylthioester hydrolase. Together, these components of the complex catalyze the overall reaction:

acetyl-CoA + n malonyl-CoA + $2n$ NADPH + $2n$ H$^+$ →
$$CH_3CH_2\text{-}(CH_2\text{-}CH_2)_n\text{-}1\text{-}CH_2COOH + n\ H_2O + n\ CO_2 + 2n\ NADP^+$$

2. *Cold Lability*

Both the rat liver and rat mammary gland enzymes dissociate into their component half-molecular-weight subunits on exposure to the cold (0°). The cold-induced dissociation follows first-order kinetics and the rate constants are similar for the rat liver and rat mammary gland enzymes. The dissociation process has been studied in detail in the case of the mammary gland enzyme (Smith and Abraham, 1971b; Smith, 1971) and shown to be accompanied by a loss in enzyme activity. The cold-induced inactivation of the enzyme also follows first-order kinetics. Substitution of D_2O for H_2O in the buffer medium results in a retardation of both the dissociation and inactivation processes (Table VIII). The enzyme can be reassociated and thus reactivated by warming. Maintenance of the quaternary structure of the enzyme is also markedly influenced by the ionic strength of the medium; thus at pH 7 and 0°, the half-life of the complex is 33 hours in 250 mM potassium phosphate, but only 5 hours in 4 mM potassium

Table VIII

EFFECT OF D_2O ON FIRST-ORDER RATE CONSTANTS FOR COLD-INDUCED INACTIVATION AND DISSOCIATION OF RAT MAMMARY FAS[a]

Rate constant:	Percentage D_2O		
	100	50	0
	(days)$^{-1}$		
$K_{inactivation}$	0.18	0.24	0.44
$K_{dissociation}$	0.15	0.26	0.56

[a] Data adapted from Smith (1971).

phosphate (Smith, 1971; Smith and Abraham, 1975). The observed effects of temperature, D_2O, and ionic strength on the stability of the complex have been interpreted to indicate that hydrophobic interactions are of major importance in the maintenance of the native enzyme structure (Smith and Abraham, 1971b; Smith, 1971).

3. Phosphopantetheine Content

In common with all other mammalian fatty acid synthetases, both the rat liver and rat mammary gland enzymes contain one 4'-phosphopantetheine moiety per molecule of enzyme. Recently it has been demonstrated that the 4'-phosphopantetheine moiety is associated with the subunit which contains β-ketothioester reductase activity; the other subunit, which contains the acetyl-CoA transacylase activity, is devoid of 4'-phosphopantetheine (Lornitzo et al., 1974). The 4'-phosphopantetheine moiety of the liver fatty acid synthetase has been shown to turn over independently of the rest of the protein (Tweto et al., 1971; Tweto and Larrabee, 1972). Yu and Burton (1974) have suggested that the increase in fatty acid synthetase activity which occurs in the livers of fasted-refed rats, might be due in part to the insertion of the 4'-phosphopantetheine into the inactive apoenzyme. As yet no studies have been performed to evaluate the significance of apoenzyme–holoenzyme interconversions in regulation of the activity of the mammary gland enzyme.

4. Amino Acid Composition

The fatty acid synthetases (FAS) from liver and mammary gland of the rat have very similar amino acid compositions (Table IX). The native enzymes contain approximately 60 sulfhydryl groups about 80% of which are readily accessible to 5,5'-dithiobis (2-nitrobenzoate). Blocking as few as four of these sulfhydryl groups with p-chloromercuribenzoate results in a 50% loss of enzyme activity (Smith and Abraham, 1971b).

5. Turnover Number

The turnover numbers for both rat liver and mammary gland enzymes are both of the order 3–4 μmoles acetyl-CoA converted to fatty acid per minute per mole enzyme.

6. Primer Specificity

Both the rat liver and rat mammary gland fatty acid synthetases show a preference for butyryl-CoA over acetyl-CoA as primer for the synthesis of fatty acids. Effectiveness of acyl-CoA's primers decreases

Table IX

COMPARISON OF AMINO ACID COMPOSITIONS OF FAS
FROM RAT LIVER AND LACTATING RAT MAMMARY GLAND

Amino acid	Moles %	
	Rat liver[a]	Rat mammary[b]
Lysine	4.04	4.07
Histidine	2.62	2.93
Arginine	4.57	4.95
Aspartic	7.86	7.88
Threonine	4.96	5.19
Serine	6.86	7.59
Glutamic	10.08	10.78
Proline	5.66	6.05
Glycine	8.39	8.01
Alanine	9.00	8.63
Cysteine	1.62	1.49
Valine	7.67	7.10
Methionine	1.96	1.83
Isoleucine	3.82	3.59
Leucine	13.64	12.17
Tyrosine	2.12	2.32
Phenylalanine	3.23	3.35
Tryptophan	1.87	2.07

[a] Data from Smith (1973).
[b] Data from Smith and Abraham (1970).

with increasing chain length above C_4 (Lin and Kumar, 1972; Smith and Abraham, 1971a).

7. *Thioesterase Activity*

The activity responsible for the transfer of acyl moieties from the fatty acid synthetase multienzyme complex of animals has been referred to as thioesterase since the terminal step involves the reaction:

$$\text{enzyme-S-acyl} + H_2O \rightarrow \text{enzyme-SH} + \text{fatty acid}$$

The chain-length specificities of the thioesterase activity of the rat mammary gland and rat liver fatty acid synthetases are very similar, both showing optimal activity toward thioesters containing 16 to 18 carbon atoms (Table X). *In vivo*, the rat liver and rat mammary gland fatty acid synthetases synthesize different chain length fatty acids. Thus the thioesterase specificity, while it may prevent growth of the

Table X
THIOESTERASE SPECIFICITY OF FAS FROM RAT LIVER
AND LACTATING RAT MAMMARY GLAND

| Acyl-CoA | Thioesterase (% of maximum activity) | |
	Mammary[a]	Liver[b]
$<C_{12:0}$	Trace	Trace
$C_{12:0}$	7	6
$C_{14:0}$	17	26
$C_{16:0}$	100	100
$C_{18:0}$	89	61

[a] Data adapted from Smith and Abraham (1971b).
[b] S. Smith, unpublished data.

acyl chain beyond 16 or 18 carbon atoms, cannot account for the different chain length fatty acids synthesized by the liver and mammary gland.

8. *Products*

Under optimum cofactor conditions, that is, conditions favoring maximum rate of malonyl-CoA-dependent NADPH oxidation, fatty acid synthetases purified from lactating rat mammary gland and rat liver, as well as from rat adipose tissue, mouse liver, and lactating mouse mammary gland, synthesize mainly palmitic acid (Table XI). The chain length of the products can, however, be modified under certain conditions (see Section VI,B).

Table XI
CHAIN LENGTH OF FATTY ACIDS SYNTHESIZED BY VARIOUS
FATTY ACID SYNTHETASES[a]

| | Percentage distribution of radioactivity | | | | | |
| | Chain length | | | | | |
FAS type	8:0	10:0	12:0	14:0	16:0	18:0
Rat mammary gland	0.6	0.3	0.5	3.2	90.8	4.6
Rat liver	0.8	2.2	3.7	8.1	82.0	3.2
Rat adipose	0.7	0.7	1.1	7.0	88.0	2.5
Mouse mammary gland	0.3	0.3	0.9	5.6	84.8	8.1
Mouse liver	1.3	0.8	0	4.7	87.3	5.9

[a] Data from Smith (1973). The labeled substrate was [1-^{14}C]-acetyl-CoA.

9. *Immunological Properties*

The cross-reactivity of a number of homogeneous rat and mouse fatty acid synthetases has been studied by Ouchterlony immunodiffusion (Fig. 8). Reactions of complete identity were obtained between the rat liver, rat mammary gland, and rat adipose enzymes, and also between the mouse liver and mouse mammary gland enzymes. Reactions of partial identity were obtained between fatty acid synthetases of different species, irrespective of the tissue of origin.

The evidence documented above strongly suggests that within a given species, the liver and mammary gland fatty acid synthetases are very similar proteins. It follows therefore, that their different physiological roles probably do not result from inherent differences in enzyme structure and that some external factor must be responsible for the observed product specificity.

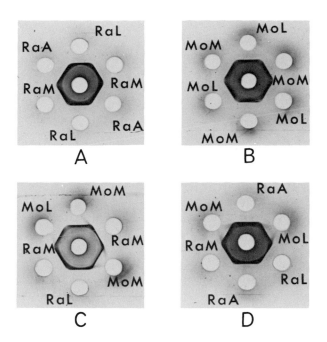

FIG. 8. Ouchterlony immunodiffusion analyses of homogeneous FAS's. Center wells contained 0.32 mg anti-(rat mammary gland)-FAS γ-globulin. The fatty acid synthetases (45 μg) in the outer wells are identified by the notation Ra = rat, Mo = mouse, A = adipose, M = mammary, L = liver. From Smith (1973).

B. FACTORS MODIFYING THE CHAIN LENGTH OF PRODUCTS SYNTHESIZED BY THE FATTY ACID SYNTHETASE

The realization that the ability of the mammary gland to synthesize short-chain length fatty acids is not due to specific properties inherent in the mammary fatty acid synthetase has prompted us to reconsider the possibility that some other characteristic of the mammary gland environment may be involved. Several factors are known to influence the chain length of fatty acids synthesized by the fatty acid synthetase enzyme.

1. Substrate Concentrations

In 1964, Smith and Dils reported that when homogenate fractions of lactating rabbit mammary gland were incubated with the cofactors required for conversion of labeled acetate to fatty acid, the chain length of the products could be altered by including citrate in the medium (Table XII). Thus the average chain length of the synthesized fatty acids increased as the citrate concentration was increased. The chain length of the products was later found to be influenced by all the components required for the acetyl-CoA carboxylase reaction, ATP, CoA, $MnCl_2$, and bicarbonate : increasing the concentration of these reactants increased the chain length of the fatty acids synthesized (Smith, 1965; Smith and Dils, 1966). We were therefore somewhat less than surprised when it was discovered that the modification

Table XII

THE EFFECT OF CITRATE ON CHAIN LENGTH OF FATTY ACIDS
SYNTHESIZED BY CYTOSOL OF LACTATING RABBIT MAMMARY GLAND[a,b]

Citrate (mM)	Acetate incorporated (nmoles/mg protein/hr)	Percentage distribution of radioactivity in fatty acids						
		Chain length						
		4:0	6:0	8:0	10:0	12:0	14:0	16:0
0	18.1	66.9	13.8	11.0	8.3	0	0	0
1	35.2	62.7	10.8	13.3	8.2	2.5	2.5	0
3	86.0	40.0	7.2	13.0	24.1	9.4	5.1	1.2
25	95.4	22.2	6.5	10.7	28.0	15.2	12.8	4.6

[a] Data from Smith and Dils (1964).

[b] The incubation medium (1.0 ml) contained 0.15 mM CoA, 3.3 mM $MnCl_2$, 15 mM $KHCO_3$, 1.5 mM glucose 6-phosphate, 0.2 mM NADP, 150 mM potassium phosphate buffer (pH 6.6), 10 mM sodium [1-^{14}C]-acetate (10μ Ci), 5 mM ATP, and 3 mg cytosol protein.

of chain length could also be achieved when malonyl-CoA was added directly to the system rather than generated by carboxylation of acetyl-CoA (Smith, 1965; Smith and Dils, 1966). In this case, increasing the proportion of malonyl-CoA to acetyl-CoA increased the chain length of the products synthesized (Table XIII). It appeared therefore that the ability of citrate to alter the products of fatty acid synthesis resulted from the ability of this compound to stimulate the production of malonyl-CoA via the acetyl-CoA carboxylase reaction. The concept that the relative concentrations of malonyl-CoA and acetyl-CoA could control the product chain length in the fatty acid synthetase reaction later formed the basis for a model equation which attempted to rationalize the process of chain termination in the yeast enzyme (Sumper *et al.*, 1969). The theory that substrate levels might regulate the chain length of fatty acids synthesized by the multienzyme complex has received considerable attention, but can be criticized on two major counts:

(a) The fatty acid synthesizing systems of mammary gland (Carey and Dils, 1970), liver (Hanson *et al.*, 1970), and yeast (Sumper *et al.*, 1969), all respond in a similar manner *in vitro*, to changes in the malonyl-CoA:acetyl-CoA ratio. *In vivo* however, only the mammary gland produces short- or medium-chain fatty acids; such fatty acids are

Table XIII

THE EFFECT OF MALONYL-CoA CONCENTRATION ON CHAIN LENGTH
OF FATTY ACIDS SYNTHESIZED BY CYTOSOL FROM LACTATING
RABBIT MAMMARY GLAND[a,b]

Malonyl-CoA (μM)	Acetate incorporated (nmoles/mg protein/hr)	Percentage distribution of radioactivity in fatty acids						
		Chain length						
		4:0	6:0	8:0	10:0	12:0	14:0	16:0
0	8.2	98	1.0	1.0	0	0	0	0
40	24.0	75	0.3	0.2	5.4	2.9	3.3	12.9
200	31.0	61	0.1	0.1	0.2	4.8	4.8	29.0
560	44.2	36	0	0	0	2.7	6.8	54.3

[a] S. Smith and R. Dils, unpublished data.

[b] The incubation medium (1.0 ml) contained 0.15 mM CoA, 3.3 mM MnCl$_2$, 1.5 mM glucose 6-phosphate, 0.2 mM NADP, 100 mM potassium phosphate buffer (pH 6.6), dithiothreitol 1 mM, 5 mM sodium [1-^{14}C]-acetate (1 Ci), 5 mM ATP, and 1 mg cytosol protein. Sufficient avidin was added to completely inhibit the acetyl-CoA carboxylase activity in the cytosol.

never found in the liver, despite the fact that the concentrations of malonyl-CoA and acetyl-CoA are known to fluctuate according to the nutritional state of the animal (Guynn et al., 1972).

(b) The fatty acid synthetases purified from a variety of tissues all synthesize predominantly palmitic acid when acetyl-CoA and malonyl-CoA are used in concentrations favoring maximum rate of synthesis (Smith, 1973; Carey and Dils, 1970; Hsu et al., 1965); shorter chain length fatty acids can be synthesized at low malonyl-CoA:acetyl-CoA ratios, when the total rate of synthesis is very low (Smith and Abraham, 1970; Hanson et al., 1971). Thus although the spectrum of fatty acids synthesized under those conditions resembles that found in secreted milk fat, the rate of synthesis is too low to account for the rapid production of these acids which we observe in the tissue slice (Smith et al., 1969).

2. Hydrogen Ion Concentration

We have recently discovered that the chain length of products synthesized by the fatty acid synthetase is dependent on the pH of the medium (Table XIV). The chain length of the products decreases with increasing pH over the range 5.6 to 8.1. The effect on chain length is unrelated to the rate of synthesis as this shows the characteristic optimum at pH 6.6. Since changes in pH can have a profound effect on protein structure (Steinhardt and Beychok, 1964), it is tempting to speculate that perhaps by changing the pH of the environment, we induce the fatty acid synthetase to assume a configuration which favors synthesis of shorter chain length fatty acids. While pH changes per se are unlikely to perform a regulatory role in the process of chain termi-

Table XIV

EFFECT OF pH ON CHAIN LENGTH OF FATTY ACIDS
SYNTHESIZED BY FAS FROM LACTATING RAT MAMMARY GLAND[a]

| | | Percentage distribution of radioactivity in fatty acids | | | | | |
| | | Chain length | | | | | |
pH	FAS activity	8:0	10:0	12:0	14:0	16:0	18:0
5.6	8.7	0	0	2.1	7.8	80.7	9.4
6.1	10.6	5.5	2.4	2.5	9.1	76.3	4.2
6.6	12.2	3.0	2.0	3.0	12.2	72.2	7.6
7.1	2.9	2.2	4.8	7.0	18.9	63.1	3.9
8.1	1.5	21.4	5.1	7.7	27.1	36.9	1.8

[a] Smith, unpublished results. The labeled substrate was [1-^{14}C]-acetyl-CoA.

nation, it is conceivable that by manipulating the pH, we are mimicking the effect of some physiological agent which *in vivo* is responsible for maintaining the appropriate configuration of the fatty acid synthetase for the synthesis of shorter chain length fatty acids. This appropriately brings us to the third factor which we know will modify the chain length of fatty acids synthesized by the fatty acid synthetase.

3. *Chain Length Modifying Factor*

At the International Conference on the Biochemistry of Lipids in The Hague in 1972, an informal discussion on the mechanism of chain termination opened up the possibility that perhaps there was a hitherto unidentified factor in mammary gland which was involved in the chain termination process. A reexamination of data obtained from previous experiments with crude homogenate fractions indicated that there might be a relationship between protein concentration in the assay system and the chain length of the products of fatty acid synthesis. The new light shed on our old data provoked us to begin a new series of experiments. First, we discovered that when only the fatty acid synthetase was present in the assay system, the concentration of enzyme had no effect on the chain length of the products (Table XV). In the presence of the cytosol fraction from lactating rat mammary gland, however, an increase in the concentration of fatty acid synthetase caused a decrease in the average chain length of the products (Table XV). The results were exciting in that for the first time we had been able to induce the fatty acid synthetase to synthesize predominantly medium-chain length fatty acids in the presence of optimum concentrations of acetyl-CoA and malonyl-CoA. To determine whether under these conditions the rate of synthesis of medium-chain fatty acids could account for the rate observed in tissue slices, we carried out another experiment. We compared the fatty acids synthesized from [U-^{14}C]-glucose by slices of lactating mammary gland the synthesis from malonyl-CoA and [1-^{14}C]-acetyl-CoA by a concentrated extract of the soluble cytoplasm of lactating mammary gland. The extract was obtained by concentrating the 100,000-gm supernatant on an Amicon PM 30 Ultrafilter. The results are shown in Table XVI. We estimated that the rate of synthesis by the extract was sufficient to account for the rate of synthesis by the slices and clearly the type of fatty acids synthesized was quite comparable with that produced by the tissue slices. The difference in design of this experiment was simply the concentration of soluble cytoplasm used. In previous experiments we had used much lower concentrations of soluble cytoplasm, usually not more than the equivalent of 100 μg protein, or 10

Table XV

EFFECT OF MAMMARY GLAND FAS CONCENTRATION ON CHAIN LENGTH OF
FATTY ACIDS SYNTHESIZED IN THE PRESENCE AND ABSENCE OF
MAMMARY GLAND CYTOSOL FRACTION[a,b]

FAS (units)	Cytosol fraction (mg protein)	Mole % fatty acid synthesized						
		C_a	8:0	10:0	12:0	14:0	16:0	18:0
35	0	15.6	0	0.4	1.8	17.6	75.9	4.3
142	0	15.6	0.3	1.5	2.5	11.5	81.8	2.3
708	0	15.6	0.2	1.5	2.3	14.3	78.5	3.2
35	1.5	14.2	0.3	13.4	15.5	17.5	50.1	3.2
142	1.5	13.4	0.1	25.3	17.4	18.6	38.1	0.5
708	1.5	12.7	11.8	21.0	18.0	20.0	29.3	0

[a] S. Smith, unpublished data.

[b] Incubations contained in a final volume of 0.5 ml: potassium phosphate buffer, pH 7.0 (50 μmoles), NADPH (7.5 μmoles), malonyl-CoA (23 nmoles), [1-^{14}C]-acetyl-CoA (22 nmoles, 55 nCi), and mammary gland FAS and cytosol fraction (100,000g for 1 hour) as indicated. Reactions were carried out at 30°. Fatty acids were extracted and analyzed by gas–liquid radiochromatography. A unit of FAS activity is the amount of enzyme which catalyzes the malonyl-CoA dependent oxidation of 1 nmole NADPH per minute at 30°. C_a = average chain length of fatty acids synthesized, calculated from the formula $C_a = \dfrac{\Sigma n\ (C \times \text{mole}\,\% \text{ fatty acid})}{100}$ where C is the number of carbon atoms in the fatty acid and n, the number of fatty acids in the mixture. It was assumed that [1-^{14}C]-acetyl-CoA contributed only the two methyl-terminal carbon atoms of every fatty acid so that moles % fatty acid synthesized was equivalent to the moles % of acetyl-CoA incorporated.

units of fatty acid synthetase. Perhaps it is worth mentioning that we use the expression milligrams of protein as a measure of soluble cytoplasm only for convenience, and we certainly do not preclude the possibility that the effect could be produced by a nonprotein component of the cytoplasm.

To determine whether the "chain-shortening" effect could be demonstrated by maintaining a constant level of fatty acid synthetase and increasing the concentration of soluble cytoplasm, the experiment described in Table XVII was performed. In this case the fatty acid synthetase was first removed from the high speed supernatant by titration with specific antibodies. The results supported the idea that indeed there was an interaction between fatty acid synthetase on the one hand and a component of the high speed supernatant on the other. As a result of the interaction, the fatty acid synthetase was induced to synthesize shorter chain length fatty acids. Some preliminary attempts

Table XVI

Comparison of the Rates of Synthesis of Fatty Acids of Various
Chain Lengths by Slices and Concentrated Extracts of
Lactating Rat Mammary Gland[a]

Preparation	Mole % fatty acid synthesized							Rate of synthesis[c]
	Chain length[b]							
	8:0	10:0	12:0	14:0	16:0	18:0	C_a	
Tissue slice	8.5	34.1	28.8	15.7	11.6	1.1	11.88	8 (37°)
Concentrated extract	10.8	32.1	20.7	17.8	16.3	2.1	12.1	>22 (30°)

[a] S. Smith, unpublished data.

[b] C_a = average chain length synthesized.

[c] μmoles of acetyl equivalents incorporated per gram tissue per hour.

Slices of tissue (100 mg) were incubated in 1.0 ml Krebs-Henseliet bicarbonate buffer pH 7.3, containing [U-^{14}C]-glucose (25 mM, 2 μCi) for 3 hours at 37° with 95 % O_2–5 % CO_2 as gas phase. Fatty acid synthesis by the concentrated extract (at a protein concentration equivalent to 50 % of that found in the tissue) was measured using [1-^{11}C]-acetyl-CoA as described in Table XV. Data from both experiments were converted to mole % fatty acid synthesized, to facilitate comparison. The rate of synthesis at 50 % tissue concentration was too fast to be measured accurately. It can be assumed however, that the rate must be at least as fast as that measured at 25 % tissue concentration (i.e., >370 nmoles NADPH oxidized per minute per 0.5 ml assay system). On extrapolation to 100 % tissue concentration, we have therefore assumed that the rate would be >370 nmoles NADPH oxidized per minute per 0.5 gm tissue, i.e., >22 μmoles acetyl equivalents incorporated per minute per gram tissue.

Table XVII

Effect of Cytosol Fraction, Depleted of Fatty Acid
Synthetase, on Fatty Acids Synthesized by Fatty Acid Synthetase[a,b]

Antibody-treated cytosol fraction (mg protein)	Average chain length synthesized
0	15.6
0.08	15.1
1.1	13.2

[a] S. Smith, unpublished data.

[b] FAS was removed from mammary gland cytosol fraction by titration with a specific anti-rat mammary gland γ-globulin preparation. Incubations were performed as outlined in Table XV.

to purify and characterize the factor from lactating mammary gland indicate that the component is of high molecular weight ($>30,000$), that
it is precipitable by a broad concentration range of ammonium sulfate,
and that it is heat stable. We suspect that perhaps the agent is a protein, a glycoprotein, or a smaller molecular weight component bound
to a protein. Evidence for the existence of such a chain-length modifier has also been obtained by J. Knudsen, E. M. Carey, and R.
Dils in Europe (personal communications).

Modification of the biological activity of an enzyme by a second protein in such a way as to alter its product specificity is not a commonly
observed phenomenon. In fact the only comparable situation to have
been described so far in the literature is the lactose synthetase system
(Brew, 1970). It is particularly intriguing that both the fatty acid
synthetase and the chain-length modifier and the lactose synthetase
and its modifier (α-lactalbumin) are found in the lactating mammary
gland. Both the fatty acid synthetase and the lactose synthetase A protein (a galactosyl transferase) are found widely distributed in animal
tissues, including the nonlactating mammary gland, where they perform roles different from those in the lactating mammary gland. The
fatty acid synthetase is responsible for the synthesis of long-chain fatty
acids and the A protein is involved in glycoprotein metabolism. In the
lactating mammary gland it appears that these same enzymes are
present but that, in some species, their specificities are altered by the
presence of other proteins, the chain-length modifier and the lactose
synthetase B protein, for fatty acid synthesis and lactose synthesis
respectively.

A considerable amount of speculation (Brew, 1970) has been made
as to the evolutionary significance of the lactose synthetase system in
terms of the development of organ specificity [the mammary gland appears to have been derived from the skin, according to embryological
evidence (Long, 1969)]. A further understanding of the operation of
the chain-length modifier, and perhaps in the more distant future, an
understanding of its evolutionary origins, could provide valuale information for establishing general principles relating to organ specificity and its development.

C. STEREOSPECIFICITY IN MILK FAT TRIGLYCERIDE SYNTHESIS

Two routes for the synthesis of triglycerides are known to operate in
animal tissues, the glycerol phosphate pathway (Kennedy, 1957) and
the monoglyceride pathway (Clark and Hübscher, 1960, 1961). It is
well established that the glycerol phosphate pathway is operative in

lactating mammary gland but whether the monoglyceride pathway plays any significant role is somewhat doubtful. Several investigators have compared the effectiveness of monoglyceride and glycerol phosphate as acceptors for glyceride synthesis in mammary gland. In the rat and the goat monoglyceride apparently will not function as an acceptor (Bickerstaffe and Annison, 1971; Dils and Clark, 1962; Pynadath and Kumar, 1964), but in the sow and guinea pig there is some evidence to the contrary (Bickerstaffe and Annison, 1971; McBride and Korn, 1964). The key question in this matter is really whether the chylomicron triglycerides are broken down completely to glycerol and fatty acid by the endothelial cells or whether some monoglyceride may be produced and transported into the epithelial cells for re-esterification. West *et al.* (1972) seem to feel that at least in the goat, hydrolysis of the plasma triglycerides proceeds to completion. On the other hand, Scow *et al.* (1973) are rather less certain.

Studies in our laboratory (Tanioka *et al.*, 1974) have confirmed that in the lactating rat mammary gland the glycerol phosphate pathway is operative (Dils and Clark, 1962). The acyl transferases involved in this pathway are found predominantly in the microsomal fraction (C. Y. Lin, S. Smith, and S. Abraham, unpublished results; Tanioka *et al.*, 1974) supporting the autoradiographical evidence of Stein and Stein (1967, 1971) which showed that labeled fatty acids collected over the endoplasmic reticulum prior to secretion into the milk in the form of triglycerides.

We have been particularly concerned in providing a rational explanation at the level of enzyme specificity, for the nonrandom distribution of fatty acids in milk fat triglycerides. When the acylation of 3-*sn*-[U-^{14}C]-glycerol phosphate was studied, the reaction was found to continue to the stage of diacylglycerol phosphate and diglyceride; no monoacylglycerol phosphate accumulated. Thus no distinction was made between the enzymes acylating positions 1 and 2 of the glycerol moiety (Fig. 9). Taken together, these two acyl transferases showed a marked specificity for long-chain acyl-CoA's (Tanioka *et al.*, 1974) (Table XVIII).

When the acylation of 1,2-diglyceride was studied however, no marked specificity for any particular chain-length acyl-CoA was observed (C. Y. Lin, S. Smith, and S. Abraham, unpublished results). Furthermore, the acyl specificity, or nonspecificity, was independent of the type of 1,2-diglyceride acceptor used.

Thus, the specificities of the acyl transferases involved in milk triglyceride synthesis are such that medium-chain fatty acids are likely to be excluded from the 1- and 2-positions, but not from the 3-

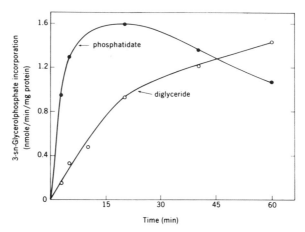

Fig. 9. Time sequence for appearance of products of the acylation of 3-*sn*-glycerol phosphate. Reaction mixtures contained in a total volume of 0.5 ml: potassium phosphate buffer pH 6.5 (100 mM), MgCl₂(4 mM), dithiolthreitol (2 mM), 3-*sn*-[U-¹⁴C]glycerol phosphate (0.5 mM, 10 μCi/μmole), plamityl-CoA (2 μM) and microsomes e3e33μg protein). From Tanioka *et al.* (1974).

position. These results are therefore compatible with the observed stereospecific distribution of fatty acids in milk fat triglycerides. Our observation that in the last step in triglyceride synthesis, the type of diglyceride acceptor does not influence the specificity for acyl donor supports the theory of noncorrelative acylation.

The apparent preference of the acyl-CoA:1,2-diglyceride, acyl transferase for medium-chain diglycerides is difficult to reconcile

Table XVIII
CHAIN-LENGTH SPECIFICITY IN GLYCERIDE SYNTHESIS
BY MICROSOMES FROM LACTATING RAT MAMMARY GLAND

| Acyl-CoA chain length | Substrate acylated (nmoles)/mg protein/minute | |
	3-*sn*-glycerol phosphate; acyl-CoA, acyl transferase[a]	1,2-diglyceride; acyl-CoA, acyl transferase[b]
10:0	0.1	6.0
12:0	0.2	7.9
14:0	1.0	9.0
16:0	1.8	7.0
18:0	1.1	9.6

[a] Data from Tanioka *et al.* (1974).
[b] C. Y. Lin, S. Smith, and S. Abraham, unpublished data.

with the observation that enzymes acylating 3-*sn*-glycerol phosphate are more likely to favor synthesis of long-chain diglycerides. It is possible however that this may be more a reflection of the physical state of the 1,2-diglyceride substrate than of enzyme specificity : perhaps in our experiments the more hydrophobic diglycerides were not presented to the enzyme system in a suitable physical form.

VII. Concluding Remarks

In the scheme shown in Fig. 10, we have tried to summarize some of the important features of the process of milk fat production. Before discussing the details of the scheme, we should like to express some reservations we have concerning its accuracy. There are considerable differences in the type of fatty acid found in milk fat of even closely related species (e.g., the rodents) and also in the substrates utilized by the mammary gland for lipogenesis (e.g., ruminants and nonruminants). The scheme must therefore be regarded as an idealized one which probably applies only to nonruminants which have medium-chain fatty acids present predominantly in the 3-position of the milk triglycerides. As we go along, we will endeavor to point out some of the many exceptions to the situation depicted by the scheme.

The ultimate source of milk fat is of course blood glucose and blood lipid, and already we come to the first exception, for, in ruminants and some herbivores, blood acetate is probably a more important precursor for fatty acids than is glucose. The blood lipid, in the form of chylomicrons (Scow *et al.*, 1973) or very low density lipoproteins is hydrolyzed at the luminal surface of the mammary gland endothelial cells by the action of lipoprotein lipase. The importance of this enzyme in milk fat production is illustrated by the observation that in the rat, the activity increases 50-fold during late pregnancy and lactation. Fatty acids produced by hydrolysis of the triglycerides are released into the circulation and the partial glycerides are absorbed into microvesicles within the endothelial cell. Thus, further hydrolysis may take place resulting in the formation of fatty acid, glycerol, and monoglyceride. Most of the free glycerol is probably re-secreted into the circulation, but some may be transferred to the epithelial cell and used as a precursor for glyceride-glycerol. The importance of glycerol as a precursor for glyceride-glycerol has been hotly debated for some time. Certainly, glycerol kinase, the enzyme required for phosphorylation of glucose is present in the epithelial cells of the mammary glands of most mammals (Abraham *et al.*, 1972; Kinsella, 1968; Mc-

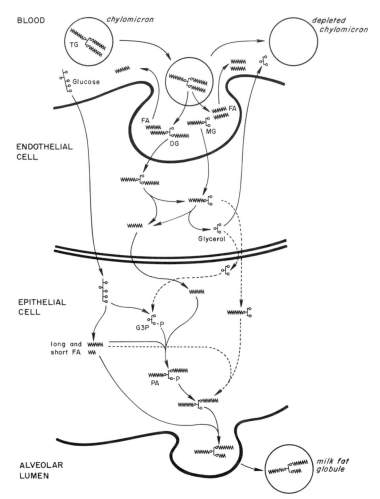

FIG. 10.   Pathways for conversion of blood glucose and lipid to milk fat triglyceride by the lactating mammary gland. The major form of blood lipids involved are the chylomicrons and very low density lipoproteins. Components of the scheme are shown diagrammatically using a tripod structure with three circles to represent the basic glycerol backbone of the glycerides; the chain length of the fatty acids is denoted by the length of the   symbol. TG = triglyceride, DG = diglyceride, MG = monoglyceride, FA = fatty acid, G3P = glycerol 3-phosphate, PA = phosphatidic acid. The dotted lines represent pathways whose significance is somewhat in doubt.

Bride and Korn, 1964), and its activity increases significantly at the onset of lactation (Baldwin and Milligan, 1966). However, estimates as to the contribution of free glycerol to milk glyceride-glycerol vary considerably. Popjak *et al.* (1953) have calculated that in rabbit milk 65–95% of the glyceride-glycerol is derived from glucose rather than from glycerol. Estimates for other species are somewhat lower, 70% in the cow (Luick and Kleiber, 1961) and 40% in the sow (Linzell *et al.*, 1969). Numerous estimates have also been made as to the contribution of the fatty acid component of blood triglycerides to milk fat triglycerides and here again there is considerable variation from one species to another. Since the medium-chain fatty acids found in some milk fats are formed exclusively by *de novo* synthesis within the mammary gland, one can assume that the proportion of medium-chain acids in the milk represents the minimum contribution of endogenous *de novo* synthesis. Thus in the rabbit, where $C_8 + C_{10}$ fatty acids account for 70% of the milk fatty acid, the contribution of blood triglyceride to milk triglyceride cannot exceed 30%. However, this type of prediction is of less value in the case of species which contain only small amounts of medium-chain acids in their milk (e.g., guinea pig). Estimates based on metabolic experiments with the goat and cow have given values ranging from 25 to 82% for the contribution of blood lipids to milk fat production (Annison *et al.*, 1967; Bishop *et al.*, 1969; Glascock *et al.*, 1956; Riis *et al.*, 1960).

The products of lipolysis, fatty acid and perhaps some monoglyceride and free glycerol, are transferred from the endothelial cell to the epithelial cell where they are reutilized for the production of milk fat. Much of the fatty acid is probably used without any structural modification, although some desaturation has been shown to take place in lactating cow, goat, and mouse mammary glands (Annison *et al.*, 1967; Glascock *et al.*, 1956; Linzell *et al.*, 1967; Rao and Abraham, 1974). Although the mammary glands of many species contain large numbers of adipocytes, little is known as to the function of these cells. The mammary epithelial cells can apparently perform all the lipogenic functions associated with milk fat synthesis and the adipocytes are thought not to play a significant role in this process (Abraham *et al.*, 1972; Pitelka *et al.*, 1969). Within the epithelial cell, glucose transported from the blood is used to synthesize glycerol phosphate and a spectrum of fatty acids characteristic of the species of mammal. In those animals which produce a milk containing short- or medium-chain length fatty acids, the chain length of products synthesized by the fatty acid synthetase may be specified by a modifier unique to lactating mammary gland. The longer chain fatty acids derived from the chylomicron triglyceride and perhaps also from *de novo* synthesis are esterified by microsomal acyl transferases to the *sn*-1- and *sn*-2-positions of glycerol phosphate. The phosphatidic acid formed is converted to diglyceride by a cytosolic enzyme, phosphatidate phosphohydrolase, and this step is probably the rate-limiting one (Askew *et al.*, 1971; Bickerstaffe and Annison, 1971; C. Y. Lin, S.

Smith, and S. Abraham, unpublished results). In the final step of the sequence, catalyzed by a microsomal acyl transferase, the sn-1,2-diglyceride is esterified at the sn-3-position by predominantly medium- or short-chain fatty acids (C. Y. Lin, S. Smith, and S. Abraham, unpublished results). The synthesized triglycerides aggregate into globules and are secreted from the luminal surface of the epithelial cells into the milk.

In presenting the scheme, we emphasized that there were probably many exceptions to any of the general rules which we were attempting to illustrate. This is, of course, particularly true in the case of the chain length of the fatty acids found in the various positions of the glycerol backbone. For example, in the case of rabbit milk which contains 70% $C_8 + C_{10}$, clearly these fatty acids cannot be confined to the sn-3-position. At the other extreme, guinea pig milk contains no medium-chain fatty acid, yet the arrangement of fatty acid is nonrandom (Breach et al., 1973). In this case there must be stereospecific incorporation of particular long-chain fatty acids into the various positions on the glycerol backbone. The stereospecific location of particular long-chain fatty acids in milk triglycerides has received little attention, yet appears to be a relatively common occurrence. For example, palmitic acid is enriched in the sn-2-position of human (Breckenridge et al., 1969) and rat (N. Mozes, C. Y. Lin, and S. Smith, unpublished results) milk triglycerides; myristic acid is enriched in the sn-2-position of the milk triglycerides of cow (Pitas et al., 1967), sheep (Kuksis et al., 1973), and goat (Kuksis et al., 1973). To provide a rational explanation for these observations will necessitate differentiation between the specificities of the acyl transferases acylating the sn-1- and sn-2-positions. The other aspect of milk fat biosynthesis which will undoubtedly receive close attention from enzymologists in the near future concerns the nature of the chain-length modifier and its mechanism of action. Hopefully, the next review on this subject will include more data and rather less speculation.

ACKNOWLEDGMENTS

We are particularly grateful to Dr. Nandi, Dr. Nemanic, Dr. Pitelka, Dr. Saacke, and Dr. Heald for supplying us with prints of their excellent micrographs. We would also like to express our thanks to the other authors mentioned in the text for allowing us to use their previously published data, and to Jolyce Hardesty for her help in preparing the typescript.

References

Abraham, S., and Chaikoff, I. L. (1959). *J. Biol. Chem.* **234**, 2246–2253.
Abraham, S., Hirsch, P. F., and Chaikoff, I. L. (1954). *J. Biol. Chem.* **211**, 31–38.
Abraham, S., Cady, P., and Chaikoff, I. L. (1960). *Endocrinology* **66**, 280–288.

Abraham, S., Matthes, K. J., and Chaikoff, I. L. (1961). *Biochim. Biophys. Acta* **49**, 268–285.

Abraham, S., Katz, J., Bartley, J. C., and Chaikoff, I. L. (1963). *Biochim. Biophys. Acta* **70**, 690–693.

Abraham, S., Kerkoff, P. R., and Smith, S. (1972). *Biochim. Biophys. Acta* **261**, 205–218.

Annison, E. F., and Lindsay, D. B. (1961). *Biochem. J.* **78**, 777–785.

Annison, E. F., Linzell, J. L., Fazakerley, S., and Nichols, B. W. (1967). *Biochem. J.* **102**, 637–647.

Askew, E. W., Emery, R. S., and Thomas, J. W. (1971). *Lipids* **6**, 326–331.

Baldwin, R. L., and Milligan, L. P. (1966). *J. Biol. Chem.* **241**, 2058–2066.

Balmain, J. H., Folley, S. J., and Glascock, R. F. (1952). *Biochem. J.* **52**, 301–306.

Bargmann, W., and Knoop, A. (1959). *Z. Zellforsch. Mikrosk. Anat.* **49**, 344–356.

Bauman, D. E., and Davis, C. I. (1074). *In* "Lactation: A Comprehensive Treatise" (B. L. Larson and V. R. Smith, eds.), Vol. 2, pp. 51–75. Academic Press, New York.

Bauman, D. E., Brown, R. E., and Davis, C. L. (1970). *Arch. Biochem. Biophys.* **140**, 237–244.

Bauman, D. E., DeKay, D. E., Ingle, D. L., and Brown, R. E. (1972). *Comp. Biochem. Physiol.* **43**, 479–486.

Bauman, D. E., Mellenberger, R. W., and Derrig, R. G. (1973). *J. Dairy Sci.* **56**, 1312–1318.

Bergman, E. N., Roe, W. E., and Kon, S. K. (1966). *Amer. J. Physiol.* **211**, 793–799.

Bickerstaffe, R., and Annison, E. F. (1971). *Int. J. Biochem.* **2**, 153–162.

Bintarningsih, Lyons, W. R., and Johnson, R. E. (1957). *Anat. Rec.* **127**, 266–267.

Bishop, C., Davies, T., Glascock, R. F., and Welch, V. A. (1969). *Biochem. J.* **113**, 629–633.

Breach, R. A., Dils, R., and Watts, R. (1973). *J. Dairy Res.* **40**, 273–287.

Breckenridge, W. C., and Kuksis, A. (1967). *J. Lipid Res.* **8**, 473–478.

Breckenridge, W. C., Marai, L., and Kuksis, A. (1969). *Can. J. Biochem.* **47**, 761–768.

Brew, K. (1970). *Essays Biochem.* **6**, 93–114.

Brockerhoff, H. (1965). *J. Lipid Res.* **6**, 10–15.

Brockerhoff, H. (1973). *Lipids* **8**, 439.

Carey, E. M., and Dils, R. (1970). *Biochim. Biophys. Acta* **210**, 388–399.

Chappell, J. B., and Robinson, B. H. (1968). *Biochem. Soc. Symp.* **27**, 123–133.

Clark, B., and Hübscher, G. (1960). *Nature (London)* **185**, 35.

Clark, B., and Hübscher, G. (1961). *Biochim. Biophys. Acta* **46**, 479–494.

Cowie, A. T. (1957). *J. Endocrinol.* **16**, 135–147.

Cowie, A. T. (1969). *In* "Lactogenesis: The Initiation of Milk Secretion at Parturition" (M. Reynolds and S. J. Folley, eds.), pp. 157–169. Univ. of Pennsylvania Press, Philadelphia.

Cowie, A. T., and Tindal, J. S. (1971). *In* "The Physiology of Lactation" (H. Davson *et al.*, eds.), p. 136. William & Wilkins, Baltimore, Maryland.

Cowie, A. T., Folley, S. J., Cross, B. A., Harris, G. W., Jacobson, D., and Richardson, K. C. (1951). *Nature (London)* **168**, 421.

Denamur, R. (1971). *J. Dairy Res.* **38**, 237–264.

Dils, R., and Clark, B. (1962). *Biochem. J.* **84**, 19p.

Folley, S. J. (1947). *Brit. Med. Bull.* **5**, 142–148.

Folley, S. J., and French, T. H. (1949). *Biochem. J.* **45**, 117–125.

Folley, S. J., Balmain, J. H., and Glascock, R. F. (1954). *Biochem. J.* **56**, 234–239.

Forsyth, I. A. (1971). *J. Dairy Res.* **3**, 419–444.

Forsyth, I. A., Strong, C. R., and Dils, R. (1972). *Biochem. J.* **129**, 929–935.

Foster, D. W., and Bloom, B. (1963). *J. Biol. Chem.* **238**, 888–892.

Garton, G. A. (1963). *J. Lipid Res.* **4**, 237–254.
Glascock, R. F., Duncombe, W. G., and Reinius, L. R. (1956). *Biochem. J.* **62**, 535–541.
Glass, R. L., and Jennes, R. (1971). *Comp. Biochem, Physiol. B* **38**, 353–359.
Glass, R. L., and Jennes, R. (1971). *Comp. Biochem. Physiol. B* **38**, 353–359.
Glock, G. E., and McLean, P. (1954). *Biochem. J.* **56**, 171–175.
Gul, B., and Dils, R. (1969). *Biochem. J.* **112**, 293–301.
Gumaa, K. A., Greenbaum, A. L., and McLean, P. (1971). *In* "Lactation" (I. R. Falconer, ed.), pp. 193–238. Butterworth, London.
Guynn, R. W., Veloso, D., and Veech, R. L. (1972). *J. Biol. Chem.* **247**, 7325–7331.
Hallowes, R. L., Wang, D. Y., Lewis, D. J., Strong, C. R., and Dils, R. (1973). *J. Endocrinol.* **57**, 265–276.
Hanson, H., Carey, E. M., and Dils, R. (1970). *Biochim. Biophys. Acta* **210**, 400–410.
Hanson, H., Carey, E. M., and Dils, R. (1971). *Biochim. Biophys. Acta* **248**, 391–405.
Herb, S. F., MAgidman, P., Luddy, F. E., and Riemenscheider, R. W. (1962). *J. Amer. Oil Chem. Soc.* **39**, 142–147.
Hilditch, T. P., and Williams, P. N. (1964). *In* "The Chemical Constitution of Natural Fats," 4th ed., pp. 142–165. Chapman & Hall, London.
Hsu, R. Y., Wasson, G., and Porter, J. W. (1965). *J. Biol. Chem.* **240**, 3736–3746.
Jensen, R. G. (1973). *J. Amer. Oil Chem. Soc.* **50**, 186–192.
Karlsson, B. W., and Carlsson, E. I. (1968). *Comp. Biochem. Physiol.* **25**, 949–971.
Katz, J., and Wals, P. A. (1972). *Biochem. J.* **128**, 879–899.
Keenan, T. W., Morré, D. J., Olsen, D. E., Yunghans, W. N., and Patton, S. (1970). *J. Cell Biol.* **44**, 80–93.
Kennedy, E. P. (1957). *Annu. Rev. Biochem.* **26**, 119–148.
Kinsella, J. E. (1968). *Biochim. Biophys. Acta* **164**, 540–549.
Kleiber, M., Smith, A. H., Black, A. L., Brown, M. A., and Tolbert, B. M. (1952). *J. Biol. Chem.* **197**, 371–379.
Kopelovich, L., Abraham, S., McGrath, H., DeOme, K. B., and Chaikoff, I. L. (1966). *Cancer Res.* **26**, 1534–1546.
Kuksis, A., Marai, L., and Myher, J. J. (1973). *J. Amer. Oil Chem. Soc.* **50**, 193–201.
Lardy, H. A., Paetkav, V., and Walter, P. (1965). *Proc. Nat. Acad. Sci. U. S.* **53**, 1410–1415.
Leng, R. A., Steel, J. W., and Luick, J. R. (1967). *Biochem. J.* **103**, 785–790.
Lin, C. Y., and Kumar, S. (1972). *J. Biol. Chem.* **247**, 604–606.
Linzell, J. L., Annison, E. F., Fazakerley, S., and Leng, R. A. (1967). *Biochem. J.* **104**, 34–42.
Linzell, J. L., Mepham, T. B., Annison, E. F., and West, C. E. (1969). *Brit. J. Nutr.* **23**, 319–332.
Long, C. A. (1969). *BioScience* **19**, 519–523.
Lornitzo, F. A., Qureshi, A. A., and Porter, J. W. (1974). *J. Biol. Chem.* **249**, 1654–1656.
Luick, J. R., and Kleiber, M. (1961). *Amer. J. Physiol.* **200**, 1327–1329.
Lyons, W. R., and Johnson, R. E. (1958). *Recent Progr. Horm. Res.* **14**, 219–254.
McBride, O. W., and Korn, L. D. (1964). *J. Lipid Res.* **5**, 442–447.
McCullagh, K. G., Lincoln, H. G., and Southgate, D. A. T. (1969). *Nature (London)* **222**, 493–494.
McLean, P. (1958a). *Biochim. Biophys. Acta* **30**, 303–315.
McLean, P. (1958b). *Biochim. Biophys. Acta* **30**, 316–324.
Mellenberger, R. W., and Bauman, D. E. (1974). *Biochem. J.* **138**, 373–379.
Moretti, R. L., and Abraham, S. (1966). *Biochim. Biophys. Acta* **124**, 280–288.
Nandi, S. (1959). *Univ. Calif., Berkeley, Publ. Zool.* **65**, 1–128.
Nandi, S., and Bern, H. A. (1961). *Gen. Comp. Endocrinol.* **1**, 195–210.
Nemanic, M. K., and Pitelka, D. R. (1971). *J. Cell Biol.* **48**, 410–415.

Novello, F., and McLean, P. (1968). *Biochem. J.* **107**, 775–791.
Patton, S. (1973). *J. Amer. Oil Chem. Soc.* **50**, 178–185.
Peeters, G., Debackere, M., and Sierens, R. (1957). *Arch. Int. Physiol. Biochim.* **65**, 324–336.
Pitas, R. E., Sampugna, J., and Jensen, R. G. (1967). *J. Dairy Sci.* **50**, 1332–1340.
Pitelka, D. R., Kerkof, P. R., Gagné, H. T., Smith, S., and Abraham, S. (1969). *Exp. Cell Res.* **57**, 43–62.
Popjak, G., Folley, S. J., and French, T. H. (1950). *Arch. Biochem.* **23**, 509–510.
Popjak, G., Hunter, G. D., and French, T. H. (1953). *Biochem. J.* **54**, 238–247.
Pynadath, T., and Kumar, S. (1964). *Biochim. Biophys. Acta* **84**, 251–263.
Rao, A., and Abraham, S. (1974). *Lipids* **9**, 269–271.
Riis, P. M., Luick, J. R., and Kleiber, M. (1960). *Amer. J. Physiol.* **198**, 45–47.
Saacke, R. G., and Heald, C. W. (1974). *In* "Lactation: A Comprehensive Treatise" (B. L. Larson and V. R. Smith, eds.), Vol. 2, pp. 147–189. Academic Press, New York.
Scow, R. O., Mendelson, C. R., Zinder, O., Hamosh, M., and Blanchette-Mackie, E. (1973). *In* "Dietary Lipids and Postnatal Development" (G. Jacini, A. Pecile, and C. Galli, eds.), pp. 91–114. Raven Press, New York.
Smith, S. (1965). Ph.D. Thesis, University of Birmingham, England.
Smith, S. (1971). *Biochim. Biophys. Acta* **251**, 477–481.
Smith, S. (1973). *Arch. Biochem. Biophys.* **156**, 751–758.
Smith, S., and Abraham, S. (1970). *J. Biol. Chem.* **245**, 3209–3217.
Smith, S., and Abraham, S. (1971a). *J. Biol. Chem.* **246**, 2537–2542.
Smith, S., and Abraham, S. (1971b). *J. Biol. Chem.* **246**, 6428–6435.
Smith, S., and Abraham, S. (1975). *In* "Methods in Enzymology" (J. M. Lowenstein, ed.), Vol. 35, pp. 65–74. Academic Press, New York.
Smith, S., and Dils, R. (1964). *Biochim. Biophys. Acta* **84**, 776–778.
Smith, S., and Dils, R. (1966). *Biochim. Biophys. Acta* **116**, 23–40.
Smith, S., Watts, R., and Dils, R. (1968). *J. Lipid Res.* **9**, 52–57.
Smith, S., Gagné, H. T., Pitelka, D. R., and Abraham, S. (1969). *Biochem. J.* **115**, 807–815.
Stein, O., and Stein, Y. (1967). *J. Cell Biol.* **34**, 251–263.
Stein, O., and Stein, Y. (1971). *In* "Advances in Lipid Research" (R. Paoletti and D. Kritchevsky, eds.), pp. 1–72. Academic Press, New York.
Steinhardt, J. and Beychok, S. (1964). *In* "The Proteins" (H. Neurath, ed.), Vol. 2, pp. 139–304. Academic Press, New York.
Strong, C. R., Forsyth, J. O., and Dils, R. (1972). *Biochem. J.* **128**, 509–519.
Sumper, M., Oesterhelt, D., Riepertinger, C., and Lynen, F. (1969). *Eur. J. Biochem.* **10**, 377–387.
Tanioka, H., Lin, C. Y., Smith, S., and Abraham, S. (1974). *Lipids* **9**, 229–234.
Turner, C. W. (1939). *In* "Sex and Internal Secretions" (E. Allen, C. H. Danfirth, and E. A. Doisy, eds.), 2nd ed., pp. 740–803. Williams & Wilkins, Baltimore, Maryland.
Tweto, J., and Larrabee, A. R. (1972). *J. Biol. Chem.* **247**, 4900–4938.
Tweto, J., Liberati, M., and Larrabee, A. R. (1971). *J. Biol. Chem.* **246**, 2468–2471.
Wang, D. Y., Hallowes, R. L., Bealing, J., Strong, C. R., and Dils, R. (1972). *Endocrinology* **53**, 311–321.
Wellings, S. R. (1969). *In* "Lactogenesis: The Initiation of Milk Secretion at Parturition" (M. Reynolds and S. J. Folley, eds.), pp. 5–25. Univ. of Pennsylvania Press, Philadelphia.
West, C. E., Bickerstaffe, R., Annison, E. F., and Linzell, J. L. (1972). *Biochem. J.* **126**, 477–490.
Wooding, F. B. P. (1971). *J. Cell Sci.* **9**, 805–811.
Yu, H. L., and Burton, D. N. (1974). *Arch. Biochem. Biophys.* **161**, 297–305.

Author Index

Numbers in italics refer to the pages on which the complete references are listed.

A

Abraham, S., 200, 201, 202, 206, 207, 211, 219, 220, 221, 222, 226, 231, 232, 233, 235, *237, 238, 239*

Abrams, R. L., 122, *126*

Acosta, J. M., 184, *189*

Adamson, G. L., 41, 45, *86*

Adler, R. D., 148, 185, *189, 191*

Admirand, W. H., 155, 156, 157, 164, 165, 166, *189*

Aggerbeck, L. P., 7, 18, 22, 24, *80, 86, 87*

Agostini, B., 28, *88*

Ahrens, E. H., Jr., 169, *192*

Aladjem, F., 16, 24, 25, *80, 82, 86*

Alaupovic, P., 5, 10, 13, 14, 21, 22, 28, 37, 64, *80, 83, 84, 85, 88*

Albers, J. J., 13, 25, 27, 62, 63, *80, 83, 87*

Alcindor, L. G., 33, *80*

Alexander, C., 7, *80*

Alexander, M., 139, 141, 142, 143, 144, 145, 146, 147, 148, 149, 150, 151, 152, 153, 154, 156, 157, 158, 161, 164, 167, 177, 178, *192*

Alkan, M., 28, *89*

Allan, J. C., 94, 102, 103, 113, 114, 122, *126, 129*

Almond, H. R., 185, *189*

Altshuler, H. L., 98, *126*

Anderson, D. R., 116, *126*

Anderson, P. J., 95, 111, *127*

Annison, E. F., 208, 231, 235, *237, 238, 239*

Anver, M. R., 139, *189*

Applegate, K. R., 62, 63, *83*

Archibald, F. M., 4, *88*

Arora, R. B., 94, 102, 103, 125, *126*

Arreaza, C., 29, *82*

Ashworth, L. A. E., 18, *81*

Askew, E. W., 235, *237*

Assman, G., 10, 11, 25, 26, 30, 37, 62, 71, *81, 86*

Ausman, L. M., 105, 121, *126*

Avigan, J., 70, *89*

Ayotte, R. A., 97, 117, *132*

Ayrault-Jarrier, M., 12, *81*

B

Bagdade, J. D., 35, *81*

Baggenstass, A. H., 169, *193*

Baginsky, M. L., 14, 37, 70, *82*

Bailey, J. M., 70, *81*

Baker, H. N., 10, *81, 82, 85*

Balasse, E. O., 40, *84*

Baldwin, R. L., 206, 234, *237*

Balint, J. A., 177, *189*

Ballinger, W. F., 112, *133*

Balmain, J. H., 207, 216, *237*

Bandyopadhyay, A., 94, 100, 102, 103, 119, *126, 127*

Banerjee, S., 94, 100, 102, 103, 110, 119, *126, 127*

Barclay, K. R., 4, *88*

Barclay, M., 4, *88*

Bargmann, W., 202, *237*

Bargoot, F. G., 24, *89*

Barnett, W. O., 187, *189*

Bar–on, H., 34, 35, *81, 89*

Barter, P. J., 33, 41, *81*

Barthel, C. H., 121, *131*

Bartley, J. C., 207, *237*

Basabe, J. C., 119, *129*

Basso, L. V., 40, *84*

Bates, S. R., 70, *81*

Bauman, D. E., 206, 207, 208, *237, 238*

Bealing, J., 201, 202, *239*

Beck, P., 95, 101, 124, *127*

Beeler, D. A., 177, *189*

Beisel, W. R., 95, 118, *128*

Belfrage, P., 36, 38, *86*

Bell, C. C., Jr., 157, 172, 174, 177, 179, 181, 185, *189, 193*

Bell, F. P., 99, 100, 102, 115, *131*

Bell, G. D., 164, 168, 169, *189, 191*

Bell, S., 140, 168, *190*

Bellon, E. M., 185, *193*

Bennett, B. I., 32, 34, *86*

Bennett, P. H., *192*

Bensadoun, A., *81*

Berenson, G. S., 7, *88*, 102, *134*

Berg, K., 27, 28, *81, 84*

Berger, J., 174, 177, *190*

241

Subject Index

A

Abetalipoproteinemia, 35
Acetonuria, 108
Acetyl coenzyme A, 207–209
Acidosis, 93, 110
Adrenal glands, effect of, on carbohydrate metabolism, 122, 123
Adrenal steroids, 199
Adrenalectomy, 123
Adrenocortical hormones, 201
Alloxan, 110, 111, 115
Amyloidosis, 107, 109
Apolipoproteins, 7–16
Apoprotein(s) A, 10, 11
  in HDL, 24, 25, 61
  human, 10, 11
  nonhuman, 11
Apoprotein B, 11–12
  human, 11, 12, 43–48
  in LDL, 21–24
  in nonhumans, 12
  in rats, 49–55
  in synthesis of chylomicrons and VLDL, 34, 35
  in VLDL, 19
Apoprotein C, 12–14
  in HDL, 24–26
  human, 12–14, 42, 43, 46–48
  in LDL, 21, 22
  nonhuman, 14
  in rats, 49–55
  in VLDL, 19
Arteriosclerosis, 2
Atherosclerosis, 92, 101, 103, 105, 108
  gallstones and, 136–138

B

Bile
  composition of, 171–174
    in nonhuman primates, 162–166
  crystal growth in, 149–163
  crystallization of cholesterol from, 159–162
  gallbladder, 143, 144
    of nonhuman primates, 162–166
  hepatic, 143, 144, 158, 159
  solubility of cholesterol in, 153–159
Bile pigments, 141
Bile salts, 155, 162
  in nonhuman primates, 171–174, 181, 182
Biliary lipids, 135–188
  gallstone formation and, 153–166
Biliary physiology, 170–182
Bilirubin, 145, 150, 187
Blood glucose, 233
  effect of fasting on, 93–99
  of stress on, 117
Blood lipids, 93, 233

C

Cachexia, 106
Carbohydrate(s)
  metabolism, effect of stress on, 116–125
    in nonhuman primates, 94–99
Calcium, in gallstones, 141, *see also* Gallstones
Cataracts, 106, 108, 109, 112
Central nervous system, effect of, on carbohydrate metabolism, 120, 121
Chenodeoxycholic acid, 168, 169, 173, 179
Cholelithiasis, 136, 143, 148
Cholesterol, 3ff.
  crystallization from bile, 159–162
  in diabetic primates, 101, 102
  in gallstones, 141, *see also* Gallstones
  in induced diabetes, 113, 115
  in nonhuman primates, 162–166
  secretion into bile, 174–177
  solubility in bile, 153–159
Cholesteryl esters in VLDL, 50
Cholestyramine, 33, 57
Cholic acid, 169, 173, 179
Chorionic somatomammotropin, 201
Chylomicrons, 3–80, 113, 202, 203, 233
  catabolism of lipid moiety, 35–41
    of protein moiety, 41–52
  composition of, 16
  fate of lipids, 38–40